37th Biennial Conference of the Institute for Briquetting and Agglomeration (IBA 2022)

Denver, Colorado, USA
18 – 22 September 2022

ISBN: 978-1-7138-6662-6

Printed from e-media with permission by:

Curran Associates, Inc.
57 Morehouse Lane
Red Hook, NY 12571

Some format issues inherent in the e-media version may also appear in this print version.

Printed with permission by Curran Associates, Inc. (2024)

For permission requests, please contact the Institute for Briquetting and Agglomeration at the address below.

Institute for Briquetting and Agglomeration
10802 Amber Rd X44
Anamosa, IA 52205

Phone: (563) 920-9399

www.agglomeration.org

Additional copies of this publication are available from:

Curran Associates, Inc.
57 Morehouse Lane
Red Hook, NY 12571 USA
Phone: 845-758-0400
Fax: 845-758-2634
Email: curran@proceedings.com
Web: www.proceedings.com

TABLE OF CONTENTS

Institute for Briquetting and Agglomeration

2022 IBA CONFERENCE PAPERS

Paper Title:
Briquetting by Stiff Extrusion vs Sintering Competition or Synergy?

Presenter:
Clement Cadier

Company:
Direxa Engineering

Briquetting by Stiff Extrusion vs Sintering
Competition or Synergy?

Clement Cadier– President
Direxa Engineering

Briquetting by Stiff Extrusion vs Sintering

- The smelting of iron and steel, in addition to the well-known negative impact on the environment, is accompanied by the formation of a ***significant amount of iron-containing wastes***, the direct recycling of which is impossible without agglomeration.
- Sintering and (indurated) pellet production are the most widespread methods of industrial agglomeration and are based on ***high-temperature processing*** of iron-containing raw materials and lead to emissions of pollutants into the atmosphere (***sintering - up to 20 kg / ton sinter, pellet production - 2 kg / ton pellets***).
- For a long time, cold agglomeration turned out to be uncompetitive in comparison with sintering and pellet production due to ***insufficient productivity*** of briquette equipment and inconsistency of briquette properties which were not meeting the requirements of metallurgical processing.
- This has changed with the development of the stiff extrusion technology for briquettes **(BREX)**, which offers a viable alternative, or at the very least which has proven to be a viable and a value adding complementing technology to the first two.

Briquetting by Stiff Extrusion vs Sintering
Comparison criteria

- Metallurgical Properties
- Maximum Equipment Capacity
- Environmental aspects
- Simulation of partial replacement of Sinter by BREX in a large BF
- Could BREX be used as embryos for sinter?

Briquetting by Stiff Extrusion vs Sintering
BREX Hot Strength

- Hot strength of the **BREX** briquette from magnetite concentrate and coke fines in terms of RDI+6.3 (**ISO 4696**) exceeds RDI+6.3 of sinter with a basicity of 1.2–1.6

Agglomerated Products	RDI (+6.3), %
Brex No.4* (basicity 0,75)	96.5
Brex No.2* (basicity 1,93)	**61.9**
Sinter (basicity 1,2)	**64**
Sinter (basicity 1,4)	**60**
Sinter (basicity 1,6)	**77**

BREX components	Composition by weight, %	
	Brex No.2	Brex No.4
Portland cement	9.1	9.0
Coke breeze	-	13.5
Bentonite	-	0.9
BF sludge	54.5	-
BOF sludge	36.4	-
Iron Ore Concentrate	-	76.6

These tests were conducted in a lab in Russia in 2010

Briquetting by Stiff Extrusion vs Sintering
BREX Hot Strength

Agglomerated product	ISO 13930, %			ISO 4696-1, %		
	LTD +6.3	LTD -3.15	LTD -0.5	RDI +6.3	RDI -3.15	RDI -0.5
BREX #A	89.95	8.68	8.32	94.31	4.67	4.14
BREX #B				93.72	5.93	5.31
BREX #C				91.52	7.67	7.24
BREX #D				95.65	3.64	3.13
BREX #E				95.24	4.02	3.55
Sinter	65.03	13.93	4.47	76.54	7.57	1.32
Pellets #1	94.87	3.78	3.49	97.99	0.71	0.15
Pellets #2	80.7	10.45	7.79	80.49	10.19	5.3
Pellets #3	82.5	13.94	12.29			

BREX (diameter of 19 mm, after curing at a temperature of 24 ° C). Portland cement (from 6.0% to 6.5%) as a binder and sodium bentonite (from 1.0% to 2.0%) as a plasticizer. The density of the obtained briquettes ranged from 2.6 to 2.9 g / cm3.

Note: BREX were produced at JC Steele & Sons Lab in Statesville - NC

Briquetting by Stiff Extrusion vs Sintering
BREX Hot Strength

- Samples of BREX were heated to 1000 ° C in a neutral atmosphere (nitrogen) in 2 hours with a temperature gradient of 500 ° C per hour. After reaching 1000 ° C, the furnace was turned off and cooled for 12 hours. The purpose of the test was to determine the mass loss and assess the shape integrity.
- The mass loss of the BREX when heated to 1000 ° C in a neutral atmosphere due to the removal of hydration moisture and partial reduction of iron oxides was **8.1%**, the briquette retained its original shape (not destroyed). The cement used as a binder is destroyed at this temperature. The fact that the BREX keeps its shape is due to the formation of a matrix made of iron-calcium olivine.

Briquetting by Stiff Extrusion vs Sintering
BREX Hot Strength

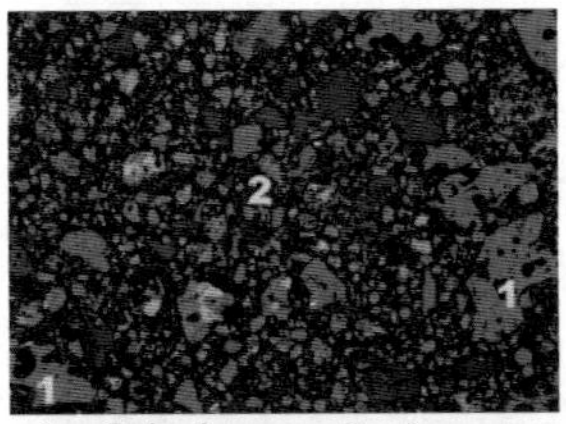

1 – Coke breeze; 2 – iron ore

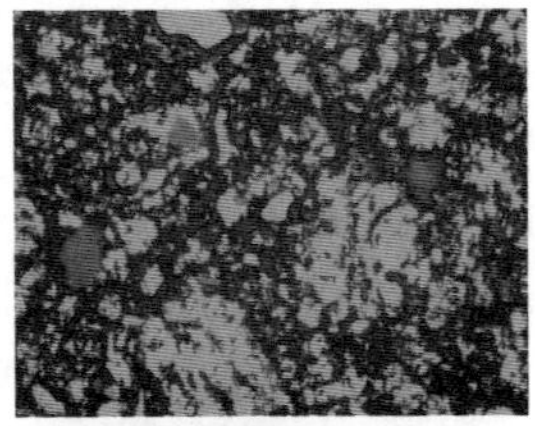

Core, 900 °C

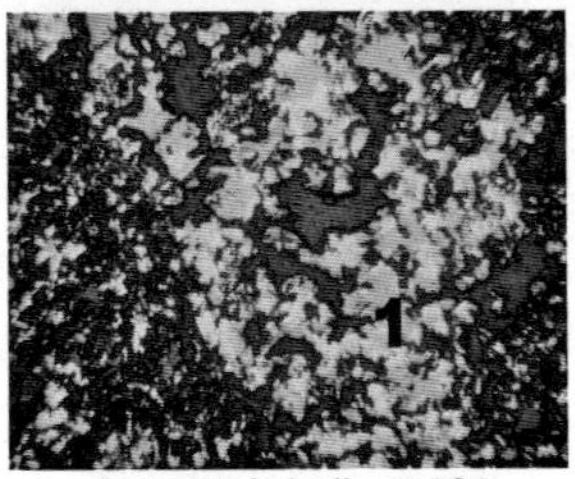

1 – metal shell, 900°C,

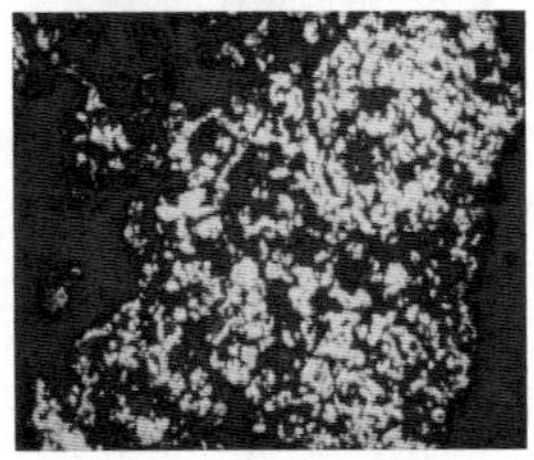

Shell, 1100 °C

Briquetting by Stiff Extrusion vs Sintering
100% BREX in BF

BF furnace performance	100% iron ore	80% BREX	100% BREX
Consumption, kg/t hot metal:			
iron ore	1,500	372	–
BREX	–	1,425	1,960
Limestone	150	–	-
dolomite	144	–	29
Scrap	132	–	-
Quartzite	–	–	13
flushing BREX of Mn ore	–	19	75
Coke	**680**	**530**	490
Iron content in the fluxed burden, %	57.6	50.4	45.5
Furnace output, t/(m^3·day)	**1.9**	**1.62**	2.0
Hot blast temperature, °C	925	900	1,000
Pressure at tuyeres, kPa	50	35-38	38-42

Note: Test was made in a 50 cu. m. Blast Furnace at Suraj - India

Briquetting by Stiff Extrusion vs Sintering
100% BREX in BF

HM chemical composition, %:	100% iron ore	80% BREX	100% BREX
Si	1.0–1.8	1.0–1.5	0.8–1.1
Mn	0.2	0.4–0.5	0.7–0.8
C	3.8–4.0	3.75–3.90	3.8–3.95
S	0.050–0.060	0.038–0.050	0.038–0.042
Hot metal temperature, °C	1,380-1,440	1,400-1,450	1,410-1,450
Chemical composition of slag, %:			
CaO	34.86	33.12	38–39
SiO_2	31.98	30.23	30.0–32.0
Al_2O_3	23.87	17.98	16.0–18.8
MgO	9.46	9.48	8.0–9.5
FeO	1.01	1.26	0.6–1.15

Note: Test was made in a 50 cu. m. Blast Furnace at Suraj - India

Briquetting by Stiff Extrusion vs Sintering
Maximum Equipment Capacity

- Capacity of sintering belt: **1,500–10,000** tons per day
- Capacity of roasting machines: **2,500–9,000** tons per day
- Capacity of extrusion plant: **2,000-7,000** tons per day; Saudi Red Bricks Plant, 1 million clay bricks per day.
- NLMK BREX-making Plant: **2,000** tons per day.
- The BREX technology has the advantage of being down-scalable to as low as **80** tons per day and still be economically viable. This is a great advantage when smaller quantities of waste are to be treated

Briquetting by Stiff Extrusion vs Sintering Environmental aspects

- The Best Available Technologies (BAT) concept was first time used in 1992 by the OSPAR Convention for the protection of the marine environment of the North-East Atlantic from all types of industrial installations.
- The Best Available Technology must meet a set of criteria:

  - the lowest level of negative impact on the environment per unit of time or volume of products (goods), or work performed, or services rendered;

  - economic efficiency of its implementation and operation;

  - application of resource-and energy-saving methods;

  - specify a period of its implementation;

  - industrial implementation of this technology on two or more projects that are having a negative impact on the environment.
- Regarding the processes for production of agglomerated iron containing materials, the list of the BAT and their technological indicators are presented in the information technology directories of the Best Available Technologies.

Briquetting by Stiff Extrusion vs Sintering Environmental aspects

What about Production of Sinter as a BAT ?

Sinter production, carried out by burning solid fuel in an air flow filtered through a layer of iron ore charge, remains a primary method of agglomeration of iron ore materials to date. As a result of physical and chemical processes in the sintering layer, emissions of pollutants are formed:

- **dust emissions** are caused by mechanical removal of the fines from the sintering layer or formed in the process of destruction of materials (sinter coming off the sintering belt; cooling, crushing and screening of the sinter cake after sintering);
- **carbon monoxide (CO) emissions** which, due to the combustion characteristics of the distributed solid fuel in the sintering layer (incomplete combustion), are technologically unavoidable; **Some CO2 emission** is of course also generated.
- **emissions of sulfur dioxide (SO_2),** depending on the sulfur content in coke fines, which is used as fuel, as well as on the composition of the iron ore charge;
- **emissions of nitrogen oxides (NO_x)** from combustion in internal combustion chamber burners, partially burning solid fuels, as well as due to the emission of "thermal" nitrogen oxides due to nitrogen content in coke fines and iron ore materials.

Briquetting by Stiff Extrusion vs Sintering Environmental aspects

What about Production of Sinter as a BAT ?

Production	Share of total emissions for various parts of the steel making process, %			
	Dust	CO	SO_2	NO_x
Sinter	31.1	77.8	61.0	26.0
Steel making	19.7	5.4	0.02	6.5
Refractory (lime-burning)	18.4	0.4	0.4	5.4
Blast furnace	17.3	3.5	0.3	3.0
Thermal power station-steam and air blower station	7.4	n/d	36.7	36.6
Coke making	2.0	7.8	1.0	9.1
Rolling production	1.2	n/d	0.2	10.5
Repair	1.0	4.9	0.02	1.5
Other	1.9	0.2	0.36	1.4
Total:	100	100	100	100

Briquetting by Stiff Extrusion vs Sintering Environmental aspects

What about Production of sinter as a BAT ?

A primary source of emissions during sinter production are the various processes of combustion. To minimize the impact on the environment and reduce the consumption of resources, as mandated by BAT, the following relevant technical solutions in the sinter production are applied:

- reduction of fuel consumption due to **rational charge preparation** (optimization of size distribution of charge components, the components composition of the charge. the size of coke fines, etc.);

- increased height of the sintered layer (in most cases requires some amount of retrofitting of the sintering machine);

- improvement of the combustion conditions of coke fines in the layer by increasing the gas permeability of the charge (**optimization of the pelletizing process**, the introduction of lime, the use of modulators of combustion (water mist));

- recirculation of waste gas heat (depending on the process requirements, different amounts of recirculation are possible, but under the moisture content conditions, it cannot exceed 35%; in any case, the processing of sinter gases requires a mandatory additional supply of air (oxygen); improving the flow of sinter gases is associated with an additional power consumption).

- The above measures, improving the traditional sintering technology, essentially provide no more than **20%** reduction in emissions; the most radical technical solution (recycling of sinter gases) at the maximum possible amount of recycling reduces emissions to **50%** (and thus leads to a specific emission level of about **10 kg/t** instead of **20 kg/t** of sinter).

Briquetting by Stiff Extrusion vs Sintering
Environmental aspects

Production of indurated pellets as a BAT ?

- Pellets production refers to pyro-metallurgical technologies, since the strengthening of agglomerated granules (raw pellets) requires high temperature (1250-1350 °C) firing.
- The emissions generated by the pellets production are due solely to the combustion of natural gas to ensure the heat requirements of firing and the chemical transformation of the components of the charge (oxidation of sulfur compounds):

  - **emissions of NO_x** from the combustion process in heated sections of the induration machine hearth;

  - **emissions of SO_2**, determined by the sulfur content in iron ore material (concentrate);

  - **dust emissions** due to mechanical removal of dispersed particles of raw pellets, indurated pellets during unloading from the induration machine, their sieving, loading;

  - **emissions of CO_2** due to stoichiometric combustion of natural gas, there is no chemical "under burning", so carbon monoxide is practically not formed, however a large amount of CO2 is released.
- Measures to reduce emissions of NOx are associated with the use of burners of special design with low formation of nitrogen oxides, or technology of selective catalytic reduction of nitrogen oxides (efficiency up to 60%).
- All considered, we are still looking at about **2 kg/t** of pollutants for this technology

Briquetting by Stiff Extrusion vs Sintering
Environmental aspects

Stiff extrusion briquetting as a BAT?

- As mentioned earlier, pyro-metallurgical technologies of agglomeration are associated with the release of substantial emissions.
- The technology of briquetting by the method of stiff extrusion under vacuum conditions doesn't have such disadvantages. The technology does not require any heat treatment of raw materials or briquettes but still allows to produce a durable material.
- The main sources of environmental impact in the production of BREX is dust at the following stages:

  - warehouse storage of raw materials (unloading operations of charge materials, storage and feed into the technological process);

  - stages of dosing, mixing, extrusion (although very limited due to water addition);

  - BREX unloading, stacking and each handling step (attrition of the fine fraction, shipment to consumers);
- <u>Most of this dust can actually be collected and simply recycled into the process.</u>
- The main component of emissions into the atmospheric air in the production of BREX is inorganic dust. According to various assessments, the specific emission of inorganic dust in the production of BREX does not exceed 0.05 kg/t.

Briquetting by Stiff Extrusion vs Sintering & Indurating Environmental Aspects Comparison

	BAT criterion	Agglomerated iron-containing material		
		Sinter	Pellet	Brex
1	The minimum level of impact on the environment, kg/t:			
	- dust	≤1.2	≤0.6	0.05
	- nitrogen oxide	≤0.55	≤0.535	0
	- sulphur dioxide	≤4.0	≤0.5	0
	- carbon oxide	≤14.0	~0	0
	Total emissions, kg / t:	≤20 (≤10?)	≤2	≤0.05
2	Resources consumption:			
	- solid fuel, kg/t**	23.6-48.9	0	0
	- gaseous fuel, m^3/t	2.45-6.3	9.5-15.0	0
	- Electricity, kWh / t	23.0-48.7	29.0-48.5	25.0-35.0

Briquetting by Stiff Extrusion vs Sintering
Comparison of Agglomeration Technologies - Environmental aspects.
In 2017 Stiff Extrusion has been included into the List of Prospective Agglomeration Technologies of Russian Manual of BAT (Chapter 7., p. 7.1)

ФЕДЕРАЛЬНОЕ АГЕНТСТВО ПО ТЕХНИЧЕСКОМУ РЕГУЛИРОВАНИЮ И МЕТРОЛОГИИ

ИНФОРМАЦИОННО-ТЕХНИЧЕСКИЙ СПРАВОЧНИК ПО НАИЛУЧШИМ ДОСТУПНЫМ ТЕХНОЛОГИЯМ

ИТС 26–2017

ПРОИЗВОДСТВО ЧУГУНА, СТАЛИ И ФЕРРОСПЛАВОВ

Москва Бюро НДТ 2017

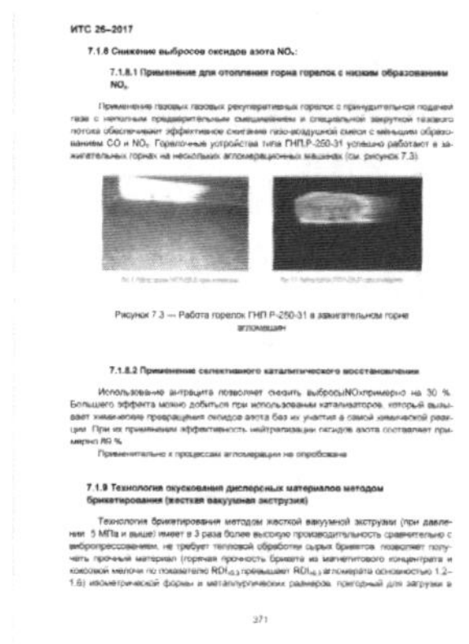

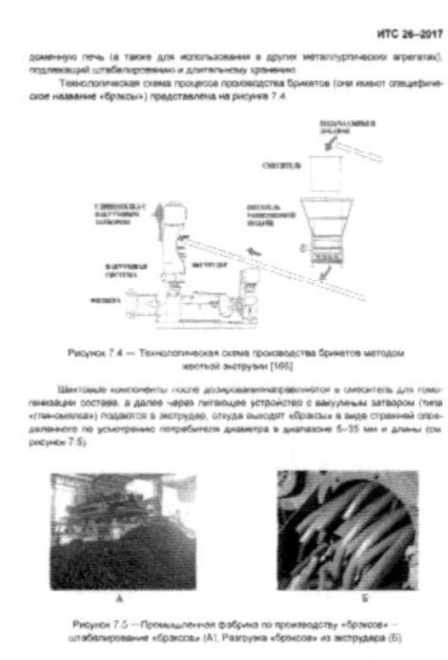

Briquetting by Stiff Extrusion vs Sintering
Partial Substitution of Sinter - Numerical Simulation

- The effectiveness of BREX in the charge of large blast furnaces was estimated by the method of mathematical modeling of blast furnace smelting using the "**DOMNA**" software.
- The blast furnace smelting in a furnace with a volume of 4297 m^3, operating under the conditions of NLMK, was modeled.
- Simulation of blast-furnace smelting was carried out for a mixture consisting of 3 components - **sinter, pellets and BREX**.
- The share of pellets is determined by the capacity of the pelletizing plant (Stoilensky GOK, **6 million tons of pellets per year**).
- The basicity of a BREX made from iron ore concentrate and low coking coal is determined from the content of cement (6%) and bentonite (1%) in the composition of the BREX, themselves based on the results of preliminary testing, and also taking into account the content of coal in the mixture. At the indicated contents of cement and bentonite, the basicity of BREX (B2) is **0.50 - 0.55**.

Briquetting by Stiff Extrusion vs Sintering
Partial Substitution of Sinter - Numerical Simulation

- The required basicity of the sinter is back calculated based on the accepted concept of replacing the sinter with BREX of a certain basicity.
- When replacing 50% of the sinter in the blast furnace charge with BREX, the basicity of the sinter should be between **2.8 and 3.2**.
- It should be noted that with such basicity in the structure of the sinter, the "flux" phases predominate, providing an increase in its strength compared to the sinter with basicity in the range of **1.5–1.7** that is characteristic of the sinter produced at NLMK.
- The coal content in BREX was back calculated by observing at what point the structural composition of BREX after heating in a reducing atmosphere to 1400 °C and after reaching almost complete metallization, unreacted coke breeze particles remained in the BREX structure due to its excessive content in the mixture for briquetting.

Briquetting by Stiff Extrusion vs Sintering
Partial Substitution of Sinter - Numerical Simulation

- The consumption of carbon-containing material in the charge for briquetting is calculated based on the stoichiometric ratio of oxygen and iron in BREX (O/Fe) by the time they arrive in the cohesion zone, where the temperature exceeds 1100 ° C and reduction takes place only with the participation of solid carbon.
- To simulate the blast smelting mentioned in the previous slide, the calculated compositions of sinters are shown for a basicity of **1.70 and 3.02.**
-

Materials	FeO	Fe_2O_3	SiO_2	Al_2O_3	CaO	MgO	C	SO_3
Portland cement	-	4.71	20.64	4.98	63.58	1.15	-	2.55
Bentonite	0.5	4.37	59.25	14.27	2.07	3.62	-	0.14
Coking coal	-	1.2	2.7	1.5	0.4	0.1	68.9	0.36
SGOK pellets	1.51	90.31	7.04	0.32	0.22	0.45	-	0.12
SGOK Iron ore concentrate	29.2	62.3	6.62	0.18	0.26	0.1	-	0.05
Sinter (1.70)	11.81	66.0	6.70	0.72	11.37	2.51	-	0.05
Sinter (3.02)	10.0	60.8	6.30	0.7	19.0	3.0	-	0.06
BREX	24.83	53.28	7.67	0.71	4.09	0.19	5.5	0.22

Briquetting by Stiff Extrusion vs Sintering
Partial Substitution of Sinter - Numerical Simulation

BF operation parameters	Base – no BREX	Variant 1	Variant 2
Sinter consumption (B2 = 1.7), kg/t	1109	-	-
Sinter consumption (B2 = 3.0), kg/t	-	557	575
SGOK pellets consumption, kg/t	546	557	541
Brex consumption , kg/t	-	557	575
SGOK iron ore consumption, kg/t	-	17	-
Fe content in charge, %	58.2	57.45	57.15
Coke rate, kg/t	391	354	284
Natural gas consumption, nm^3/t	125	125	35
Pulverized coal consumption, kg/t	-	-	160
Blast rate, m^3/min	7483	7568	7340
Blast temperature, °C	1240	1240	1240
O_2 content in blast, %	30.5	30.5	30.5
Blast humidity, g/m^3	10	10	20
Top gas yield, m^3/t	1545	1540	1470
Top gas pressure, kPa	240	240	240
CO,%	24.4	24.9	26.2
CO_2, %	23.2	22.6	23.9
H_2, %	9.7	9.9	8.2
Slag ratio, kg/t	318	314	323
Slag basicity, B2	1.01	1.01	1.02
Capacity, t/day	12465	12624	12708
Capacity, $t/m^2 \cdot day$	92.48	93.66	94.3
Reduction efficiency,%	94.2	94.2	94.2

- The simulation was carried out for [Si] = 0.4 %; [C] = 4.8 %; $T_{pig\ iron}$=1500 ° C;
- The results showed that due to the carbon contained in the BREX, the coke consumption for hot metal production is reduced compared to the base case by **10%**.
- When blowing natural gas with a consumption of 125 m^3/t of hot metal, coke consumption of **354 kg /t** of hot metal is achieved.
- When pulverized coal is injected with a flow rate of 160 kg/t of hot metal, coke consumption of **284 kg/t** of hot metal is achieved.

Briquetting by Stiff Extrusion vs Sintering Synergy of both Technologies

- When replacing 50% of the sinter production with the production of briquettes:
  - reduced consumption of iron ore concentrate;
  - eliminated sinter returns, by improving the quality of sinter;
  - limestone consumption increases;
  - increases the consumption of dolomite;
  - the consumption of skip sinter is reduced;
  - reduced consumption of dry skip coke takes place;
  - increases the basicity of the sinter (> **3.0**);
  - reduced the mass fraction of iron in the sinter;
  - 50% reduction in emissions (CO2 emissions by **32%**, dust by **50%**, sulfur dioxide by **43%**).
- The cost of production of 1 ton of BREX, with a line capacity of **700 kty**, is comparable to the cost of sinter with a sinter plant productivity of **7 million tons per year**.

Briquetting by Stiff Extrusion vs Sintering Embryos for Sintering?

Another possible important advantage of extrusion agglomeration is the preference for using extrusion for the preparation of nucleating agents for the production of sinter, revealed in industrial experiments carried out in Ukraine (link below). A number of essential parameters of sintering, including efficiency of sintering process in general, were improved by using embryos prepared on an extruder. According to this research, traditional methods of nucleation - the use of pellets or crushed roll briquettes - are said to be inferior in terms of extrusion efficiency.

Reference: **Pilyugin E.I., Semakova V.B. POSSIBLE APPLICATION OF ADDITIONS OF RECYCLED SELECTED SINTER FINES TO SINTER CHARGE.** ***Izvestiya. Ferrous Metallurgy.*** **2013;56(10):48-49. (In Russ.)** https://doi.org/10.17073/0368-0797-2013-10-48-49

Extrusion vs Sintering - Synergy

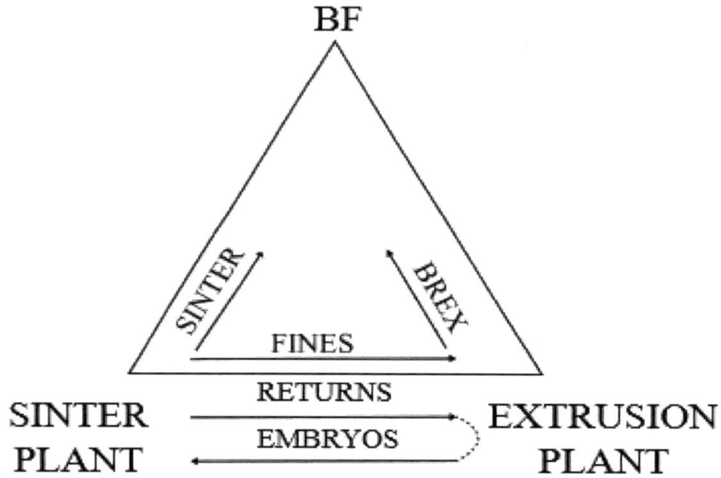

Thank You For Your attention

Direxa ENGINEERING

STEELE Since 1889

Clement Cadier – President / Direxa Engineering

DOI 10.1007/s11015-021-01208-8

Metallurgist, Vol. 65, Nos. 7-8, November, 2021 (Russian Original Nos. 7-8, July–August, 2021)

SINTERING AND BRIQUETTING SYNERGY IN BLAST FURNACE SMELTING

A. M. Bizhanov[1] **and C. Aubertot**[2]

UDC 669.162.1:662.788.3

The article describes the concept of partially replacing the sinter in a blast furnace charge with extrusion briquettes to form the basis for sintering and briquetting synergy. The comparability criteria for sinter and extrusion briquette (brex) properties and production parameters were analyzed along with a substantiation of the fundamental possibility of partially replacing sinter with brexes. Such replacement of 50% of the sinter in the blast furnace charge, leading to a proportional decrease in its production, was established to result in a twofold decrease in the harmful emissions of the sinter plant and the production of higher strength sinter due to the structure of the modified blast furnace charge. At the stage of sinter production, such an alteration will lead to a decrease in the total consumption of iron ore concentrate, as well as allowing blast furnace and aspiration fines used in the sinter charge to be output to briquetting. As a result of improved sinter quality, the formation of fines can be significantly reduced against the background of increased dolomite, limestone, and solid fuel consumption. The modified blast furnace charge is also characterized by a decrease in skip sinter and dry skip coke consumption. The results of calculating the options of 10, 20, and 30% partial sinter replacement in the charge are provided.

Keywords: sinter, pellets, extrusion briquette (brex), synergy, partial replacement of sinter, blast furnace charge.

In addition to the well-known negative impact on the environment, smelting of iron and steel is accompanied by the formation of significant quantities of iron-containing wastes, the direct processing of which is impossible or difficult without agglomeration. The most common currently used industrial agglomeration technologies are sintering and pelletizing. Both these techniques, which are based on the high-temperature processing of iron-containing raw materials, are associated with significant emissions of pollutants into the atmosphere (up to 20 kg/ton of sinter and 2 kg/ton of pellets for sintering and pelletizing, respectively).

Until recently, the third technique of briquetting was uncompetitive in comparison with sintering and pelletizing due to the insufficient capacity of briquetting equipment and the inconsistency of briquette properties with metallurgical processing requirements.

The situation changed with the advent on the agglomeration market of a rigid extrusion technology adapted for the production of extrusion briquettes (brexes), already widely used in more than 60 countries around the world for the production of ceramic bricks. The success of the first implemented projects confirmed the possibility of using this competing technology in place of sintering.

In order to further substantiate this possibility, we will compare the considered agglomeration technologies from the point of view of metallurgical properties of sinter and extrusion briquettes, the production of sintering and extrusion equipment, as well as their respective environmental impact.

[1] J. C. Steele & Sons, Inc., Statesville, North Carolina, USA; e-mail: abizhanov@jcsteele.com.

[2] Direxa Engineering, LLC, Denver, Colorado, USA; e-mail: CAubertot@direxa.com.

Translated from Metallurg, Vol. 65, No. 7, pp. 20–28, July, 2021. Russian DOI 10.52351/00260827_2021_07_20. Original article submitted May 19, 2021.

0026-0894/21/0708-0699

Table 1
Tumbler Test Strength of a Mill-Scale Brex

Parameter	Briquette sample			
	1	2	3	4
Initial mass m_0	15012	15001	14999	15000
m_1 (+ 6.30 mm)	12917	12948	12943	12909
m_2 (+ 0.5 mm)	239	215	229	221
m_3 (– 0.5 mm)	1690	1658	1685	1735
$d = m_0 - m_1 - m_2 - m_3$, g	166	180	142	135
$D = d/m_0$, %	1.1	1.2	0.9	0.9
TI = m_1/m_0, %	86.0	86.3	86.3	86.1
AI = $(m_0 - m_1 - m_2)/m_0$, %	12.4	12.3	12.2	12.5
TI (average), %	86.2	–	–	–
AI (average), %	12.3	–	–	–

Table 2
Component Composition of Sludge and Ore-Coke Brexes

Brex components	Mass fraction of components,%	
	brex 2	brex 4
Portland cement PC 500	9.1	9.0
Coke breeze	–	13.5
Bentonite	–	0.9
Blast furnace sludge	54.5	–
Converter sludge	36.4	–
Iron ore concentrate	–	76.6

It appears advisable to compare the mechanical strength of sinter and extrusion briquettes during tumbler tests in accordance with ISO 3271 (GOST 15137-77 "Iron and manganese ores, sinters, and pellets. Determination of tumbler strength"). This method is based on the mechanical processing of briquettes in a rotating steel tumbler (diameter 1000 mm, length 500 mm, 200 revolutions at a tumbler rotation frequency of 25 ± 1 min^{-1}). The subsequent determination of the change in the particle size distribution of the sample (– 0.5 mm, 0.5–6.3 mm, and + 6.3 mm) by screening characterizes the ability of briquettes to resist impact and abrasion during

Table 3
Results of Determining the Reduction-Disintegration Index of Brexes and Sinters of Various Basicity

Agglomerated material	RDI (+ 6.3), %
Brex 4* (basicity 0.75)	96.5
Brex 2* (basicity 1.93)	61.9
Sinter with a basicity of:	
1.2	64
1.4	60
1.6	77

transportation and overloading. The relative proportion of the – 0.5 mm fraction characterizes a briquette's resistance to abrasion (AI, Abrasion Index), while the proportion of the coarse fraction (+ 6.3 mm) designates its impact strength (TI, Tumble Index). According to this method, the quality of the sinter is considered satisfactory if its impact strength (Tumble Index) is not lower than 70%. Table 1 shows the results of measuring the strength of brexes made of mill scale using a cement binder. As can be seen, in terms of the impact strength, brexes exceed the rejection limit for sinter. The slightly higher abrasion index values presented in the study [1] are explained by the numerical modeling results of the brex tumbler test. The obtained results associate the increase in abrasion with the peculiarities of briquettes falling on the steel surface of the tumbler and create the basis for revising the rejection limits of the briquette abrasion strength in such tests, which will result in an adequate comparison of this parameter with that for the sinter.

A comparison of the reduction-disintegration indices for sinter and brexes of various composition was carried out in [2]. The authors studied the metallurgical properties of brexes made from blast furnace and converter sludge, as well as iron-carbon brexes composed of Stoilenskii MPP iron ore concentrate and coke breeze (Table 2), which were also considered as a promising blast furnace charge component.

Reduction-disintegration tests of sludge and concentrate brexes performed according to ISO 4696 demonstrated the significant advantage of concentrate brexes ($RDI_{+6.3}$ = 96.5%) as compared to sludge brexes ($RDI_{+6.3}$ = 61.8%). This is explained by the absence of any hematite in the former and, conversely, by the presence in the sludge brexes (in the particles of both blast furnace and converter sludge) of secondary hematite having a crystal lattice rearranged by increasing geometric parameters during low-temperature and slow reduction. This causes mechanical stress and disintegration of material pieces containing hematite.

For comparison, the reduction-disintegration indices of sinters with a basicity $(CaO+MgO)/(Al_2O_3+SiO_2)$ of 1.2, 1.4, and 1.6, obtained from the PJSC "NLMK" conventional charge, were simultaneously evaluated according to the same standard (Table 3). The reduction-disintegration index of the sludge brexes is comparable to that of a sinter having a basicity of 1.2 and 1.4 (64 and 60%), which is explained by the similar content of secondary hematite in these materials. The reduction-disintegration indices of a sinter having a basicity of 1.6 (77%) is higher than that of a sludge brexes due to a new phase of calcium ferrites already appearing in the sinter at a basicity of 1.6, which strengthens its structure and reduces its disintegration during low-temperature reduction. Due to the strength of the cement binder and the absence of ore particle disintegration during low-temperature reduction, the reduction-disintegration index ($RDI_{+6.3}$) of brexes produced from magnetite iron ore concentrate and coke breeze was experimentally established to significantly exceed the reduction-disintegration index of sinters having a basicity (B4) of 1.2, 1.4, and 1.6.

The reduction-disintegration mechanism is qualitatively illustrated in Figs. 1 and 2, where provided brex structures following reduction at 1400°C demonstrate the formation of a characteristic network metallic iron within which wustite microzones are located. The metal precipitated from the glass phase develops silicates in uncrystallized form.

Thus, after the binding capacity of the cement has been lost, the low reduction-disintegration index of the brex is provided as a result of the formation (even during gas reduction) of a surface metal frame-shell and an iron silicate matrix, from which iron can be reduced at temperatures above 1100°C using coke breeze carbon.

At the beginning of 2021, studies were performed to investigate the metallurgical properties of extrusion briquettes based on iron-containing electrostatic precipitator dusts with cement binder (8%) and bentonite plasticizer (0.8%). An independent laboratory (CCI, part of the COTEGNA GROUP) carried out a set of studies, including:

- determination of the relative reducibility according to the ISO 7215 standard; here, the sample is exposed to a reducing gas mixture consisting of CO (30%) and N_2 (70%) for 180 min at a temperature of 900°C; the final reduction index is determined by the mass loss during the reduction process; reducing gas consumption – 15 Liter/min; diameter of the test sample – 19 mm; length – 19–120 mm;

- determination of the free-swelling index according to the ISO 4698 standard (for pellets); the sample is exposed to a reducing gas mixture consisting of CO (30%) and N_2 (70%) for 60 min at a temperature of 900°C; the free-swelling index is defined as the difference between sample volumes before and after reduction; reducing gas consumption – 15 L/min; diameter of the test sample – 19 mm; length – 19–120 mm;

- determination of the low-temperature reduction-disintegration index;

- dynamic grinding according to ISO 13930; the sample in the rotating tube is exposed to a reducing gas mixture consisting of CO (20%), CO_2 (20%), H_2 (2%), and N_2 (58%) for 60 min at a temperature of 500°C; the low-temperature reduction-disintegration index is determined depending on the size class: + 6.3 mm, – 3.15 mm, and – 0.5 mm; reducing gas consumption – 20 Liter/min; diameter of the test sample – 19 mm; length – 19–120 mm.

The results of measuring the metallurgical properties of the samples are given in Table 4 and Figs. 3-6.

According to CCI, the test results for iron briquettes fall within in the range of values obtained for iron ore pellets and sinter samples of a good quality. Thus, both the mechanical strength and the reduction-disintegration index of the brexes demonstrate that their respective properties are at a level exceeding that of sinter. Long-term practical experience of operating a number of briquette plants as part of blast furnace shops (Russia, Japan, India, Chile, etc.) confirms the high metallurgical properties of brexes, achieved at a significantly lower binder content than when using alternative briquette technologies.

From the point of view of comparing the production rate of sinter and briquette plants, the undoubted superiority of sinter plants according to this parameter should be recognized. Moreover, the already accumulated logistic experience of large-scale plants for brex production indicates the possibility of achieving a production rate of 2000–7000 ton of brexes per day. The production rate of sinter strand and indurating machine comprises 1500–10000 and 2500–9000 ton/day, respectively. By comparison, the world's largest ceramic brick factory, Saudi Red Brick Plant, produces 1 million bricks a day using rigid extrusion technology.

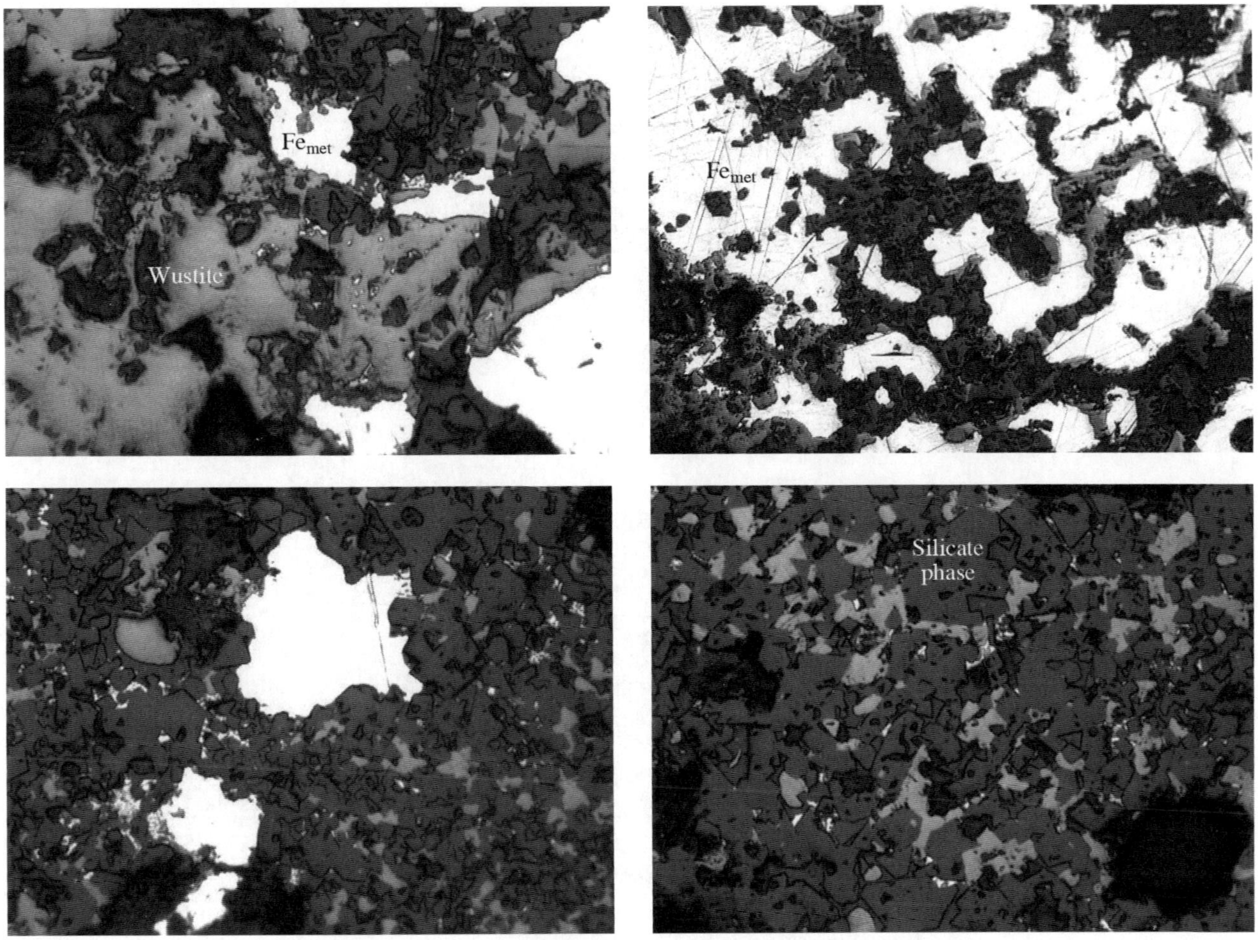

Fig. 1. Optical microscopy image of brex following reduction heating at 1400°C, × 200.

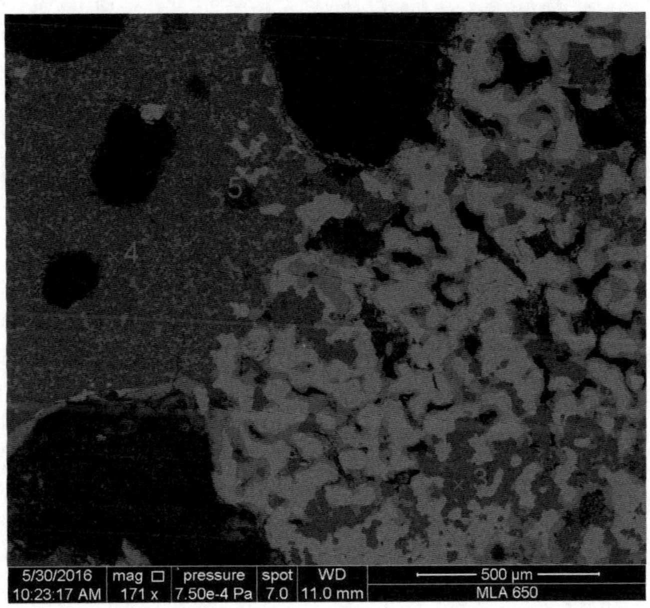

Fig. 2. SEM image of brex following reduction heating at 1400°C: 1 – α-iron; 2 – wustite; 3, 4 – glass phase; 5 – wustite.

Fig. 3. Sample appearance before testing.

Fig. 4. Sample appearance after measuring the relative reducibility (ISO 7215).

Fig. 5. Sample appearance after free-swelling test (ISO 4698).

Fig. 6. Sample appearance after low-temperature reduction-disintegration test (ISO 13930).

Table 4
Independent Testing Results of Briquette Metallurgical Properties

Indicator	Regulations	Results
Total iron Fe_t, %	ISO 2597-1	47.61
Fe(II) oxide, %	ISO 9035	10.23
Final degree of reduction index R_{180}, %	ISO 7215	88.8
Free-swelling index FSI, %	ISO 4698	9.4
Low-temperature disintegration index:		
+ 6.3 mm – $LTD_{+6.3}$, %		86.1
– 3.15 mm – $LTD_{-3.15}$, %	ISO 13930	13.8
– 0.5 mm – $LTD_{-0.5}$, %		13.6

The sintering process is carried out by burning solid fuel in an air stream filtered through a layer of iron ore charge. As a result of physical and chemical processes in the sinter layer, emitted pollutants include:

– dust emissions caused by the mechanical removal of a finely dispersed charge from the layer or formed during the destruction of materials (sinter when coming off the sinter strand; sinter cake when cooled, crushed, and screened following sintering);

– emissions of carbon monoxide CO, technologically justified due to the peculiarities of combustion of the solid fuel distributed in the sinter layer (incomplete combustion);

– emissions of sulfur dioxide SO_2, depending on the sulfur content in coke breeze and coal, used as fuel, as well as on the composition of the iron ore charge;

– emissions of nitrogen oxides NO_x from the combustion process in the ignition hood and of solid fuel partly, as well as due to the emission of "thermal" nitrogen oxides caused by the nitrogen contained in coke breeze and iron ore materials.

Sintering has significant environmental impacts. At a typical integrated metallurgical enterprise, sintering occupies a leading position in the quantity of pollutant emissions generated for all the most significant emission components (dust, carbon monoxide, sulfur dioxide, nitrogen oxides) (Table 5) [3].

By contrast with the sintering process, in rigid vacuum extrusion (pressure range 1.5–3.5 MPa or even higher; mixture moisture content of 12–16%), no heat treatment of raw briquettes is required. The strong obtained material (see Table 3) of isometric shape and dimensions is suitable for loading into a blast furnace, withstanding stacking, multiple handling, and long-term storage in ambient conditions. As in the case of non-fired pellets, a binder is necessarily introduced into the charge of the brex production; however, its consumption is reduced as compared to the production of non-fired pellets [4]. In some cases (for certain charge types), the addition of a plasticizer is required for the production of brexes.

Table 5
Atmospheric Emissions of the Main Production Facilities of the Iron and Steel Industry

Production	Share of production in the total volume of component emissions, %			
	dust	CO	SO_2	NO_x
Sintering	31.1	77.8	61.0	26.0
Steelmaking	19.7	5.4	0.02	6.5
Refractory	18.4	0.4	0.4	5.4
Blast furnace	17.3	3.5	0.3	3.0
Energy (TPP-TBS)	7.4	No data	36.7	36.6
By-product coke-making	2.0	7.8	1.0	9.1
Rolling	1.2	No data	0.2	10.5
Repair	1.0	4.9	0.02	1.5
Other	1.9	0.2	0.36	1.4
Total:	100	100	100	100

The main sources of environmental impact during the production of brexes include the following (in aggregate):

- warehouse of raw materials (operations of unloading charge materials, storage, and supply to the technological process);
- dosing, mixing, extrusion department;
- unloading of brexes, stacking, and processing of a stack (screening of fines, shipment to consumers);
- shop space aspiration system.

Inorganic dust represents the priority component of air emissions in brex production. According to estimates, the specific emission of inorganic dust in the production of brexes does not exceed 0.05 kg/ton.

A comparison of the main industrial agglomeration technologies according to the criteria of the best available technologies (BAT) [5–6] is presented in Table 6. As can be seen, under reduced sinter production, half of the released capital funds is sufficient for the construction of a brex production plant.

The undoubted competitive advantage of extrusion agglomeration consists in its minimal environmental impacts due to the absence of energy consumption for high-temperature processing of raw brexes. Thus, the possibility of effective partial replacement of sinter with brexes is substantiated according to the criteria listed above (metallurgical properties, equipment production rate, and environmental impacts).

When fine-dispersed waste (dust and sludge) is used in the sintering, additional energy and material resources are expended. Moreover, not all such materials can be effectively used as part of sinter charge, leading to a constant increase in dumps (technogenic deposits) at the territory of enterprises. Depending on the country,

Table 6
Characteristics of Various Agglomeration Technologies According to the Criteria of Best Available Technologies (Bat)

BAT criterion	Agglomerated iron ore feedstock		
	sinter	pellets	brexes
Minimum level of environmental impact, kg/ton:			
dust	≤ 1.2	≤ 0.6	0.05
nitrogen oxides	≤ 0.55	≤ 0.535	0
sulfur dioxide	≤ 4.0	≤ 0.5	0
carbon monoxide	≤ 14.0	~ 0	0
Total emissions, kg/ton	≤ 20.0	≤ 2.0	≤ 0.05
Resource consumption:			
solid fuel, kg/ton	23.6–48.9	0	0
gaseous fuel, m^3/ton	2.45–6.3	9.5–15.0	0
electricity, kWh/ton	23.0–48.7	29.0–48.5	15.0–33.0
Investments, RUB/ton	≈ 5000	≈ 5500	≈ 2000
Implementation period, years	3	3	2
Implementation (at one or more enterprises)	Yes	Yes	Yes

the disposal of such waste is either prohibited or allowed only following its neutralization involving significant costs.

Since its composition is close to that of a blast furnace charge, blast furnace dust represents a very valuable material. However, the poor agglomeration ability of the material due to its high carbon content and fineness hinders its use in sinter production. Although metallurgists have partially solved the problems of using blast furnace dust in the composition of the sinter charge, a number of experts believe that a significant proportion of the dust is not incorporated in the sinter cake due to its poor agglomeration ability, instead being carried away with sinter gases to pass once more into the sludge. Although the carbon of the blast furnace dust does not react during the sintering process, carbon of the blast furnace dust can be effectively used for the reduction of oxides in the composition of the briquette, leading to a decrease in coke consumption.

Although converter dust and sludge can be used as an additive in sinter production, this leads to a significant decrease in the production rate of sintering machines associated with the deterioration in agglomeration and gas permeability, as well as a significant quantity of alkalis and zinc entering the blast furnace to negatively effect blast furnace operation. Due to the unstable chemical and granulometric composition of technogenic raw materials of various genesis, their use in sinter charges at plants lacking the possibility of dosing in a homogenization stockpile negatively affects the stability of the composition and quality of the sinter.

The partial replacement of sinter with brexes was discussed for the first time in [7] in connection with achieving a high proportion of briquettes in a blast furnace charge (up to 100%). In the present study, this concept has been revised and developed in the form of a statement about the possibility and feasibility of achieving

Table 7
Proportion of Sinter in the Charge Depending on the Slag Basicity*

Sinter basicity	Slag basicity				
	1.00	1.05	1.10	1.15	1.20
1.04	1.000	–	–	–	–
1.20	0.796	0.873	0.951	–	–
1.30	0.718*	0.790	0.860	0.930	1.000
1.40	0.648	0.710	0.773	0.836	0.899
1.50	0.591	0.648	0.705	0.762	0.819
1.60	0.544	0.596	0.648	0.700	0.753
1.70	0.503	0.551	0.599	0.647	0.696
1.80	0.469	0.514	0.558	0.604	0.649
1.90	0.438	0.480	0.522	0.564	0.606
2.00	0.411	0.450	0.490	0.529	0.569
2.10	0.388	0.425	0.462	0.499	0.537
2.20	0.367	0.402	0.437	0.472	0.507
2.30	0.348	0.381	0.414	0.447	0.481
2.40	0.331	0.362	0.394	0.425	0.457
2.50	0.315	0.345	0.375	0.405	0.436
2.60	0.301	0.330	0.358	0.387	0.416
2.70	0.289	0.316	0.343	0.371	0.398
2.80	0.277	0.303	0.329	0.356	0.382
2.90	0.266	0.291	0.316	0.341	0.367
3.00	0.256	0.280	0.304	0.328	0.353

Comments: * Basic variant without brexes, consisting of sinter and pellets in amount of 0.718 and 0.282, respectively; in variants with a higher slag basicity, the lower proportion of pellets is provided by addition of brexes; in other variants, the proportion of pellets is preserved.

synergy between sintering and extrusion briquetting, obtained as a result of a 50% reduction in sinter production. Such a synergy results in a twofold decrease in emissions and a proportional decrease in the amount of sinter in the blast furnace charge, which is compensated by adding brexes made of materials removed from the sintering process. As a result, the strength of the modified charge (sinter + brex) increases, firstly, due to the use of stronger brexes, and secondly, due to the production of a stronger sinter (with or without a reduced proportion of secondary materials having higher basicity). Ultimately, this will lead to a decrease in the formation of fine fractions in the sintering and blast-furnace processes.

As follows from calculations for the conditions of one of the plants (Table 7), a decrease in the proportion of sinter in the blast furnace charge requires an increase in sinter basicity. The calculation conditions included

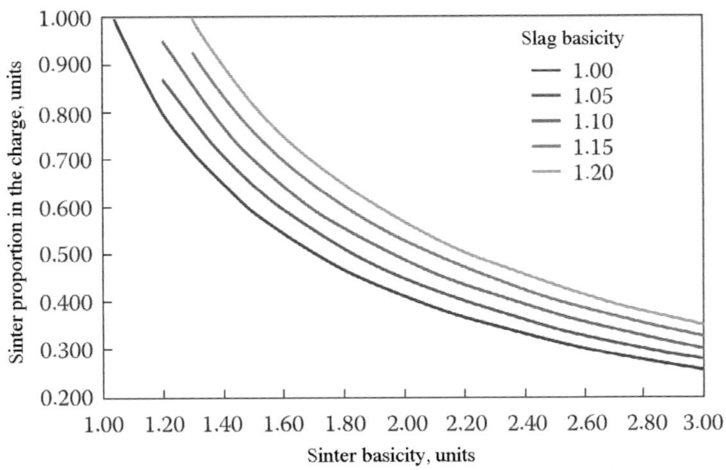

Fig. 7. Dependence of the sinter proportion in the blast furnace charge on the basicity of the sinter and slag.

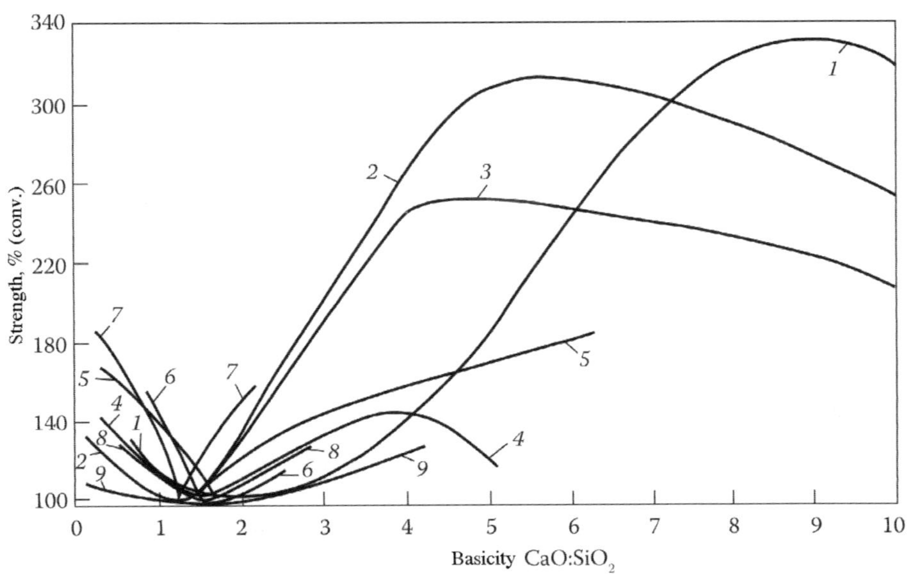

Fig. 8. Influence of the basicity of the sinter on its strength, depending on the quality of raw materials [8]: *1–3* – finely ground concentrate, rich, medium, and poor in iron, respectively; *4* – a mixture of ores; *5* – fine concentrate and dusty ore mixture; *6* – magnetite ore; *7* – hematite ore; *8, 9* – ore mixture

the use of brexes offering a stable proportion of fluxed pellets and maintaining the basicity of the blast furnace slag, as well as the exclusion of wet fluxes from the blast furnace process.

Figure 7 shows the graphical dependence of the sinter proportion in the charge on its basicity.

According to Table 7 and Fig. 7, for the basicity of a blast furnace slag at the level of 1.00–1.10, which is characteristic of almost all blast furnace premises in Russia, a decrease in the proportion of sinter in the charge to below 0.5 will require sinter basicity of at least 1.7. Similarly, at a sinter proportion below 0.3, basicity approaches the value of 3 ("iron flux" value).

For a sinter proportion in the blast furnace charge of less than 50%, the basicity of the sinter is shown in Table 8.

In turn, an increase in the basicity of the sinter (above the minimum values of 1.3–1.5 [8]) is known to result in enhanced strength characteristics for almost all types of iron ores (Fig. 8).

Table 8
Sinter Basicity Depending on Its Proportion in the Blast Furnace Charge

Operating parameters under maintained sinter basicity B = 1.315	Consumption of briquettes, % of iron ore mixture			
Consumption, kg/t of cast iron	0 (base)	10	20	30
Sinter	1193	1037	879	719
Pellets	443	449	450	454
Briquettes	0	165	332	503
Coke (dry skip)	426	426	425	423
Limestone	0	40	60	80
Dolomite	0	0	10	20
Correction of sinter basicity				
Recommended sinter basicity to exclude wet flux from blast furnace smelting	1.32	1.53	1.79	2.21
Consumption, kg/t of cast iron		167.01	169.94	173.08
Sinter	1193	1051	899	743
Pellets	443	453	461	469
Briquettes	0	167	340	519
Coke (dry skip)	426	417	409	401
Limestone	0	0	0	0
Dolomite	0	0	0	0

Comments: The basicity of the slag is 0.99; the proportion of pellets in the charge is 27.1%; gas utilization and slag composition rates are constant. Briquettes are composed by 80% of a concentrate mixture (Mikhailovskii and Lebedinskii 3:1), 13% of coke breeze, 6% of cement, and 1% of bentonite.

In accordance with Fig. 8, for the conditions of calculations, whose results are provided in Tables 7–8 and Fig. 7, replacing 50% of the sinter by brexes with a corresponding increase in the basicity of the sinter will lead to an increase in its strength by 60–80% (only by increasing the basicity!). An additional strength increase achieved by removing dust and sludge from the sinter charge in contributes to a more than twofold increase in total strength.

When "acidic" pellets are used, the sinter is initially more basic. Nevertheless, an increase in its basicity to a level of at least 2.0–2.5 will also provide the possibility of using brexes in the blast furnace charge to remove secondary materials from the sintering.

Thus, in addition to a twofold decrease in harmful emissions, a twofold reduction in the proportion of sinter in the blast furnace charge will result in increased strength of the produced sinter and, subsequently, a significant (to a minimum) decrease in the oversize at the blast furnace plant. At older facilities where no sinter screening operation is available, this will minimize the harmful effect of this factor on the process indicators (every 1% decrease in the content of a 5–0 mm fine fraction in an iron ore charge will lead to a decrease in coke consumption and an increase in production rate by 0.5 and 1.0%, respectively [3]. In addition, the following changes in the sinter charge are expected:

– secondary materials such as blast furnace and aspiration dust, as well as sludge, are partially or completely removed from the sintering;

– the consumption of limestone and dolomite is increased;

– solid fuel consumption is increased;

– specific consumption of iron ore concentrate is increased while absolute consumption is reduced.

In blast furnace smelting, the implemented concept of partial replacement of sinter with brexes is expected to result in:

– reduced consumption of skip sinter along with a significant increase in strength characteristics;

– the possibility of increasing the proportion of pellets in the charge;

– decreased specific consumption of coke and an increased production rate as a result of a decrease in the proportion of fines.

– a change in the mass fraction of iron depending on the composition of the brexes and the proportion of charge components.

The possibility of achieving a high briquette proportion in the blast furnace charge is demonstrated in the studies of [9–12] devoted to the analysis of the results of a pilot smelting performed at PJSC "NLMK" in 2003.

When smelting a pilot batch of briquettes (2475 tons) from a mixture of iron ore concentrate, coke breeze, and Portland cement (15% of the briquette mass), the level of briquette consumption exceeded 303 kg/ton of cast iron. The results of the smelting confirmed such briquettes to comprise a self-reducing blast furnace charge component, ensuring a decrease in coke consumption proportional to briquette consumption during blast furnace smelting. The proportion of such a component in the blast furnace charge, which is only slightly limited by a decrease in the furnace production rate as a result of a decrease in the charge iron content, can reach 50% or more. The maximum achieved value of the briquette proportion in the ore part of the charge was about 19%. Achieving this level required a serious "dilution" of the charge using 15% of cement. For extrusion briquettes, the required reduction-disintegration index is provided by 6–9% of cement. Further reductions in binder consumption achieved using polymer binders will increase the degree of technically feasible replacement of sinter with brexes.

CONCLUSION

In general, the partial replacement of sinter by brexes in a blast furnace charge will improve the quality of the sinter both as a result of the necessary increase in basicity and due to the possible removal of secondary materials from the sinter charge, leading not only to reduced coke consumption and increased production rate at the blast furnace, but also to a decrease in total emissions and consequent environmental impact.

REFERENCES

1. A. M. Bizhanov and S. A. Zagainov, "Testing of briquettes for mechanical strength," *Metallurg,* No. 3, 11–18 (2021).
2. I. F. Kurunov, A. M. Bizhanov, D. N. Tikhonov, and N. R. Mansurova, "Metallurgical properties of brexes," *Metallurg,* No. 6, 44–48 (2012).
3. Yu. A. Frolov, *Sintering: Technology, Heat Engineering, Management* [In Russian], Metallurgizdat, Moscow (2016).
4. V. E. Lotosh, *Non-Firing Agglomeration of Finely Dispersed Materials and Minerals* [In Russian], Publ. "Filantrop," Yekaterinburg (2009).
5. *ITS NDT 26 "Production of Cast Iron, Steel, and Ferroalloys"* [in Russian], Electronic resource: /www.burondt.ru/NDT/NDTDocsDetail/.
6. *ITS NDT 25 "Extraction and Beneficiation of Iron Ores"* [in Russian], Electronic resource: /www.burondt.ru/NDT/NDTDocsDetail/.
7. A. M. Bizhanov and I. F. Kurunov, *Extrusion Briquettes (Brexes) – a New Stage in the Agglomeration of Raw Materials in Ferrous Metallurgy* [in Russian], Metallurgizdat, Moscow (2017).
8. E. F. Vegman, B. N. Zherebin, A. N. Pokhvisnev, and Yu. S. Yusfin, *Cast Iron Metallurgy* [in Russian], Metallurgiya, Moscow, 184–204 (2004).
9. I. F. Kurunov, E. M. Shcheglov, A. I. Kononov, O. G. Bol'shakova, et al., "Study of the metallurgical properties of briquettes from technogenic and natural raw materials with an assessment of their application effectiveness in a blast furnace smelting. Part 1," *Byul. NTiEI "Chernaya Metallurgiya,"* No. 12. 39–48 (2007).
10. I. F. Kurunov, E. M. Shcheglov, A. I. Kononov, O. G. Bol'shakova, et al., "Study of the metallurgical properties of briquettes from technogenic and natural raw materials with an assessment of their application effectiveness in blast-furnace smelting. Part 2," *Byul. NTiEI "Chernaya Metallurgiya,"* No. 1, 8–16 (2008).
11. I. F. Kurunov, T. Ya. Malysheva, and O. G. Bol'shakova, "Study of the phase composition of iron ore briquettes for assessing their behavior in a blast furnace," *Metallurg,* No. 10. 41–46 (2007).
12. I. F. Kurunov, O. G. Bol'shakova, E. M. Shcheglov, et al., "Experience of washing the hearth of blast furnaces with scale briquettes," *Metallurg,* No. 6, 36–39 (2007).

Institute for Briquetting and Agglomeration

2022 IBA CONFERENCE PAPERS

Paper Title:

Cold-Bonded Briquette Testing Methodology and Standards Used for Traditional Furnace Feedstocks

Presenter:

Mac Steele and Mark T. Ford

Company:

J.C. Steele and Sons, Inc

Cold-Bonded Briquette Testing Methodology and Standards Used for Traditional Furnace Feedstocks

Mac Steele, Mark T. Ford

J.C. Steele and Sons, Inc
710 South Mulberry Street, NC, USA, 28677
Phone: 704.872.3681
Email: macsteele@jcsteele.com

ABSTRACT

Alternative feedstocks, like all feedstocks, must meet certain requirements for use in furnaces. This paper compares one alternative feedstock, cold-bonded briquettes, to other feedstocks: iron ore pellets (IOP), lump iron ore, and coking coal. It also evaluates various tests to predict briquette performance in the furnace, including tumble index and shatter index. Does an accurate prediction of acceptable performance require a new test or a combination of tests? At what point do the increased additives required to meet the mill's existing raw material standards have a negative impact on the furnace performance?

Keywords: Cold-Bonded Briquettes, Extrusion, Briquettes, Briquetting, Circular Economy, Tumble Test, Shatter Test, Byproducts, Recycling

1. INTRODUCTION

The steel industry dates to the beginning of the Iron Age, 4000 years ago, while modern industrial steelmaking began in the mid-nineteenth century. Early steelmakers used a wide variety of raw materials, which affected the quality of their product. As steelmaking evolved, steelmakers learned to prefer the highest quality and consistency in their raw materials. Webster defines quality as a "peculiar and essential character." In steelmaking, quality in raw materials meets defined physical, chemical, and metallurgical process requirements. Consistency, which Webster defines as "tending to be arbitrarily close to the true value of the parameter estimated as the sample becomes larger," is equally important. When it comes to processing steel and adding iron-making byproducts for reuse to an existing process, these two definitions are almost contradictory. The raw materials are byproducts, or impurities removed from raw materials themselves during a prior steelmaking process. Regardless of the challenge of taking impurities captured in industrial quantities and reshaping them into furnace feedstock for reuse, the goal is the same: raw material of consistently high quality. For years, iron and steelmakers have refined their process to handle similar raw materials with similar qualifications. Because of tighter regulatory control over the environmental impact of these byproducts, there are now more reasons to recover and reuse them in production. In "*Characterization of Iron Oxide Pellets used in the Production of Iron and Steel*," presented at the 2019 International Briquetting and Agglomeration conference, Battle [1] focused on testing standards used for iron ore pellets in Direct Reduced Iron (DRI) plants. His findings were consistent with the challenges facing extruded briquettes, i.e., the tests for extruded briquettes are common, but not necessarily relevant to the product being tested. This raises the question of how to define the new, cold-bonded recycled feedstock.

To narrow the focus to the type of furnace targeted, we reviewed blast furnace burdens. The primary raw materials for blast furnaces are pelletized ore, lump ore, sinter, and coke, as shown in Table 1. Blast Furnace Burden Materials. Briquettes made with stiff extrusion are typically used as a supplemental burden, to help recover value in waste streams that are unusable in their existing shape or form (they may be too fine, too coarse, or too wet). J.C. Steele and Sons' stiff extrusion technology works with a range of raw materials that would otherwise be landfilled or sold at a loss. There are other cold-bonding technologies, of course, and like stiff extrusion, they also have limitations in moisture and particle size distribution (PSD). This paper focuses on using stiff extrusion to produce cold-bonded briquettes. There are multiple papers that address cold-bonded briquetting [e.g. 2, 3, 4, 5] and feeding the briquettes into the blast furnaces. The challenge that arises is the range of different methodologies used to test the physical and metallurgical properties of these extruded briquettes.

Table 1. Blast Furnace Burden Materials

Material	Iron Ore Pellets	Lump Iron Ore	Sinter	Coke	Cold-Bonded Briquettes
Purpose	Primary >65% Fe feedstock	Primary >67% Fe feedstock	Primary iron bearing burden material with some contained flux; Consumes some byproduct streams from the plant	Thermal - provides heat, Chemical - provides carbon, Physical - provides permeable layer and structural support (Silveira; et al., 2017)	Burden additive - consumes some byproduct streams from the mill
Generic Material Makeup	Ironbearing feedstock	Ironbearing feedstock	Ironbearing feedstock with some flux and carbon	Carbon	Ironbearing and carbon bearing byproducts
Testing Methodology Used	ISO 3271 - >6.3 mm min 95%; <0.5 mm max 5%	ISO 3271 - >6.3 mm min 85%; <0.5 mm max 10%	ISO 3271 - >6.3 mm min 95%;	ISO/DIS 616 - Shatter Index	None specifically defined. It is an aggregate of some combination of known testing procedures.

Each burden is qualified in the following "buckets" for its respective role:

General Characteristics: Size, Shape, Density, Porosity, Moisture, Chemistry, Grain Size, Binder Selection, Drying/Curing Times

Performance, Physical: Drop Test, Split Tensile Strength Test, Single-Point Break Strength, Compressive Strength, "Shatter" Test, Tumble Test, Abrasion Test

Performance, Metallurgical: Determination of Relative Reducibility, Swelling Index, Gas Permeability, Softening Temperatures, Reduction Disintegration Index (RDI) or Fines Production, Chemistry, Mineralogy

Cost: Both calculated costs, such as production of pellets and cost savings (waste streams and the ancillary benefits of a more positive ecological profile for shareholders and public), satisfying regulatory bodies, meeting benchmarks on recycling (company set, contracted, or legislated), "carbon credits," etc.

Cold-bonded briquette recipes are typically made by taking the greatest quantity of byproducts available and consuming them. The chemistry is not altered significantly in the cold-bonding process, apart from whatever binding system is used, especially when using a Portland cement (PC) system, which adds a small percentage of calcium into the mix. Therefore, chemistry restrictions placed on the finished product are a result of introducing raw materials into the cold-bonding process. This paper will focus solely on the physical tests performed on cold-bonded briquettes produced with stiff extrusion.

2. METHODS

There are many methods available to characterize feedstocks. We focused solely on cold strength testing, using the raw materials testing traditionally requested by integrated mills. These tests represent the market standard for physically qualifying raw materials and assessing their suitability for extruded products:

ASTM E279-18/ISO 3271 Determination of Abrasion Resistance of Iron Ore Pellets, Lump, and Sinter by the Tumbler Test

ASTM E382-12/ISO 4700 Determination of Crushing Strength of Iron Ore Pellets

IS 9963: Determination of Shatter Index for iron ore lumps, sinter and pellets - Bureau of Indian Standards (BIS) – Indian Specific

ISO/DIS 616:2020(E) — Coke (Determination of shatter indices)

2.1. TUMBLE TESTING

The ISO 3271 test is the most requested test. The Test Plant at J.C. Steele and Sons uses the procedure shown below in Figure 1 based on the ISO 3271 Fourth Edition 2007-10-01.

SOP.09 – ISO 3271-JCSS PELLET TUMBLE TEST

REV.16.10.12.JFF

This procedure is based on ISO 3271 Fourth Edition 2007-10-01 ***Iron ores for blast furnace and direct reduction feedstocks – Determination of the tumble and abrasion indices***

TEST # / DESCRIPTION: ______________________ DATE: ____________ SAMPLE ______ OF ______

1. Dry 60 kg of the test sample at 105°C down to 0.1% or less wet basis moisture
2. Return to room temperature
3. Prepare a 15 kg ± 0.15 kg sample of pellets
4. Record mass: ________________ grams (m_0)
5. Place sample in the ISO 3271 compliant tumbler with lifting bars installed
6. Tightly fasten door
7. Set drum rotation to 25 r/min ± 1 r/m

   ⚠CAUTION

   Pellet tumbling is loud. Hearing protection is required.
8. Rotate drum 200 revolutions
9. Stop drum and wait 2 minutes
10. Remove all material from the drum, dry sieve and record:
    a. Retained ISO 3310 screen (6.30mm) ______________ grams (m_1)
    b. Retained ISO 3310 screen (500 micron) ______________ grams (m_2)
    c. Passing ISO 3310 screen (500 micron) ______________ grams (m_3)

NOTE ***If the difference between the initial mass of the test portion and the total mass of the fraction m_1, m_2, and m_3 exceeds 1.0%, the test is rejected.***

11. Photograph results
12. Place the retained 500 micron sample (m_2) and the minus 500 micron sample (m_3) in sealed plastic bags
13. Place bags in larger sealed container with remainder of tumbled sample (m_1)
14. Calculate results:
    a. Tumble Index $TI = (m_1/m_0)x100$
    b. Abrasion Index $AI = (m_0-m_1-m_2)x100/m_0$
15. Repeat steps 3 through 14 on three additional 15 kg samples

J.C. STEELE & SONS, INC. • 710 S Mulberry Street • Statesville, NC 28677 • P.O. Box 1834 (28687)
+1.704.872.3681 • 800.278.3353 • www.jcsteele.com

Figure 1. J.C. Steele SOP.09 – ISO 3271 Pellet Tumble Test

2.2. COMPRESSION TESTING

The second common test is the ASTM Standard E0382 and ISO 4700, which Thomas Battle referred to in his 2019 IBA paper. This test evaluates selected spherical pellets. Since extruded briquettes are not spherical, we modified our test to account for the cylindrical shape of the extruded product. J.C. Steele uses two tests for compression testing: split tensile and single-point break tests. Our split tensile testing is an interpretation of ASTM C1006, Paragraph 7.1 shown in Figure 2. For a split tensile test, the briquettes are cylindrical in shape but must be cut to have parallel ends as shown in Figure 3. This test only uses cured pellets, as green pellets do not rupture during testing, they deform, which skews our data.

Certain pellets were evaluated for splitting tensile strength per ASTM C1006, Paragraph 7.1:

$$T = 2P/\pi DL, \text{ where:}$$

T = Splitting tensile strength, psi
P = Splitting force, lbf
D = Pellet diameter, inches
L = Pellet length, inches

Figure 2. Splitting Tensile Strength per ASTM C1006, Paragraph 7.1

SOP.13 – PELLET SPLIT TENSILE STRENGTH

REV.16.11.22.JFF

Either green or cured cylindrical pellets can be evaluated for splitting tensile strength per ASTM C1006, Paragraph 7.1. However, in most cases, green pellets will not rupture, but simply deform and be smashed.

Force is applied to the diameter of the pellet held between two platens:

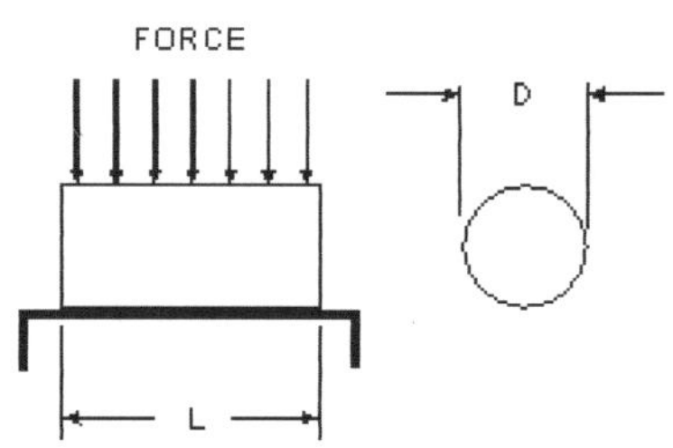

$T = 2(\text{FORCE})/\pi DL$, where:

T = Splitting tensile strength, MPa [Newton/mm^2]

FORCE = Newtons required to split the pellet along its length

D = Pellet diameter, mm

L = Pellet length, mm

NOTE

Pellets can be either cut to length or random lengths. The pellet must be straight and parallel to the platen surfaces to achieve continuous edge contact with both platens.

Any result other than a split along the pellet axis is disregarded.

J.C. STEELE & SONS, INC. • 710 S Mulberry Street • Statesville, NC 28677 • P.O. Box 1834 (28687)
+1.704.872.3681 • 800.278.3353 • www.jcsteele.com

Figure 3. J.C. Steele SOP.13 – Pellet Split Tensile Strength

Figure 4 shows an interpretation of crushing a spherical pellet between two platens. The method of applying force is similar, but the loading is different. A concavity or convexity in the extruded briquette can misrepresent compressive strength. We have tested extruded briquettes with compressive forces over 250 Kgf. The binding system is important, but less so than particle size distribution and the raw materials themselves. Diameter of the extruded briquette also has an impact, so the ASTM C1006 test, Paragraph 7.1, specifies a pellet no greater than 16 mm. The paper, "*Cohesive strength of iron ore granules,*" [6] has an excellent image pictured in Figure 6 which shows platen contact with an iron ore pellet. In contrast, Figure 5 illustrates how platen contact differs with an extruded briquette.

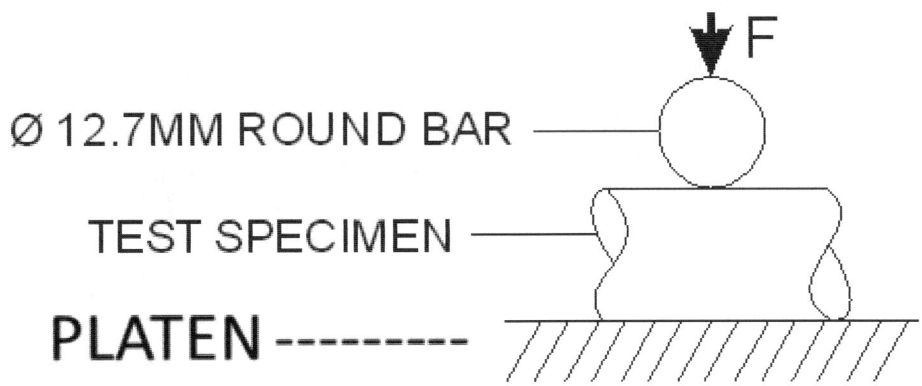

Figure 4. Single-Point Break Illustration on Extruded Briquette

Figure 5. Single-Point Break Test on Extruded Briquette

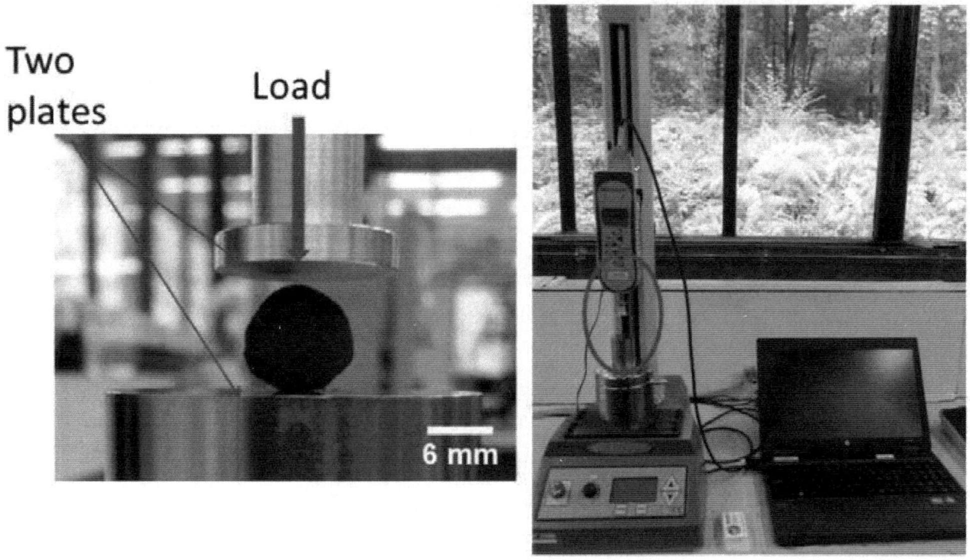

Figure 6. Compression Testing Setup - Photo Credit - Edouard Izard

2.3. SHATTER TESTING

Extruded briquettes are rarely used for structural support or to increase permeability, so we discarded the ISO Standard 616 Shatter Index. This is not to say that the structural integrity and permeability of extruded briquettes are unimportant during qualifications, but neither is their primary value. We use a version of the shatter index test or "Drop Test" that works with both green and cured pellets. J.C. Steele and Sons customers often specify this test for qualification, as it is similar to conveyor belt transfers. It is replicable in both laboratory and plant settings, without a dedicated shatter test device. Plant engineers can use a few sets of screens and a plastic bag to assess the quality of extruded briquettes. The J.C. Steele SOP is shown in Figure 7.

The ISO 3271 testing method for Tumble Index and Abrasion Index is an industry recognized test consistently used for certain extruded briquettes. See Table 2, Table 3, and Table 4 for samples (note: not every J.C. Steele and Sons customer requires this test based on customer assessment of extruded briquettes). The test requires 60 kilograms of raw materials, often with multiple mixes of mill byproducts. We do not always have this quantity, so we use Figure 7 to qualify the materials when ISO 3271 quantities are not requested.

SOP.11 – PELLET DROP TEST PROCEDURE

REV.16.12.01.JFF

This procedure can be performed on freshly extruded "green" pellets or cured pellets. The drop height and screening criterion can be adjusted per customer requirements. Generally, a fraction of particles smaller that the customer's desired minimum size is determined during the test.

NOTICE **Generally, drop test is performed on cured pellets. If testing green pellets, perform the test within one hour after extrusion.**

Sample # ______________________ Date & Time________________________

1. Determine pellet density: _________ g/cc
2. Collect a sample of 180 ±5 cc's of pellets using this formula:
    - Weight of sample = (180 cc) X (Pellet Density ~ g/cc) = _________ g
3. Place sample in plastic bag (gallon size – approximately 25 cm square)
4. Squeeze air from bag but pellets must be free to move and tumble
5. Seal the bag
6. Drop onto a concrete surface or steel plate at least 3/4" thick four times from a height of one meter.
7. Repeat steps 2 through 6 on three samples
8. Screen each sample -4 mesh (4.75mm) __________g
9. Weight of entire sample __________g
10. CPFT 4 mesh = Weight of -4 mesh fraction/Total sample weight _________%
11. Measure pellet moisture __________% wbm

Figure 7. J.C. Steele - SOP.11 – Pellet Drop Test Procedure

3. MILL SCALE EXTRUDED BRIQUETTE – J.C. STEELE AND SONS R&D TEST

In 2016, J.C. Steele and Sons explored the benefits of extra mechanical processing of material, or shearing, followed by souring. We conducted a pilot test with our HD-10 Extruder at TMS International facilities in Middletown, Ohio, using 9% Portland cement (PC) and 1% sodium bentonite clay.

We used various die and auger combinations to evaluate extruder performance with these mix conditions:

1. Single Pass Extrusion – We mixed and moisturized all raw materials, which were immediately extruded using the HD-10 Extruder.

2. Sheared – We sheared the raw material mix (less PC) by passing it through the HD-10 Extruder once with a shearing plate/die mounted on the extruder exit. Next, we added the PC and necessary water, remixed the batch and then extruded.

3. Sheared and Soured – Same as above, with the sheared mix stored in one cubic meter bags for four days before final blending with PC, mixing with water and extrusion.

All dies used for this test produced 0.75" or 19 mm diameter pellets.

We conducted 3EX laboratory extruder testing concurrently, evaluating cured pellets for each mix condition with ISO 3271 tumble testing on both the 3EX Lab Extruder and HD10 Extruder.

Table 2. Single Pass Extrusion with ISO 3271 Results

		Machine and Process	Lab Extruder - Single Pass				HD-10 - Single Pass	
		TEST # and/or DATE/TIME	2016-0310-01 Millscale - Single Pass				3/29/2016 13:51	
		Comments	No Shear/No Sour				No shear/No Sour	
		SAMPLE #	1	2	3	4	1	2
Test Sample	m_0	grams	15012	15001	14999	15000	15000	15001
Plus 6.30 mm	m_1	grams	12917	12948	12943	12909	11202	11327
Plus 500 micron	m_2	grams	239	215	229	221	798	743
Minus 500 micron	m_3	grams	1690	1658	1685	1735	2752	2761
m_0-m_1-m_2-m_3	d	grams	166	180	142	135	248	170
d/m_0	D	%	1.1	1.2	0.9	0.9	1.7	1.1
(m_1/m_0)	TI	%	86.0	86.3	86.3	86.1	74.7	75.5
$(m_0-m_1-m_2)/m_0$	AI	%	12.4	12.3	12.2	12.5	20.0	19.5
		TI (avg)	86.2				75.1	
		AI (avg)	12.3				19.8	

Table 3. Sheared Mix Extrusion with ISO 3271 Results

		Machine and Process	Lab Extruder - Shear Only				HD-10 - Shear Only	
		TEST # and/or DATE/TIME	2016-0311-01 Millscale - Shear Only				3/29/2016 11:30	
		Comments						
		SAMPLE #	1	2	3	4	1	2
Test Sample	m_0	grams	15001	15000	15002	14998	15001	15002
Plus 6.30 mm	m_1	grams	13056	12893	13048	13223	12583	12790
Plus 500 micron	m_2	grams	265	311	268	207	292	211
Minus 500 micron	m_3	grams	1580	1715	1583	1451	1947	1803
m_0-m_1-m_2-m_3	d	grams	100	81	103	117	179	198
d/m_0	D	%	0.7	0.5	0.7	0.8	1.2	1.3
(m_1/m_0)	TI	%	87.0	86.0	87.0	88.2	83.9	85.3
$(m_0-m_1-m_2)/m_0$	AI	%	11.2	12.0	11.2	10.5	14.2	13.3
		TI (avg)	87.0				84.6	
		AI (avg)	11.2				13.8	

Table 4. Sheared and Soured Mix Extrusion with ISO 3271 Results

		Machine and Process	LE - Shear/Sour		HD-10 Shear/Sour		HD-10 Shear/Sour		HD-10 Shear/Sour	
		TEST # and/or DATE/TIME	160314-01		3/14/2016 16:00		3/15/2016 14:20		3/15/2016 14:47	
		Comments							noted good vacuum	
		SAMPLE #	1	2	1	2	1	2	1	2
Test Sample	m_0	grams	15002	15000	15001	14999	14998	15000	15001	14999
Plus 6.30 mm	m_1	grams	12790	12827	12906	12637	12549	12388	13096	13103
Plus 500 micron	m_2	grams	337	354	309	464	522	620	299	296
Minus 500 micron	m_3	grams	1643	1700	1669	1733	1784	1879	1503	1495
m_0-m_1-m_2-m_3	d	grams	232	119	117	165	143	113	103	105
d/m_0	D	%	1.5	0.8	0.8	1.1	1.0	0.8	0.7	0.7
(m_1/m_0)	TI	%	85.3	85.5	86.0	84.3	83.7	82.6	87.3	87.4
$(m_0-m_1-m_2)/m_0$	AI	%	12.5	12.1	11.9	12.7	12.8	13.3	10.7	10.7
		TI (avg)	85.4		85.1		83.1		87.3	
		AI (avg)	12.3		12.3		13.1		10.7	
					85.2	Average of three sheared and soured runs on the HD-10				
					12.0					

We reached the following conclusion from our test results: in general, there was good correlation between the 3EX laboratory extruder and HD-10 produced pellets. However, single-pass pellets (no shearing or souring) from the 3EX laboratory extruder trials performed significantly better. This may be due to more careful handling of the pellets produced by the 3EX. All three mixes were successfully extruded on the HD-10, but single-pass pellets (no shearing or souring) will require careful design of the handling system post-extrusion.

Results from the ISO 3271 Tumble Test Index and Abrasion Index showed that all three samples were within the minimum and maximum specifications defined in the paper, *"Iron Ore Sintering: Quality Indices."* [7] This is shown in Table 5.

Table 5. Sinter Quality Requirements - Per D. Fernandez-Gonzalez, 2017

	Minimum value	Maximum value	Typical
Coke consumption ($kg \cdot t^{-1}$ sinter)	39	54	–
Productivity ($t \cdot m^{-2}$ per 24h)	26	43	–
Fe total (%)	51	61	>56
Basicity Index			1.70
FeO (%)	4.0	11	
Al_2O_3 (%)	0.6	1.8	1.35
MgO (%)	0.7	2.2	1.65
SiO_2 (%)	5.3	5.4	
Alkalis (%)		0.11	
Phosphorus (%)		0.04	
RDI (% < 3mm)	27	33	<33
Tumbler (% > 6.3mm)	63	79	>74
Reducibility (R_{60}, %)	49	78	
% < 0.125 mm		15	
0.2 mm < % < 0.7 mm		18	

This raises the question, what is suitable? If the cold-bonded extruded briquette is sinter, it would meet the cold strength physical requirements. We concluded that having Reduction Disintegration Index (RDI), Reducibility Index (RI), and chemical analysis done in addition to ISO 3271 testing to determine metallurgical characteristics would have been useful. We plan to repeat this tumble test program and share the results of the RDI, RI, and chemical analysis in another paper. Unfortunately, because the tumble testing of the products was planned, we did not perform drop tests. The drop test will also be added to the testing requirements to draw out any consistencies in testing. The density of the extruded briquettes was consistently over 3.75 g/cc, so even the high-density briquette maintained excellent cold strength.

4. INTEGRATED STEEL MILL BLAST FURNACE EXTRUDED BRIQUETTE

In 2016, J.C. Steele and Sons partnered with TMS International to test a briquette using a variety of blast furnace byproducts. The testing was similar to what J.C. Steele and Sons did on the mill scale briquettes shown in Table 2, Table 3, and Table 4. The customer requested the highest tumble index briquette with the highest percentage of each byproduct available.

Table 6 shows the two best mixes produced. The question then came down to production cost of the extruded briquette. The addition of sodium silicate added cost to the product. The other cost was tied to the 15 mm diameter of the briquette. This diameter required mechanically processing the materials before extrusion. Ultimately, the mill chose a briquette with similar percentages of mill byproducts, without sodium silicate. The tumble test performance for products fed to the mill is consistently over 80% with a 19 mm extruded briquette. Some samples of those materials are shown in Table 7.

Table 6. Blast Furnace (BF) Byproduct Tumble Test Comparison

Specimen #	2016-0922-03	2017-0310-01
Iron Ore Fines [EM-160805-E]	23.9%	24.1%
Mill Scale [EM-160805-A]	19.3%	19.5%
BF Dust/Sludge [EM-160805-D]	27.6%	-
BF Dust [EM-170213-C]	-	10.3%
BF Sludge [EM-170213-B]	-	17.7%
Coke Fines [EM-160805-F]	21.2%	21.4%
Sodium Bentonite	1.0%	1.0%
Type 1 Portland Cement	6.0%	6.0%
N Sodium Silicate (37% solids)	1.0%	---
Extrusion Die #	130	130
Pellet Diameter (mm)	15.0	15.0
Extrusion WBM	10.1%	9.6%
Compacted Density [g/cc]	2.53	2.64
Cure Temperature °C	25	25
ISO 3271 Tumble TEST		
TI Tumble Index (+6.3mm)	86.0%	80.9%
AI Abrasion Index (-0.5mm)	12.0%	16.7%

Table 7. Extruded Briquette Tumble Index Samples – Courtesy of TMS International

N°	TI	OVER SIZE	COARSE	LARGE	MEDIUM	FINES
1	89,2%	0,38%	9,17%	28,66%	48,41%	13,38%
2	85,5%	0,05%	8,89%	35,26%	43,95%	11,84%
3	89,0%	0,00%	5,20%	33,09%	50,56%	11,15%
4	89,0%	0,22%	12,00%	29,26%	46,30%	12,22%
5	89,1%	0,23%	10,93%	31,89%	45,56%	11,39%
6	87,3%	0,31%	8,56%	28,75%	51,07%	11,31%
7	89,2%	0,34%	11,86%	32,20%	44,75%	10,85%
8	86,1%	0,32%	10,51%	31,21%	46,18%	11,78%
9	90,8%	0,35%	8,83%	27,92%	53,71%	9,19%
10	89,5%	0,36%	9,17%	31,55%	44,94%	13,99%
11	90,5%	0,31%	7,21%	29,15%	52,66%	10,66%
12	86,0%	1,15%	12,60%	27,48%	46,18%	12,60%
13	88,3%	0,16%	5,00%	26,45%	54,84%	13,55%

5. CONCLUSION

J.C. Steele and Sons has a long history and demonstrable expertise in processing and shaping a variety of raw materials. Typically, when contacted by integrated mills, we produce samples to meet a cold physical specification. After production of samples, metallurgical and hot testing is typically done by the customer themselves. Only rarely have these results been shared, as the mix makeup we see is proprietary information. Further testing and research of the cold samples will offer a more detailed picture of the impact of ISO 3271 on other criteria used to qualify burden materials. Cost is always a consideration, due to new binding systems or process requirements. The short answer is that we can always add cost to make a product stronger. The question remains, at what point does value start to diminish? The testing methods will continue to be investigated to determine what correlates best from laboratory scale up to full production usage. Commercial application data, combined with laboratory and pilot-sized trials, helps to further solidify the value of cold-bonded briquetting.

6. REFERENCES

1. Battle, T. P. (2019). Characterization of Iron Oxide Pellets Used in the Production of Iron and Steel. *36th Biennial Conference, Institute for Briquetting and Agglomeration.* Charleston.

2. Wedholm, A. (2016). Briquetting - Taking Advantage of Fine-Grained Residues in a Sustainable Manner. *In Proceedings of the SCANMET V, Luleå, Sweden 12-15 June 2016; Swerea MEFOS: Luleå, Sweden, 2016.*

3. Andersson, A., Gullberg, A., Kullerstedt, A., Ökvsit, L. S., Wikstrom, J., Ahmed, H., & Wikström, J. (2019, June 22). Recycling of Blast Furnace Sludge to the Blast Furnace via Cold-Bonded Briquettes: Evaluation of Feasibility and Influence on Operation. ISIJ International, Vol. 59 (2019), No. 10, 1786-1795.

4. Lopez C., Juan A.; Ballesteros B., Raul V.; Guispot T., Jesus M.; Ramirez, Rogelio; Altos Hornos de Mexico S.A. de C.V. Monclova Coahuila, Mexico. (1998). Development of B. F. flue dust briquette for recycling in BOF at AHMSA. *ICSTI/IRONMAKING CONFERENCE PROCEEDINGS*, (pp. 1275-1279).

5. de Bruin, Tina; Sundqvist, Lena; SSAB. (1998). Briquetting - One way of treating by-products at SSAB Tunnplat in Lulea. *ICSTI/IRONMAKING CONFERENCE PROCEEDINGS*, (pp. 1263-1273).

6. Jaimes Contreras, R. &.-F.-Y. (2017). Cohesive strength of iron ore granules. *Powders and Grains 2017 (8th International Conference on Micromechanics of Granular Media).*

7. D. Fernández-González, I. R.-B.-G. (2017). Iron Ore Sintering: Quality Indices. *Mineral Processing and Extractive Metallurgy Review*, (pp. 38:4, 254-264). doi:10.1080/08827508.2017.1323744.

Institute for Briquetting and Agglomeration

2022 IBA CONFERENCE PAPERS

Paper Title:

Agglomeration of batteries lead fines using BASF binders

Presenter:

Willy Cilengi

Company:

Agglotek VA Resources

WHO WE ARE

///Agglotek VA Resources

Agglotek Value Added Resources (Agglotek VAR) is:

- A **level 1 BBBEE** contributor to South African economy.
- Focused on **value addition and beneficiation of fines** in the mining industry through **agglomeration of fines** traditionally considered as waste due to limitations for further processing and difficulty in handling for transportation to end customers.
- Specialised in agglomeration technologies: B**riquetting, Extrusion and Pelletizing**.

WHO WE ARE

- Agglotek team has combined experience of more than **30 years in mining and chemical industries**, offering **environmentally sustainable solution** that will reduce liability associated with the ever-growing tailings and fines stockpiles, inherent to the mining operations.

- Agglotek have access to **innovative binder's chemistry,** compatible with wide range of commodities such as **coal, iron ore, ferroalloys fines, DRI dust, oxide sludge etc...**

- The combination of wealth of knowledge and expertise accumulated by some Agglotek personnel while working in the mining and chemical industry ensures **the company's ability to adapt its systems to the changing needs of customers**

OUR MISSION

Reduce tailings footprint by providing sustainable solution through operational excellence.

OUR VISION

Greening Africa and the World through elimination of minerals waste stockpiles and dams through agglomeration techniques and binding aids innovation.

OUR VALUES

Value creation

Sustainable business solutions.

Honesty and Integrity.

Customer satisfaction.

We Focus on value addition and beneficiation of mineral fines in the mining industry

ABOUT US

///Agglotek VA Resources

Level 1 BBBEE contributor

- Providing sustainable solutions

VALUE ADDITION

- Fines beneficiation
- Agglomerations of fines

Agglomeration technology

- Briquetting
- Extrusion
- Novel binder chemistry

5

///Agglotek VA Resources

ABOUT THE LEAD FINES AGGLOMERATION

- THE AUTOMOTIVE INDUSTRY IS THE BIGGEST CONTRIBUTOR TO THE ECONOMIC GROWTH IN THE WORLD.
- IT IS THE KEY SECTOR OF THE ECONOMY IN THE WORLD, REGISTERING 30 % INCREASE OVER THE PAST DECADE (1995-2005). (1).
- ALSO, THE VERY SAME AUTOMOTIVE INDUSTRY CONTRIBUTES TO POLLUTION WITH AS ENGINE OIL, TYRES, STARTERS, ALTERNATORS, WINDOWS & WINDSHIELD, SCRAP METALS, PLASTIC COMPONENTS, OIL FILTERS, ENGINES, MATS & CARPETS (2).
- SOME PARTS ARE REUSABLE SUCH AS HEADLIGHTS, BLINKERS, TAILLIGHTS, SEATS, UPHOLSTERY, EXHAUST SYSTEMS, MIRRORS, ALLY WHEELS, TRANSMISSIONS SYSTEMS AND UNDAMAGED WINDOWS AND WIND SHIELDS (2).

ABOUT THE LEAD FINES AGGLOMERATION

///Agglotek VA Resources

- OTHER PARTS ARE RECYCLABLE, SUCH AS LEAD-ACID BATTERIES.
- EVERY YEAR, AN ESTIMATED 1.8 MILLION USED BATTERIES ARE NOT RESPONSIBLY RECYCLED.
- WHEN A LEAD-ACID BATTERY IS NOT PROPERLY RECYCLED, LEAD, ACID AND MERCURY ARE DEPOSITED INTO LAKES, STREAMS AND LANDFILLS (3).
- RECYCLING OLD BATTERIES REDUCES WASTE...
- UP TO 99 % OF LEAD-ACID BATTERIES ARE RECYCLABLE. IT ALSO REDUCES THE NEED TO USE NEW RAW MATERIALS & COMPONENTS (1).

THE RECYCLING PROCESS

///Agglotek VA Resources

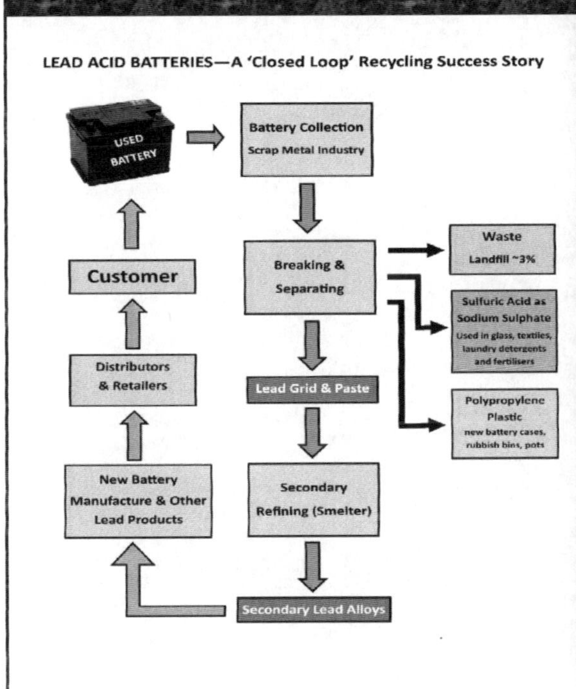

- THE OLD LEAD-ACID BATTERIES ARE BROKEN APART
- LEAD AND HEAVY MATERIALS ARE SEPARATED FROM THE PLASTIC
- LEAD IS SMELTED INTO LEAD INGOTS.
- DUST CONTAINING LEAD IS GENERATED, COLLECTED IN BAGHOUSE (HEALTH HAZARD).
- INGOTS ARE FURTHER MELTED DOWN AGAIN TO FORM LEAD PLATES AND OTHER LEAD COMPONENTS FOR NEW BATTERIES.(4)
- THE POLYPROPYLENE IS FORMED INTO PELLETS THAT ARE THEN MADE INTO NEW BATTERY CASES.
- THE ACID IS CONVERTED INTO SODIUM SULPHATE AND USED IN DETERGENT, GLASS AND TEXTILE MANUFACTURING PLANTS.

THE AGGLOMERATION PROCESS

- During smelting operation, fumes (lead dust) generated are directed to the baghouse, where the fumes are entrapped and collected to be recycled.
- Due to the fine size of the dust, they become difficult to handle.
- BASF looked at agglomeration (briquetting) of all lead-bearing dust, oxide, dross using organic binders (value addition) to feed briquettes back into the Smelter...
- Preliminary test work confirmed the capability to agglomerate such lead-bearing dust material using BASF binders such as Alcotac CB6, CB11 and FE 14, with target to obtain briquettes.

THE AGGLOMERATION PROCESS

The briquettes produced during the test were able to reach the following characteristics:

- Remain intact when dropped,
- Or if broken, this could be into pieces (> 3mm);
- Resist to weather elements when exposed;
- Resist at high temperature without breaking;
- Melt into to furnace without disintegrating into fines.

10

EXPERIMENT (6)

Scope of Test

- Agglomerate lead-based material fines using BASF binders;
- Compressive strength of briquettes from Day 0 to Day 7.

Binders Used and Dosages applied:

- Alcotac CB6: 0.6% w/w.
- Alcotac CB 11: 1.0% and 2.0 % w/w.
- Alcotac FE 14 : 0.6 w/w.

11

EXPERIMENT (6)

Equipment

- Moisture Analyser RADWAG MA 200.3Y. WM (Max. 200 g. d= 1 mg).
- Mettler 2 decimal Balance.
- Kitchen Mixer
- Komareck B50 Roller Press
- Compression Tester (Chatillon 2500 N)
- 1.000 ml beakers.

Moisture Analyser | Planetary Mixer | Komarek 25 kg/hr Roller Press | Compression Testers

12

EXPERIMENTAL PROCEDURE

///Agglotek VA Resources

- Sample of baghouse dust at 0.60 % w/w moisture and adjusted to 8.0% w/w moisture prior briquetting.
- 1500 gr of lead-based material fines were weighed and placed in the 1,000-ml beaker. 10 g were taken to determine the moisture using the moisture analyzer, which recorded (initial moisture) 0.60% w/w.
- Each selected binder (Alcotac® CB6, CB11 & FE14) was added to the sample and was thoroughly mixed for 3 minutes using the Kitchen Mixer at speed 1.

13

EXPERIMENTAL PROCEDURE

///Agglotek VA Resources

- Water was added to adjust the moisture to 8.0% w/w before briquetting. 10 g of material were taken to the Moisture Analyzer to record the moisture after binder and water addition (final moisture).
- The mixed binder-sample was transferred to Komarek B50 roller press, and briquettes produced.
- The extracted briquettes were then compressed using the Chatillon Force Gauge 2500 N tester to determine green strength (Day 0) in Newton.
- A green strength average of above 350 N was recorded depending on binder used.
- The remaining briquettes were left to air dry for 7 days.

RESULTS & DISCUSSION

///Agglotek VA Resources

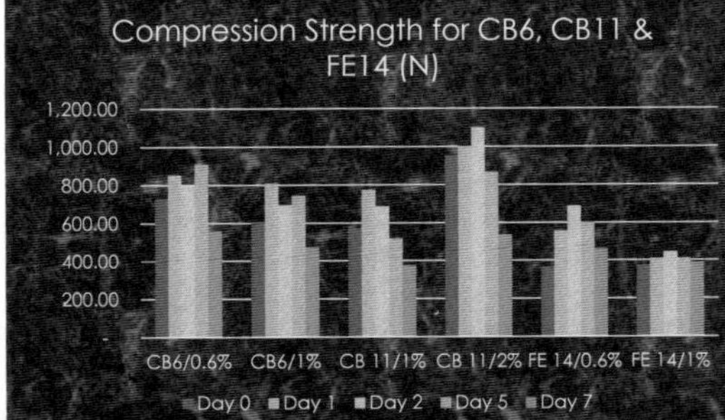

Figure 1 : Compression Strength

Test	CB6 (0.6%)	CB6 (1%)	CB 11 (1%)	CB 11 (2%)	FE 14 (0.6%)	FE 14 (1%)
Day 0	728.33	609.33	571.33	953.67	366.00	375.00
Day 1	854.67	810.33	772.67	1,001.33	556.67	409.67
Day 2	799.00	693.67	688.67	1,098.33	688.67	443.33
Day 5	912.00	745.00	519.67	866.33	601.67	408.67
Day 7	561.33	473.00	375.33	538.67	462.00	388.67

CONCLUSION & RECOMMENDATIONS

///Agglotek VA Resources

- Alcotac® CB11 & CB 6 record better compressive strength reaching 1000 N.
- Lead baghouse dust can be briquetted at controled moisture below 8.0% w/w.
- **A binder's optimisation should be considered (techno-economic case study).**

16

///Agglotek
VA Resources
3
17

///Agglotek
VA Resources
4
18

///Agglotek VA Resources

19

REFERENCE

///Agglotek VA Resources

1. http://www.autobatteries.com/en-us/installation-and-recycling. 19/Nov/2021.
2. https://www.cartakebook.com/blog/in-tht-know/recycling-week-10-car-components-that-can-be-recycled. 24/Sept/2019.
3. https://www.waste360.com/ewaste-report-recycling. 6/Jan/2022
4. https://www.recyclingmybattery.com/en-us.
5. http://www.ecocycle.com.au/battery/how/to/recycle/a/lead/battery.
6. Agglomeration of Fry's Lead Fines & Paste using BASF binders: BASF Material Handling – Agglomeration; Technical report; 23/03/2021.
7. https://www.waste360.com>e-waste>report-recycling 21/Nov/2019

CONTACT

M.M. Willy Cilengi

Business Development

info@agglotek.com

Mob: +27 82 900 1818

3, Loe Street – New Redruth

Alberton 1449 – South Africa

26.09.2022 20

Institute for Briquetting and Agglomeration

2022 IBA CONFERENCE PAPERS

Paper Title:
Agglomeration of Hygroscopic Powders

Presenter:
Jacob Sulzle

Company:
Bepex

Agglomeration of Hygroscopic Powders

Jacob Sulzle
Application Engineer Mixing
Bepex International, LLC
333 N.E. Taft Street
Minneapolis, Minnesota 55413
612-331-4370

ABSTRACT

Wet agglomeration is a widely used method in many industries to create granules from fine powders suitable for a wide variety of applications. Instant mixing is a subset of wet agglomeration using high levels of mixing intensity and short residence times to uniformly agglomerate products. Over the years Bepex has developed several processes which can agglomerate difficult to handle materials that would normally not be suitable for mechanical wet agglomeration. This paper is intended to describe one such specific process.

This paper will present the principles behind wet agglomeration, the difficulties seen when agglomerating hygroscopic, sticky materials, and solutions to those issues. A specific case is used in this paper as an example of the above-mentioned topics.

BACKGROUND

Agglomeration can be defined as "a process of particle size enlargement in which small, fine particles, such as dusts or powders, are gathered into larger masses, clusters, pellets or briquettes for use as end products or in a secondary processing step."[1]

Instant mixing wet agglomeration is typified by the high shear environment of the mixer along with a short residence time. Instant mixing can be used to dedust, improve flowability, increase the rate of dissolution or compressibility, and change the bulk density of the product. A key component behind the formation of agglomerates is the liquid loading on the individual particles. The liquid coats the surface of the particle and as it collides with other particles capillary actions and surface tension cause the particles to adhere together.

The size of the resulting agglomerates can be controlled mainly via the solids to liquids feed ratio. Figure 1 contains a typical particle size versus liquid loading curve. Low levels of liquid addition are in the mixing and coating region of the graph below. As more liquid is added, agglomerates start to form. As the liquid loading is increased further, going beyond the material's saturation point, a paste will begin to form. If the liquid loading is increased beyond that point, a slurry will be formed.

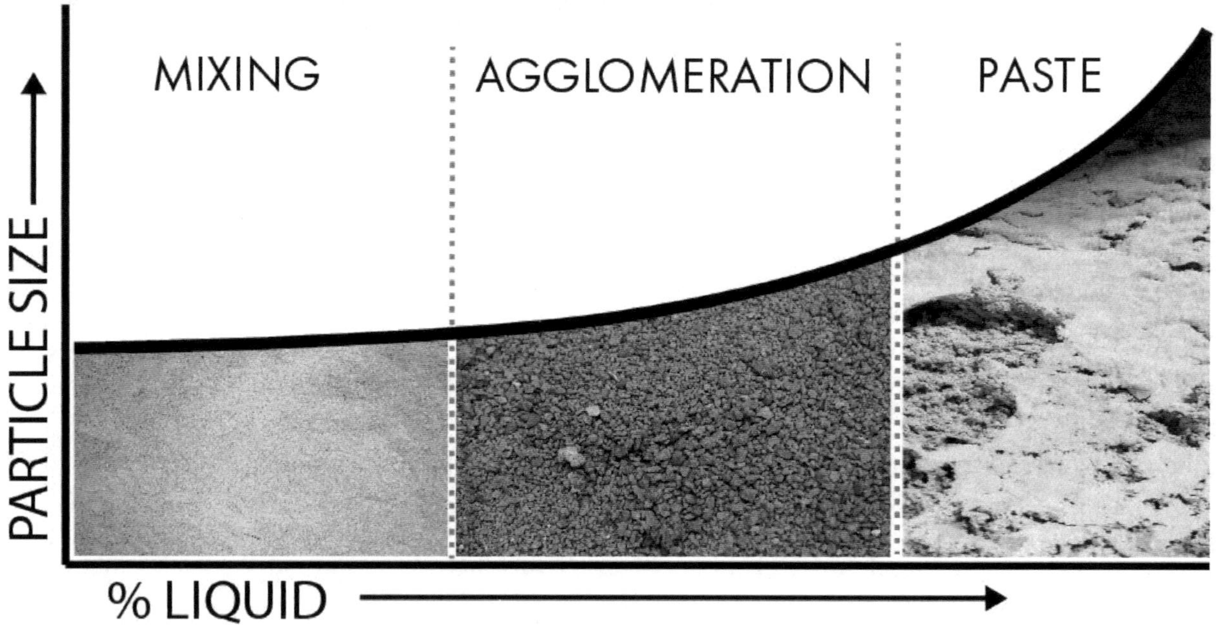

Figure 1. Graph of particle size versus liquid loading.

The area of the graph labeled as agglomeration is called the operating window. Operating within this area of the liquid loading graph will produce agglomerates, while operating outside this area will either produce dust or a paste/slurry. This operating window is material specific. Some materials have wide operating windows, allowing flexibility in the feed composition and rates while still producing acceptable product. Other materials have very narrow operating windows which require close monitoring and metering of the feed to ensure good operation.

DIFFICULTIES

Hygroscopic, sticky products are examples of materials which can have very narrow operating windows. These materials can be so sensitive that a 3%-4% change to the liquid addition rate can be the difference between de-dusting and creating a paste. These materials also tend to have lower product yields than most other materials, requiring high recycle fines rates for the system. This will increase the capital cost of the system because most of the equipment will need to be larger to handle the large recycle rate.

Another issue seen with these kinds of materials is the tendency to build up inside of the agglomeration equipment, leading to undesirable operating conditions and products. This buildup can cause plugging of the mixing device, increase the horsepower requirements of mixers, and cause undesirable "sinkers". Sinkers are pieces of compacted material that break off the mixer wall and are mixed into the rest of the agglomerated product.

SOLUTIONS

The issues of material buildup on the walls of the agglomeration device, low product yield, and narrow operating window are solved in different ways. First, to minimize build up inside the agglomeration device, a flexible wall which is mechanically flexed to remove materials from the walls is used. Bepex has developed the FlexTurbulizer and TurboFlex agglomerators for use in these situations.

The Bepex FlexTurbulizer offers the performance of a continuous high speed paddle mixer but is designed specifically to handle materials that buildup and foul conventional mixers. The FlexTurbulizer incorporates a Bepex Jet Rotor, for multipoint liquid injection, with continuous deformation of a horizontal flexible mixing chamber wall to easily process cohesive materials as they are wetted with liquid.

This wetted material tends to buildup on most mixer walls, densifying to a hard layer and building to the point of contacting the rotating paddle or mixing element. The continuous deformation of the FlexTurbulizer mix chamber wall prevents this layer from forming. The result is consistent size, shape and density granules continuously produced. A picture of the FlexTurbulizer can be seen below in Figure 2.

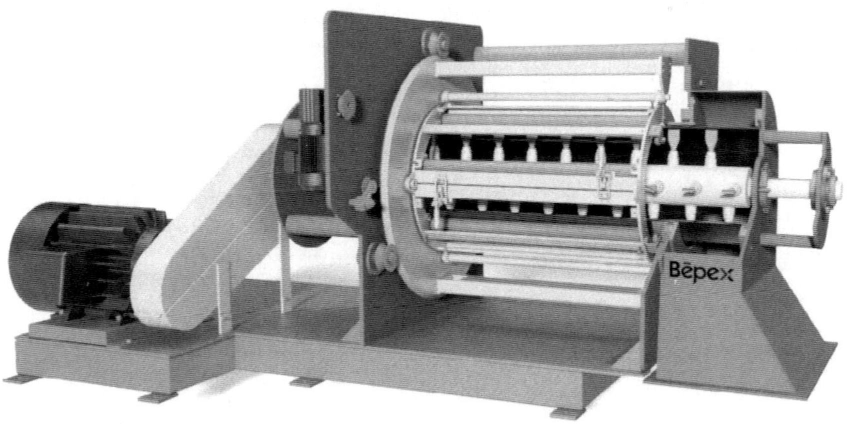

Figure 2. Cutaway of a Bepex FlexTurbulizer

The next issue is the narrow operating window. Consistent, precise control of the solids to liquid ratio is required when dealing with a material that is sensitive to the liquid loading level. Mass flow meters with feedback control to the liquid dosing systems, and loss in weight metering devices for the solids streams, will give the necessary control of the liquid loading. The solid and liquid feed moistures must also be very consistent, or variations accounted for in the liquid addition calculation. Also, using spray nozzles to add the liquid in the equipment will ensure even liquid distribution and prevent local over-saturation of the material.

The final issue to address is low first pass yield from the agglomeration device. Using spray nozzles to disperse the liquid in the agglomerator will increase the yield in comparison to non-atomized liquid addition. Another method to increase yield is to use a binder (such as starches, gums, or waxes) to help the individual particles to stick together more readily. In some cases, binders are either undesirable for the product formulation, do not increase the yield enough to justify their cost, or do not increase yield at all. Yield can also be increased by spraying additional agglomerating liquid onto the solids in the drying apparatus (in the example below a fluid bed).

CASE STUDY

One of Bepex's customers has an installation that uses a Bepex FlexTurbulizer followed by a fluid bed dryer to agglomerate a solid material using water alone as the liquid/binder. This customer tried to process a new solid feed material expecting it to work the same as other similar materials they currently run. They discovered the new material had a different operating window, which they overshot during their full-scale trials. The amount of liquid addition was too high for the new material, and they ended up in the slurry portion of the graph in Figure 1. This led to a mess in the fluid bed requiring a full day to clean, as well as damage to the FlexTurbulizer due to abrasion of the mixing paddles.

The manufacturer contacted Bepex to perform pilot scale testing at our Minneapolis facility to determine the optimal way to process the new material, rather than proceed with further full-scale trials on their system. The following elements were tested at the Bepex Process Development Center:

1. The liquid loading in the FlexTurbulizer to determine optimal liquid to solid ratio for this material.
2. Multiple binders were tested to determine the effects on the on-spec product yield.
3. Oil addition to the powder upstream of the water used to agglomerate the material.
4. Spraying liquid into the fluid bed dryer to increase yield.

Testing started with varying the liquid addition rate in the FlexTurbulizer. It was found that the material would begin to agglomerate at approximately 5% liquid addition. The liquid was successfully pushed to 8% by weight of the solids. Increasing the liquid addition rate beyond 8%, the material began to appear over-agglomerated. The liquid rate was not pushed to the point of failure, so the maximum liquid addition was not firmly established. It is unknown what liquid rate the manufacturer ran during their full-scale trial. Based on the observations from the test, a 9-10% liquid addition rate would be too high. The operating window for this material was therefore established as 5-8% liquid addition.

To maximize on-size yield the maximum liquid addition of 8% was used for further trials. The 8% liquid addition rate in the FlexTurbulizer resulted in a 30-33% on-size product yield. To further increase the yield, addition of binders, pre-coating with oil, and spraying additional liquid in the fluid bed were tested.

Two binders were tested: 25% maltodextrin with water solution and a 10% gum Arabic with water solution. Binders were used in dilute solution with the water, so a single liquid feed stream was still used. Using maltodextrin as a binder did not increase the yield compared to water alone. Using gum Arabic as a binder decreased the yield. It seemed to make the agglomerates stickier while not allowing for as much water to be added which made the agglomerates that did form smaller.

It was proposed that mixing a small amount of oil with the material prior to adding the agglomerating liquid would create a waterproof coating on the powder that would slow the absorption of the liquid; thereby allowing the liquid to stay on the surface, coat the powder, and more readily agglomerate without becoming saturated. This was tested by adding vegetable oil through the side of the FlexTurbulizer inlet housing. It was metered in to the FlexTurbulizer by a peristaltic pump and a small scale was used to measure the flow rate. It was found that the oil would coat and dedust the material well. However, downstream addition of agglomerating liquid did not agglomerate the material. Oil additions as low as 0.1% would prevent the liquid binder from agglomerating the material.

The final element tested was liquid addition in the fluid bed dryer as a second stage of agglomeration. Air atomizing nozzles were used inside the fluidizing chamber. Multiple nozzle configurations in different zones were tested. If the spray pattern was too wide it would lead to build up on the walls of the fluid bed, while too focused a spray pattern caused buildup on the fluid bed screens. Spraying liquid in the first zone of the dryer caused some lump formation because the material was still too wet from the first agglomeration step to take much more water. Spraying in the second zone of the fluid bed did not cause lump formation, and this proved successful in increasing the product yield to 42%.

The 42% yield, while low for some materials, was a significant increase. The liquid addition in the fluid bed was approximately 6% of the total liquid addition to the system. The increased yield allows the manufacturer to run more efficiently with lower rates of recycled material, increasing their overall system capacity. This technique of using spray nozzles in the fluid bed dryer can be applied to other applications involving wet agglomeration and fluid bed dryers. It would be especially useful in applications with high fines recycle rates, as decreasing the recycle rate can reduce the size of the equipment when designing the system or increase the production capacity of an existing system.

CONCLUSION

The agglomeration of hygroscopic, sticky powders can be challenging. Using the right equipment, paying attention to the material's operating window, and process optimization through testing of binders and secondary agglomeration options can help gain control of the process and increase on-size yield from the system. Working with an experienced equipment supplier and pilot testing of the process will ensure a successful project.

BIBLIOGRAPHY

1. Engelleitner, W.H., "Selection of the Proper Agglomeration Process", Proceedings of 17th Biennial Conference., The Institute for Briquetting Agglomeration, August 1981, pp. 231-233.

Institute for
Briquetting and
Agglomeration

2022 IBA CONFERENCE PAPERS

Paper Title:
Industrial Hygiene Containment Validation Factory Acceptance Test

Presenter:
Ankit Sharma

Company:
International Safety Systems, Inc.

ISS

Reducing Risk Globally...

International Safety Systems, Inc.

- Report -

Industrial Hygiene Containment Validation
Factory Acceptance Test (FAT)
TFC220 Roll Compactor
at
Freund Vector IA
October 13-14, 2020

USA:
13831 Northwest Fwy., Ste. 104,
Houston TX 77040 USA
Phone: 1-203-751-0400, 685-8808
www.issehs.com

US offices:

Pennsylvania | New Jersey | Utah| Texas

Prepared by:
Ankit Sharma, CIH, LFOH
Global Project Manager

Submitted to:
Jamie Frizzell
Technical Sales Group Manager
Freund Vector

I. Background/ Overview

An Industrial Hygiene (IH) containment verification- Factory Acceptance Test (FAT) was conducted for Roll Compactor TFC-220 at Freund Vector, Marion IA from October 13-14, 2020. Ankit Sharma, Certified Industrial Hygienist (CIH) Licentiate Faculty of Occupational Hygiene (LFOH), Global Project Manager with International Safety Systems, Inc. (ISS) conducted the assessment. Jamie Frizzell, Technical Sales Group Manager at Freund Vector provided onsite support during the assessment.

The FAT was conducted to determine containment capabilities of the Pilot Roll Compactor TFC-220, by charging 10 kg of surrogate blend (containing 30% Mannitol) from a ChargePoint's Chargebag® (single use closed transfer bag) docked via PharmaSafe® Split Butterfly Valves (SBVs) to the hopper of the roll compactor, followed by enclosed vertical tapered screw feed to the two serrated rolls (which rotate in opposite directions) to generate compacted sheets. The Roll Compactor was provided with a front cover with an inflatable air seal for contained compaction process. The material was then gravity fed through an enclosed, in-line feeding system to a mill, followed by enclosed gravity collection of the dry granulated material into an empty ChargePoint® bag connected at discharge port via PharmaSafe® SBVs. The 'Pearlitol 50C' grade of Mannitol was used as a surrogate[1]. The excipient used in the blend was pregelatinized corn starch.

The Containment Performance Target (CPT) was considered as 5 $\mu g/m^3$, as requested by Freund Vector. The selected value represents the mid-band value of Occupational Exposure Band (OEB) 4 Active Pharmaceutical Compounds (APIs) (Occupational Exposure Limits (OELs) between 1-10 $\mu g/m^3$ as adopted by most progressive pharmaceutical companies).

Three (3) repeat iterations of the roll compactor operation were planned during the containment validation. Personal breathing zone (PBZ) air samples, area air samples (at potential breach points around roll compactor) and wipe samples (on external surfaces to determine potential breach) were collected during the containment validation. The containment validation plan was developed in line with International Society of Pharmaceutical Engineers (ISPE) SMEPAC (Standardized Measurement of Equipment Particulate Airborne Concentration) guidelines[2].

The third iteration of containment validation of roll compactor was impacted by an off-incidence of a breach (perforation/damage) in the Chargebag® docked above the hopper during hopper charging, which led to leakage / fugitive emissions from the bag during the task. The bag was sealed immediately by taping around the perforation. The air samples collected during third iteration were analyzed at the request of Freund Vector. However, as the results were not representative of containment validation, the results were not included in

---

[1] The certificate of analysis (CofA) indicated that particle size (81% of particles less than 100 micron diameter) was larger than International Society of Pharmaceutical Engineers (ISPE) recommended particle size (diameter) of 75 micron or less (for 90% of particles).

[2] Except samples collected at charging/discharging PharmaSafe® SBV (1 area sample /iteration instead of 3 samples typically recommended in ISPE guideline).

evaluation of containment performance and are included separately as Table 3 presented in Appendix A.

Statistical analysis was performed for air monitoring samples from the first two iterations. However, parameters determined through statistical analysis (such as 95^{tho}%ile exposure estimate) have not been evaluated with CPT, considering limited dataset of two representative iterations. Minimum three representative task iterations are recommended to statistically analyze and derive conclusions on containment performance.

The specific Roll compactor model (TFC 220) was not equipped with a wash-in place (WIP) system, and the Roll Compactor was not cleaned in between the iterations. Therefore, the existing containment validation results are not indicative/reflective of containment performance of the Roll compactor unit during cleaning operation.

II. Results summary

Area background air samples:
The daily area air background samples collected on two days of containment validation were reported below Limit of Quantitation (LOQ) of (<) 0.019 μg/m^3 , hence indicating there was no detectable airborne contamination in the room/test suite prior to the iterations.

Personal Breathing Zone (PBZ) air monitoring results' summary:
The PBZ air monitoring results for the employee performing the roll compaction during the first and second iterations of containment validation, were 0.431 μg/m^3 and 0.445 μg/m^3 , and hence below 10% of the CPT of 5 μg/m^3.

Area air/ Static air monitoring results' summary:
A total of 14 samples were collected during the first and second iterations, at around 0.5 - 1 ft. distance from potential breach points (seven (7) locations / components of the TFC-220 Roll Compactor). The area air concentrations for:

- Seven (7) of the 14 samples collected, were below 10% of the CPT of 5 μg/m^3.
- Five (5) of the 14 samples collected, were between 10-20% of the CPT.
- One (1) of the 14 samples collected, were between 30-40% of the CPT. The sample was collected near top of hopper (below screw conveyor housing).
- One (1) of the 14 samples collected, was between 60-70% of the CPT. The sample was placed near bottom SBV connected to the Chargebag® for collecting roll compacted and milled blend

Area (distant) air monitoring results' summary:
One sample each was collected during the first and second iterations of the containment validation, at approximately 6 ft. distance from the Roll Compactor, in middle of the test suite. The area distant area air monitoring results were below 5% of the CPT.

Wipe sampling results:
Wipe samples were collected to determine containment performance of the contained Roll compactor system with Chargebag® and PharmaSafe® SBVs. A set of background wipe

samples were collected on ten surfaces, followed by wipe sampling on the same surfaces after first and second iterations of the containment validation.

- The background surface contamination levels on all surfaces of the Roll compactor were reported as detects, but below 20% of the wipe limit.
- The background surface contamination on the outer surface of the empty Chargebag® docked at the bottom SBV (discharge collection port), prior to each of the two (2) iterations, were reported below LOQ of (<) 0.01 μg/100cm^2.
- First iteration:
  - The surface contamination levels reported for two (2) of the ten samples collected at a) above the screw feeder housing (35.4 μg/100cm^2) and b) below test window (front cover) / above TFC 220 signage (30.6 μg/100cm^2), exceeded 50% of the wipe limit.
    - The wipe sampling result above screw feeder is indicative of contamination from potential leakage/emissions from Chargebag® and PharmaSafe® SBV assembly and/or spread of contamination from potentially contaminated SBV discs (during undocking of SBVs) after completion of task.
    - The wipe sampling result below test window (front cover) /above TFC 220 signage is indicative of potential leakage from air inflatable seal around the front cover.
  - Remaining results were below 50% wipe limit.
- Second iteration: The surface contamination levels reported for one (1) of the ten (10) samples collected *exceeded the wipe limit* (on fiber /cardboard mat taped at floor below discharge collection bag (result - 171 μg/100cm^2)), indicating potential leakage/emission from the discharge SBV and Chargebag® assembly and/or spread of contamination as SBVs were disconnected after completion of the task. Remaining wipe sampling results were below 20% of the wipe limit.

Conclusion:

The PBZ air and area air monitoring results are indicative (and not conclusive) that the containment system is likely to be effective for roll compaction (and in-line milling) of 10 kg of blend containing 30% surrogate (for an OEB 4 API) , with a CPT of 5 μg/m^3.

- Additional exposure monitoring (at minimum one (1) iteration) is needed to statistically conclude the containment performance.
- The area air sample collected near the PharmaSafe® SBV assembly with the Chargebag® (at the discharge/ collection port) was reported between 60-70 % of the CPT, indicating that there is a potential for leakage/ fugitive emissions during a) collection of compacted and milled blend in the Chargebag® and b) during un-docking of the SBV at the end of the task.

The wipe sampling result on the floor below the discharge collection port (Chargebag® connected to PharmaSafe® SBV) during the second iteration exceeded wipe limit, and is indicative that a) potential for leakage/fugitive emissions exist during the collection of compacted and milled blend in Chargebag® docked at the PharmaSafe® SBV and/or b) the disassembly of the SBV can lead to spread of contamination from SBV discs to the floor, which could have contributed to surface contamination level exceeding wipe limit. A visible surface contamination was observed on the PharmaSafe® SBV connected to filled Chargebag removed from discharge / collection port. Hence, the PharmaSafe® SBV assembly with Chargebag® during roll compaction, along with disassembly process at the end of the compaction process, was not effective in mitigating surface contamination levels below wipe limits.

Recommendations:

1) Conduct at minimum, one (1) additional containment validation iteration to statistically evaluate data and determine containment performance of the roll compactor system.
    a. Select a different employee/ operator for the remaining iteration to capture employee variation in handling / work practices.
    b. Ensure that adequate space / clearance is available to hold the Chargebag® upright at charging to prevent collapsing of blend near mouth of the liner, which can lead to increased tension across Chargebag® plastic liner and potentially lead to bag damage/ wear and tear.
2) Ensure that all operational parameters are verified prior to starting the roll compaction process and ensure the front cover air inflatable seal is not deflated during roll compaction.
3) Evaluate the steps for contained cleaning of the TFC-220 Roll Compactor without wash-in place system and conduct containment validation during the cleaning process.

Please review the report in conjunction with the following documents:

1) Appendix A- Results Tables
2) Appendix B – Monitoring locations
3) Appendix C- Task description and task images
4) Appendix D- AIHA accredited laboratory report
5) Appendix E - Surrogate Certificate of Analysis
6) Appendix F – Airflow calibrator – Calibration certificate
7) Appendix G- Results sheet (excel spreadsheet)

We appreciate the support received by all professionals at Freund Vector, Marion IA.

Regards,

Ankit Sharma CIH LFOH
Global Project Manager
ISS International Safety Systems Inc.

Appendix A- Results Tables

Table 1- Air monitoring results (Iterations 1 and 2)- normal operations

Date of Sampling	Sample ID	Total time (minutes)	Lab reported concentration (µg/m³)	95th %ile exposure estimate	GSD	Containment Performance Target (µg/m³)
Background						
10/13/2020	FRV-101320-MAN01	100	<0.01	NA	NA	5
10/14/2020	FRV-Oct20-MAN20	51	<0.019			5
Personal Breathing Zone (PBZ) air sample						
10/13/2020	FRV-Oct20-MAN02	96	0.431	0.455	1.02	5
10/13/2020	FRV-Oct20-MAN11	43	0.445			5
Area sample- near top SBV (AS1)						
10/13/2020	FRV-Oct20-MAN03	93	0.404	1.32	1.65	5
10/13/2020	FRV-Oct20-MAN12	42	0.822			5
Area sample near bottom of screw feeder cover -above Roller compactor and below hopper (AS3)						
10/13/2020	FRV-Oct20-MAN04	94	0.698	1.53	2.31	5
10/13/2020	FRV-Oct20-MAN13	40	0.213			5
Area sample near front cover left top (AS4)						
10/13/2020	FRV-Oct20-MAN05	92	0.904	1.96	2.28	5
10/13/2020	FRV-Oct20-MAN14	42	0.282			5
Area near top of hopper (AS2)						
10/13/2020	FRV-Oct20-MAN06	78	1.782	**6.37**	3.89	5
10/13/2020	FRV-Oct20-MAN15	43	0.261			5
Area near bottom of mill and above clamp below mill (AS6)						
10/13/2020	FRV-Oct20-MAN07	99	0.323	1.29	1.8	5
10/13/2020	FRV-Oct20-MAN16	43	0.744			5
Area near top of mill (AS5)						
10/13/2020	FRV-Oct20-MAN08	94	0.299	0.58	2.03	5
10/13/2020	FRV-Oct20-MAN17	42	0.11			
Area - near bottom SBV charge port bag (AS7)						
10/13/2020	FRV-Oct20-MAN09	92	0.924	**7.77**	2.47	5
10/13/2020	FRV-Oct20-MAN18	41	**3.324**			
Area distant						
10/13/2020	FRV-Oct20-MAN10	88	0.061	0.102	1.73	5
10/13/2020	FRV-Oct20-MAN19	50	0.028			

95th %ile estimate - The value is a statistically determined estimate below which 95% of exposures are expected to be reported. The value is indicative of upper tail of exposures for a lognormal distributed IH data

GSD- Geometric Standard Deviation- It is the measure of variability for a lognormally distributed data set.

- GSD< 2 indicates less variability, fairly reproducible data
- GSD between 2 and 3, indicates moderate variability in data
- GSD > 3 indicates relatively high variability in data, exposures likely more dependent on work practices, controls are less robust.
- GSD>4, high variability in exposure monitoring data

Table2 - Wipe Sampling Results (iterations 1 and 2)

Wipe sampling location	Area sample (cm^2)	Background Wipe Results ($\mu g/100cm^2$)	Wipe Results after 1st iteration ($\mu g/100cm^2$)	Wipe Results after 2nd iteration ($\mu g/100cm^2$)	Wipe Limit ($\mu g/100cm^2$)
Above the screw feeder housing (WS1)	100	0.835	**35.4**	6.68	50
Hopper top flange connected to screw feeder housing (WS2)	100	4.1	3.96	0.604	50
Below lower flange of hopper/ above roller compactor housing (WS3)	100	8.3	15.82	3.79	50
Below test window / Above TFC 220 signage (WS4)	100	9.2	**30.6**	2.53	50
Top of mill housing (WS5)	100	2.2	2.61	1.59	50
Mill housing front - around bearing housing (WS6)	100	1.57	1.46	0.506	50
Above lower SBV housing - top surface (WS7)	100	2.04	0.132	1.24	50
Bag mouth connected to valve- bag used for 1st iteration	100	<0.01	0.406	0.0687	50
Floor below lower SBV (WS8)	100	1.2	7.2	**171**	50
Inflatable sash right side -including handle (WS9)	100	6.1	4.8	0.879	50
Bag mouth connected to valve- bag used for 2nd iteration	100	<0.01	NA	0.0687	50

Table 3: Air monitoring results (iteration 3)- process upset/containment breach

Date of Sampling	Sample ID	Total time	Lab reported concentration ($\mu g/m^3$)	Containment Performance Target ($\mu g/m^3$)
Personal Breathing Zone (PBZ) air sample				
10/14/2020	FRV-Oct20-MAN21	43	**3.41**	5
Area sample- near top SBV (AS1)				
10/14/2020	FRV-Oct20-MAN22	48	**80.58**	5
Area sample near bottom of screw feeder cover - above Roller compactor and below hopper (AS3)				
10/14/2020	FRV-Oct20-MAN23	43	**1.95**	5
Area sample near sash left top (AS4)				
10/14/2020	FRV-Oct20-MAN24	42	**5.66**	5
Area near top of hopper (AS2)				
10/14/2020	FRV-Oct20-MAN25	42	**95.27**	5
Area near bottom of mill and above triclamp below mill (AS6)				
10/14/2020	FRV-Oct20-MAN26	41	**10.06**	5
Area near top of the mill (AS5)				
10/14/2020	FRV-Oct20-MAN27	40	**13.68**	5
Area - near bottom SBV charge port bag (AS7)				
10/14/2020	FRV-Oct20-MAN28	39	**16.64**	5
Area distant				
10/14/2020	FRV-Oct20-MAN29	43	0.24	5

Appendix B- Monitoring locations

Air monitoring locations

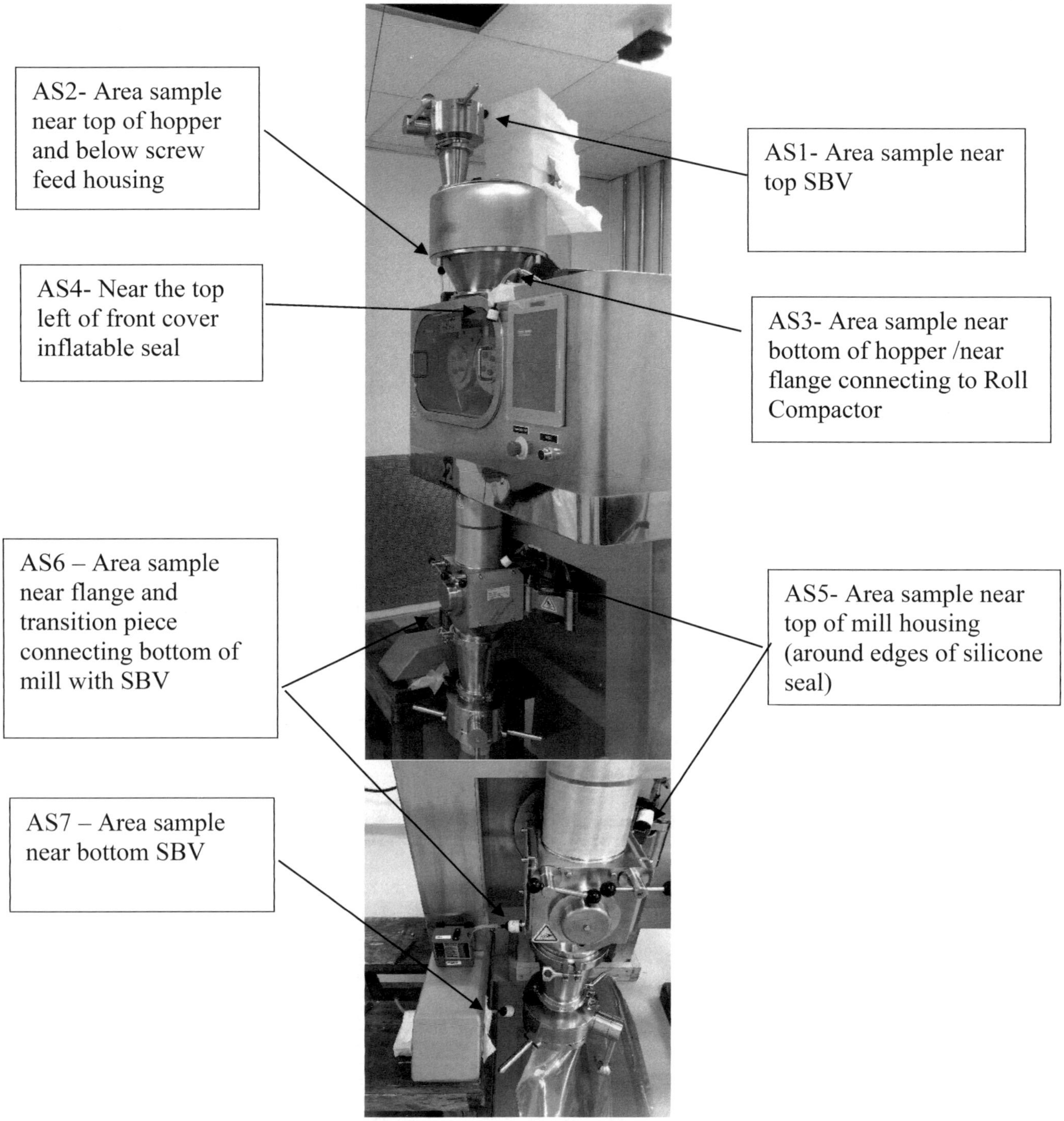

<u>Wipe sampling locations</u>

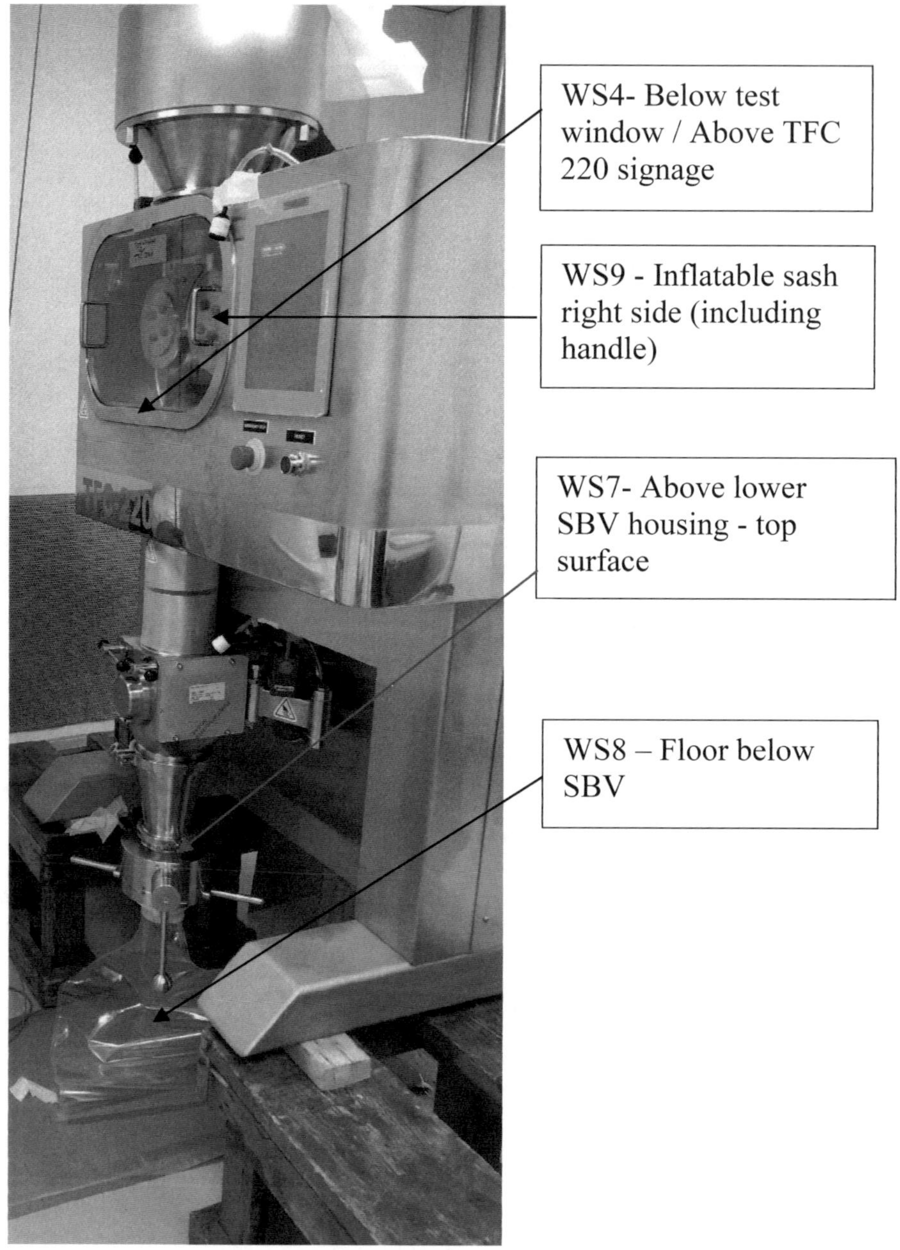
WS4- Below test window / Above TFC 220 signage
WS9 - Inflatable sash right side (including handle)
WS7- Above lower SBV housing - top surface
WS8 – Floor below SBV

Appendix C- Task description and Images

1. A temporary enclosure was created in corridor outside the test suite (in which the TFC220 Roll Compactor was housed) to create a temporary gowning/degowning area.
2. The monitored employee donned the Personal Protective Equipment (PPE), which included disposable coverall, disposable shoe covers and double layer of disposable Nitrile gloves.
3. The Roll Compactor was placed on a wooden platform to provide elevation for docking the Chargebag® at discharge port of in-line mill (below roll compactor).
4. The employee docked the empty Chargebag® connected to PharmaSafe® SBV at discharge port and locked the valve in place. The valve was operated by operating the lever handle.
5. The employee collected the Chargebag® (containing 10 kg blend containing 30% surrogate) from a 55 gallon drum which was brought in by the employee into the suite.
6. As a makeshift system to lift the Chargebag® and hold it in place, the Chargebag® was attached to hooks fixed on a wooden block and lifted by hand operated pulley lift created (using bungee cord) to hoist the bag and position it over the PharmaSafe® SBV connected to hopper of the roll compactor (one of the false ceiling tiles of the suite was removed to allow clearance height for the Chargebag® with PharmaSafe® SBV to be positioned over the hopper). The bungee cord was tied at an anchor point to hold the bag in place.
7. The employee climbed up on portable ladder positioned in front of the Roll Compactor and sat on top rung of the ladder to dock the Chargebag® with the PharmaSafe® SBV seated on the hopper.
8. The employee faced issues in operating the lever of the valve, indicating that the active-passive valve discs of the PharmaSafe® containment valve was not locked in place. It took 8-10 attempts of re-aligning the SBV in the seat, to ensure that the SBVs were locked and seated properly, which allowed the employee to operate the lever and open the valve.
    a. During first iteration, when employee was not able to open the PharmaSafe® valve, employee undocked the SBV and placed the Chargebag® on the top of Roll compactor , brought the bag down through the cord pulley lifting-lowering system, and lifting the bag again to reposition over the SBV on the hopper.
9. *First iteration*: The employee started the Roll Compactor using the COMPU control system but realized that the mill operation option was not showing in the HMI panel.
    a. While trying to locate the option to activate mill, the employee accidentally deflated the inflatable seal of the front cover. The employee quickly reinflated the seal. This step likely did not impact the containment performance as roll compaction was not performed prior to this incident.
    b. A technical engineer was called to assist in the program logic/ HMI settings. After intervention, the mill option was available on the HMI panel, and was selected.
10. The employee then opened the top SBV to allow gravity feeding of blend from Chargebag® into the hopper of the Roll compactor. The discharge bag was observed to start filling up instantaneously as soon as the compaction and in-line milling process started.
11. The settings on the COMPU Control panel, included a) mill speed of 90 rotations per minute (rpm), b) screw speed of 24 rpm, c) roll speed of 6 rpm and d) gap between the two rolls was 0.073 inches. The roll force was changed during the compaction process and maintained upto 8000 pound force (lb. f).

12. During the roll compaction and in-line milling process, the employee had to hold and shake the Chargebag® at charging port (to ensure flow of material to the hopper) and discharge port (to avoid bottleneck in the collection Chargebag®).
13. The roll compaction and in-line milling process was operated for approximately 20 minutes to compact and mill 10 kg of blend (containing 30% surrogate).
14. After the compaction was complete, the employee disconnected the PharmaSafe SBVs and immediately used 'Good and Clean' disinfectant wipes before moving the filled bag to the empty 55-gallon drum.
15. The employee changed outer layer of gloves after wipe cleaning the SBV discs.
16. The employee similarly removed the emptied Chargebag® at charging station, clean the SBV disc and change the gloves.
17. *Third iteration* - The third iteration of containment validation of roll compactor was impacted by an off-incidence of a breach (perforation/damage) in the ChargePoint® bag docked above the hopper during hopper charging, which led to leakage / fugitive emissions during the task. The bag was sealed immediately by taping around the perforation.

Employee docking the empty Chargebag® with PharmaSafe SBV at the discharge/ collection port

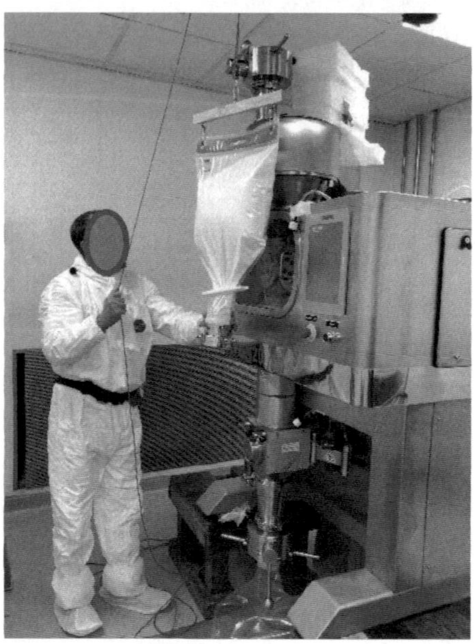

Employee moving the Chargebag® using hand operated hoist to dock at charging station.

Employee positioning the Chargebag® with PharmaSafe® at charging port

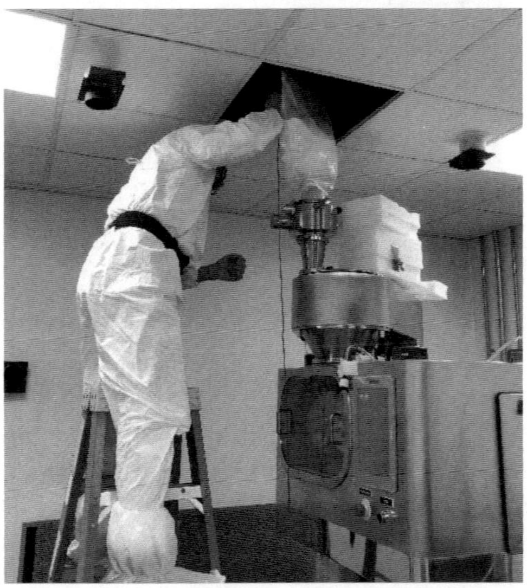

Employee positioning the Chargebag® with PharmaSafe® at charging port

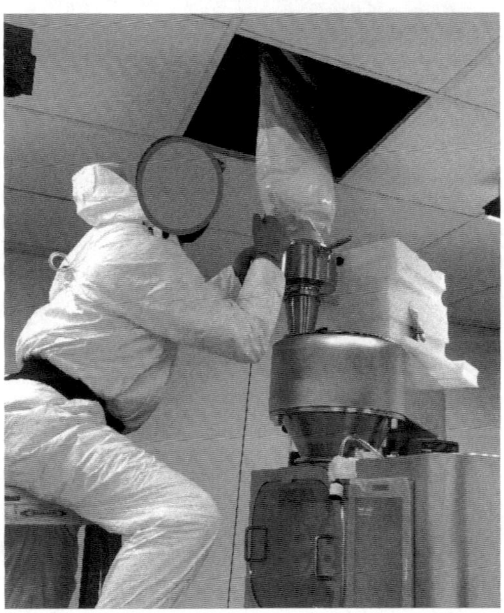

Employee trying to operate the lever to open the SBV at charging station . Employee made multiple attempts before being able to operate lever

Employee facilitating material flow from Chargebag to the screw feed and then to the Roll Compactor, where compacted sheets are generated and fed to in-line mill

The Chargebag® connected at the bottom SBV for collection of roll compacted and milled blend

The silicone sleeve connecting the Roll compactor to the Mill housing

The employee disconnecting the Chargebag SBV from the discharge port and cleaning immediately with disinfectant wipes

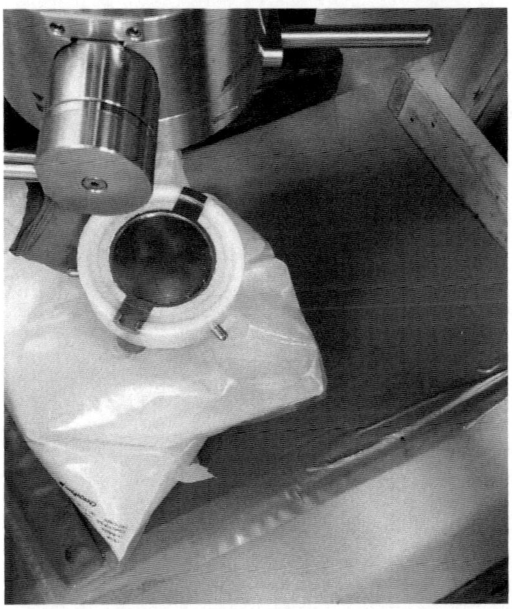

Visible contamination on the SBV disc as it is disconnected after collecting milled , roll compacted blend

Employee cleaning the PharmaSafe® SBV disc of the emptied Chargebag®

The employee removed the emptied bag using pulley bungee cord

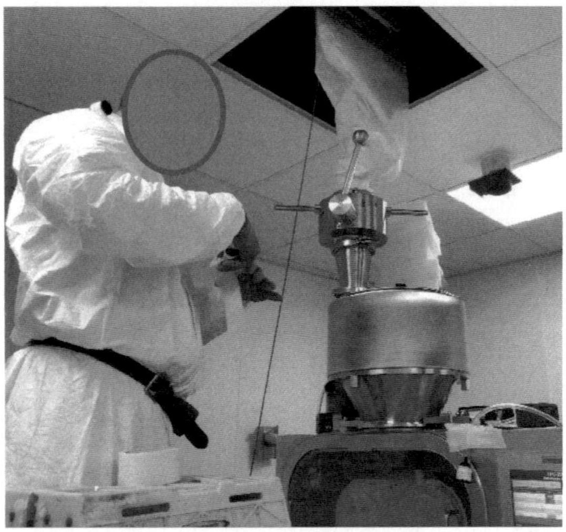

Paper tape applied around the mouth of plastic bag where perforation was observed.

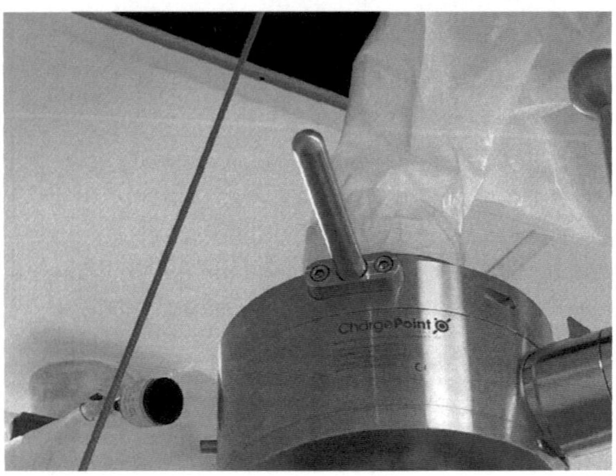

Paper tape applied around the mouth of plastic bag where perforation was observed.

Analytics Corporation
10329 Stony Run Lane
Ashland, Va 23005
Phone: (804) 365-3000 Fax: (804) 365-3002
AIHA-LAP, LLC Accreditation ID 100531

November 12, 2020

ANKIT SHARMA
ISS INTERNATIONAL SAFETY SYSTEMS INC
SUITE 104
13831 NORTHWEST FWY
HOUSTON, TX 77040

Laboratory Workorder ID: Y301104

Client Project ID: ISSUSA PROJECT IOWA
Received: October 27, 2020
Reported: November 12, 2020

Attached are the results we obtained on the analysis of your samples submitted to Analytics. Any Chains-of-Custody associated by this sample group are enclosed. Air concentrations are calculated as a convenience to the client and the overall accuracy of this result depends on both the accuracy of the air volume and the amount found by analysis. Theoretical air volumes for passive monitors are calculated using the sampling time submitted and the manufacture's listed sampling rate for each compound. Results provided in this report relate only to the items tested.

For blanks and non-detects the results indicated with a '<' value represents the reporting limit for the analysis. Unless otherwise noted results are not corrected for blank values.

Unless the signature of the appropriate manager(s) appears on this report, this report should be considered PRELIMINARY and is subject to change.

We appreciate your confidence in allowing Analytics to be your testing laboratory. Any questions regarding this report can be addressed by calling our customer services department at (800) 888-8061.

Andrew L. Teague, CIH
Technical Director

Enclosures

Analytics Corporation
10329 Stony Run Lane
Ashland, Va 23005
Phone: (804) 365-3000 Fax: (804) 365-3002
AIHA-LAP, LLC Accreditation ID 100531

Final Report

Work Order Y301104

ISS INTERNATIONAL SAFETY SYSTEMS INC
SUITE 104
13831 NORTHWEST FWY
HOUSTON, TX 77040

Customer: 42509720
Attention: ANKIT SHARMA
PO Number ANKIT SHARMA

Date Received: 10/27/20
Client Project ID ISSUSA PROJECT IOWA

Lab ID: Y301104001 Sample ID: FRV-101320-MAN01 Media: C-62,2um PTFE Filter Sample Date: 10/13/2020 Sampling Time:

Analyte	Method	Analysis Date	Volume	Reporting Limit	Front	Rear	Total	Concentration
Mannitol	IH IC 021	11/12/20	200.700 L	2.0 ng			< 2 ng	< 0.01 ug/M3

Lab ID: Y301104002 Sample ID: FRV-OCT20-MAN02 Media: C-62,2um PTFE Filter Sample Date: 10/13/2020 Sampling Time:

Analyte	Method	Analysis Date	Volume	Reporting Limit	Front	Rear	Total	Concentration
Mannitol	IH IC 021	11/12/20	199.872 L	2.0 ng			86.2 ng	0.431 ug/M3

Lab ID: Y301104003 Sample ID: FRV-OCT20-MAN03 Media: C-62,2um PTFE Filter Sample Date: 10/13/2020 Sampling Time:

Analyte	Method	Analysis Date	Volume	Reporting Limit	Front	Rear	Total	Concentration
Mannitol	IH IC 021	11/12/20	186.496 L	2.0 ng			75.3 ng	0.404 ug/M3

Lab ID: Y301104004 Sample ID: FRV-OCT20-MAN04 Media: C-62,2um PTFE Filter Sample Date: 10/13/2020 Sampling Time:

Analyte	Method	Analysis Date	Volume	Reporting Limit	Front	Rear	Total	Concentration

Analytics Corporation
10329 Stony Run Lane
Ashland, Va 23005
Phone: (804) 365-3000 Fax: (804) 365-3002
AIHA-LAP, LLC Accreditation ID 100531

Final Report

Work Order Y301104

Lab ID: Y301104004 Sample ID: FRV-OCT20-MAN04 Media: C-62,2um PTFE Filter Sample Date: 10/13/2020 Sampling Time:

Analyte	Method	Analysis Date	Volume	Reporting Limit	Front	Rear	Total	Concentration
Mannitol	IH IC 021	11/12/20	193.452 L	2.0 ng			135 ng	0.698 ug/M3

Lab ID: Y301104005 Sample ID: FRV-OCT20-MAN05 Media: C-62,2um PTFE Filter Sample Date: 10/13/2020 Sampling Time:

Analyte	Method	Analysis Date	Volume	Reporting Limit	Front	Rear	Total	Concentration
Mannitol	IH IC 021	11/12/20	186.898 L	2.0 ng			169 ng	0.904 ug/M3

Lab ID: Y301104006 Sample ID: FRV-OCT20-MAN06 Media: C-62,2um PTFE Filter Sample Date: 10/13/2020 Sampling Time:

Analyte	Method	Analysis Date	Volume	Reporting Limit	Front	Rear	Total	Concentration
Mannitol	IH IC 021	11/12/20	156.546 L	2.0 ng			279 ng	1.782 ug/M3

Lab ID: Y301104007 Sample ID: FRV-OCT20-MAN07 Media: C-62,2um PTFE Filter Sample Date: 10/13/2020 Sampling Time:

Analyte	Method	Analysis Date	Volume	Reporting Limit	Front	Rear	Total	Concentration
Mannitol	IH IC 021	11/12/20	203.033 L	2.0 ng			65.6 ng	0.323 ug/M3

Analytics Corporation
10329 Stony Run Lane
Ashland, Va 23005
Phone: (804) 365-3000 Fax: (804) 365-3002
AIHA-LAP, LLC Accreditation ID 100531

Final Report

Work Order Y301104

Lab ID: Y301104008 Sample ID: FRV-OCT20-MAN08 Media: C-62,2um PTFE Filter Sample Date: 10/13/2020 Sampling Time:

Analyte	Method	Analysis Date	Volume	Reporting Limit	Front	Rear	Total	Concentration
Mannitol	IH IC 021	11/12/20	190.898 L	2.0 ng			57.1 ng	0.299 ug/M3

Lab ID: Y301104009 Sample ID: FRV-OCT20-MAN09 Media: C-62,2um PTFE Filter Sample Date: 10/13/2020 Sampling Time:

Analyte	Method	Analysis Date	Volume	Reporting Limit	Front	Rear	Total	Concentration
Mannitol	IH IC 021	11/12/20	182.927 L	2.0 ng			169 ng	0.924 ug/M3

Lab ID: Y301104010 Sample ID: FRV-OCT20-MAN10 Media: C-62,2um PTFE Filter Sample Date: 10/13/2020 Sampling Time:

Analyte	Method	Analysis Date	Volume	Reporting Limit	Front	Rear	Total	Concentration
Mannitol	IH IC 021	11/12/20	178.273 L	2.0 ng			10.9 ng	0.061 ug/M3

Lab ID: Y301104011 Sample ID: FRV-OCT20-MAN11 Media: C-62,2um PTFE Filter Sample Date: 10/13/2020 Sampling Time:

Analyte	Method	Analysis Date	Volume	Reporting Limit	Front	Rear	Total	Concentration
Mannitol	IH IC 021	11/12/20	89.526 L	2.0 ng			39.8 ng	0.445 ug/M3

ANALYTICS

Analytics Corporation
10329 Stony Run Lane
Ashland, Va 23005
Phone: (804) 365-3000 Fax: (804) 365-3002
AIHA-LAP, LLC Accreditation ID 100531

Final Report

Work Order Y301104

Lab ID: Y301104012 Sample ID: FRV-OCT20-MAN12 Media: C-62,2um PTFE Filter Sample Date: 10/13/2020 Sampling Time:

Analyte	Method	Analysis Date	Volume	Reporting Limit	Front	Rear	Total	Concentration
Mannitol	IH IC 021	11/12/20	84.224 L	2.0 ng			69.2 ng	0.822 ug/M3

Lab ID: Y301104013 Sample ID: FRV-OCT20-MAN13 Media: C-62,2um PTFE Filter Sample Date: 10/13/2020 Sampling Time:

Analyte	Method	Analysis Date	Volume	Reporting Limit	Front	Rear	Total	Concentration
Mannitol	IH IC 021	11/12/20	82.320 L	2.0 ng			17.5 ng	0.213 ug/M3

Lab ID: Y301104014 Sample ID: FRV-OCT20-MAN14 Media: C-62,2um PTFE Filter Sample Date: 10/13/2020 Sampling Time:

Analyte	Method	Analysis Date	Volume	Reporting Limit	Front	Rear	Total	Concentration
Mannitol	IH IC 021	11/12/20	85.323 L	2.0 ng			24.1 ng	0.282 ug/M3

Lab ID: Y301104015 Sample ID: FRV-OCT20-MAN15 Media: C-62,2um PTFE Filter Sample Date: 10/13/2020 Sampling Time:

Analyte	Method	Analysis Date	Volume	Reporting Limit	Front	Rear	Total	Concentration
Mannitol	IH IC 021	11/12/20	86.301 L	2.0 ng			22.5 ng	0.261 ug/M3

Analytics Corporation
10329 Stony Run Lane
Ashland, Va 23005
Phone: (804) 365-3000 Fax: (804) 365-3002
AIHA-LAP, LLC Accreditation ID 100531

Final Report

Work Order Y301104

Lab ID: Y301104016 Sample ID: FRV-OCT20-MAN16 Media: C-62,2um PTFE Filter Sample Date: 10/13/2020 Sampling Time:

Analyte	Method	Analysis Date	Volume	Reporting Limit	Front	Rear	Total	Concentration
Mannitol	IH IC 021	11/12/20	88.186 L	2.0 ng			65.6 ng	0.744 ug/M3

Lab ID: Y301104017 Sample ID: FRV-OCT20-MAN17 Media: C-62,2um PTFE Filter Sample Date: 10/13/2020 Sampling Time:

Analyte	Method	Analysis Date	Volume	Reporting Limit	Front	Rear	Total	Concentration
Mannitol	IH IC 021	11/12/20	85.295 L	2.0 ng			9.41 ng	0.11 ug/M3

Lab ID: Y301104018 Sample ID: FRV-OCT20-MAN18 Media: C-62,2um PTFE Filter Sample Date: 10/13/2020 Sampling Time:

Analyte	Method	Analysis Date	Volume	Reporting Limit	Front	Rear	Total	Concentration
Mannitol	IH IC 021	11/12/20	81.522 L	2.0 ng			271 ng	3.324 ug/M3

Lab ID: Y301104019 Sample ID: FRV-OCT20-MAN19 Media: C-62,2um PTFE Filter Sample Date: 10/13/2020 Sampling Time:

Analyte	Method	Analysis Date	Volume	Reporting Limit	Front	Rear	Total	Concentration
Mannitol	IH IC 021	11/12/20	101.292 L	2.0 ng			2.81 ng	0.028 ug/M3

Analytics Corporation
10329 Stony Run Lane
Ashland, Va 23005
Phone: (804) 365-3000 Fax: (804) 365-3002
AIHA-LAP, LLC Accreditation ID 100531

Final Report

Work Order Y301104

Lab ID: Y301104020 Sample ID: FRV-OCT20-MAN20 Media: C-62,2um PTFE Filter Sample Date: 10/14/2020 Sampling Time:

Analyte	Method	Analysis Date	Volume	Reporting Limit	Front	Rear	Total	Concentration
Mannitol	IH IC 021	11/12/20	102.859 L	2.0 ng			< 2 ng	< 0.019 ug/M3

Lab ID: Y301104021 Sample ID: FRV-OCT20-MAN21 Media: C-62,2um PTFE Filter Sample Date: 10/14/2020 Sampling Time:

Analyte	Method	Analysis Date	Volume	Reporting Limit	Front	Rear	Total	Concentration
Mannitol	IH IC 021	11/12/20	85.979 L	2.0 ng			293 ng	3.408 ug/M3

Lab ID: Y301104022 Sample ID: FRV-OCT20-MAN22 Media: C-62,2um PTFE Filter Sample Date: 10/14/2020 Sampling Time:

Analyte	Method	Analysis Date	Volume	Reporting Limit	Front	Rear	Total	Concentration
Mannitol	IH IC 021	11/12/20	96.928 L	2.0 ng			7810 ng	80.575 ug/M3

Lab ID: Y301104023 Sample ID: FRV-OCT20-MAN23 Media: C-62,2um PTFE Filter Sample Date: 10/14/2020 Sampling Time:

Analyte	Method	Analysis Date	Volume	Reporting Limit	Front	Rear	Total	Concentration
Mannitol	IH IC 021	11/12/20	89.311 L	2.0 ng			174 ng	1.948 ug/M3

Analytics Corporation
10329 Stony Run Lane
Ashland, Va 23005
Phone: (804) 365-3000 Fax: (804) 365-3002
AIHA-LAP, LLC Accreditation ID 100531

Final Report

Work Order Y301104

Lab ID: Y301104024 Sample ID: FRV-OCT20-MAN24 Media: C-62,2um PTFE Filter Sample Date: 10/14/2020 Sampling Time:

Analyte	Method	Analysis Date	Volume	Reporting Limit	Front	Rear	Total	Concentration
Mannitol	IH IC 021	11/12/20	86.752 L	2.0 ng			491 ng	5.66 ug/M3

Lab ID: Y301104025 Sample ID: FRV-OCT20-MAN25 Media: C-62,2um PTFE Filter Sample Date: 10/14/2020 Sampling Time:

Analyte	Method	Analysis Date	Volume	Reporting Limit	Front	Rear	Total	Concentration
Mannitol	IH IC 021	11/12/20	84.707 L	2.0 ng			8070 ng	95.27 ug/M3

Lab ID: Y301104026 Sample ID: FRV-OCT20-MAN26 Media: C-62,2um PTFE Filter Sample Date: 10/14/2020 Sampling Time:

Analyte	Method	Analysis Date	Volume	Reporting Limit	Front	Rear	Total	Concentration
Mannitol	IH IC 021	11/12/20	83.913 L	2.0 ng			844 ng	10.058 ug/M3

Lab ID: Y301104027 Sample ID: FRV-OCT20-MAN27 Media: C-62,2um PTFE Filter Sample Date: 10/14/2020 Sampling Time:

Analyte	Method	Analysis Date	Volume	Reporting Limit	Front	Rear	Total	Concentration
Mannitol	IH IC 021	11/12/20	80.440 L	2.0 ng			1100 ng	13.675 ug/M3

ANALYTICS

Analytics Corporation
10329 Stony Run Lane
Ashland, Va 23005
Phone: (804) 365-3000 Fax: (804) 365-3002
AIHA-LAP, LLC Accreditation ID 100531

Final Report

Work Order Y301104

Lab ID: Y301104028 Sample ID: FRV-OCT20-MAN28 Media: C-62,2um PTFE Filter Sample Date: 10/14/2020 Sampling Time:

Analyte	Method	Analysis Date	Volume	Reporting Limit	Front	Rear	Total	Concentration
Mannitol	IH IC 021	11/12/20	76.941 L	2.0 ng			1280 ng	16.636 ug/M3

Lab ID: Y301104029 Sample ID: FRV-OCT20-MAN29 Media: C-62,2um PTFE Filter Sample Date: 10/14/2020 Sampling Time:

Analyte	Method	Analysis Date	Volume	Reporting Limit	Front	Rear	Total	Concentration
Mannitol	IH IC 021	11/12/20	87.161 L	2.0 ng			20.8 ng	0.239 ug/M3

Lab ID: Y301104030 Sample ID: FRV-OCT20-MANFB01 BLANK Media: C-62,2um PTFE Filter Sample Date: 10/13/2020 Sampling Time:

Analyte	Method	Analysis Date	Volume	Reporting Limit	Front	Rear	Total	Concentration
Mannitol	IH IC 021	11/12/20	0 L	2.0 ng			< 2 ng	--

Lab ID: Y301104031 Sample ID: FRV-OCT20-MANFB02 BLANK Media: C-62,2um PTFE Filter Sample Date: 10/13/2020 Sampling Time:

Analyte	Method	Analysis Date	Volume	Reporting Limit	Front	Rear	Total	Concentration
Mannitol	IH IC 021	11/12/20	0 L	2.0 ng			3.16 ng	--

(Mannitol found in client blank) Samples are not corrected.

ANALYTICS

Analytics Corporation
10329 Stony Run Lane
Ashland, Va 23005
Phone: (804) 365-3000 Fax: (804) 365-3002
AIHA-LAP, LLC Accreditation ID 100531

Final Report

Work Order Y301104

Lab ID: Y301104032 Sample ID: FRV-OCT20-MANMB01 BLANK Media: C-62,2um PTFE Filter Sample Date: 10/14/2020 Sampling Time:

Analyte	Method	Analysis Date	Volume	Reporting Limit	Front	Rear	Total	Concentration
Mannitol	IH IC 021	11/12/20	0 L	2.0 ng			< 2 ng	--

Lab ID: Y301104033 Sample ID: FRV-OCT20-MANFB03 BLANK Media: C-62,2um PTFE Filter Sample Date: 10/14/2020 Sampling Time:

Analyte	Method	Analysis Date	Volume	Reporting Limit	Front	Rear	Total	Concentration
Mannitol	IH IC 021	11/12/20	0 L	2.0 ng			< 2 ng	--

ANALYTICS

Analytics Corporation
10329 Stony Run Lane
Ashland, Va 23005
Phone: (804) 365-3000 Fax: (804) 365-3002
AIHA-LAP, LLC Accreditation ID 100531

Final Report

Work Order Y301104

General Laboratory Comments

Abbreviations:
ug = micrograms; mg=milligrams; g = grams, ppm=parts per million (volume), ppb = parts per billion (volume), mg/M3=milligrams per cubic meter of air, ug/M3=micrograms per cubic meter of air; Min=minutes, Qual=Qualifiers

Y301104

Chain of Custody

Client Project: ISSUSA Project Iowa

Project by: ISS Inc.

Invoice to/Bill To:
International Safety Systems, Inc.

Send results to: ankit.sharma@issehs.com

Date of Sampling	Sample ID	Analyte	Sampling Media	Total time	Average Flow Rate (L/Min)	Volume (Liter)
10/13/2020	FRV-101320-MAN01	Mannitol	25 mm PTFE	100	2.007	200.700
10/13/2020	FRV-Oct20-MAN02	Mannitol	25 mm PTFE	96	2.082	199.872
10/13/2020	FRV-Oct20-MAN03	Mannitol	25 mm PTFE	93	2.005	186.496
10/13/2020	FRV-Oct20-MAN04	Mannitol	25 mm PTFE	94	2.058	193.452
10/13/2020	FRV-Oct20-MAN05	Mannitol	25 mm PTFE	92	2.032	186.898
10/13/2020	FRV-Oct20-MAN06	Mannitol	25 mm PTFE	78	2.007	156.546
10/13/2020	FRV-Oct20-MAN07	Mannitol	25 mm PTFE	99	2.051	203.033
10/13/2020	FRV-Oct20-MAN08	Mannitol	25 mm PTFE	94	2.031	190.898
10/13/2020	FRV-Oct20-MAN09	Mannitol	25 mm PTFE	92	1.988	182.927
10/13/2020	FRV-Oct20-MAN10	Mannitol	25 mm PTFE	88	2.026	178.273
10/13/2020	FRV-Oct20-MAN11	Mannitol	25 mm PTFE	43	2.082	89.526
10/13/2020	FRV-Oct20-MAN12	Mannitol	25 mm PTFE	42	2.005	84.224
10/13/2020	FRV-Oct20-MAN13	Mannitol	25 mm PTFE	40	2.058	82.320
10/13/2020	FRV-Oct20-MAN14	Mannitol	25 mm PTFE	42	2.032	85.323
10/13/2020	FRV-Oct20-MAN15	Mannitol	25 mm PTFE	43	2.007	86.301
10/13/2020	FRV-Oct20-MAN16	Mannitol	25 mm PTFE	43	2.051	88.186
10/13/2020	FRV-Oct20-MAN17	Mannitol	25 mm PTFE	42	2.031	85.295
10/13/2020	FRV-Oct20-MAN18	Mannitol	25 mm PTFE	41	1.988	81.522
10/13/2020	FRV-Oct20-MAN19	Mannitol	25 mm PTFE	50	2.026	101.292
10/14/2020	FRV-Oct20-MAN20	Mannitol	25 mm PTFE	51	2.017	102.859
10/14/2020	FRV-Oct20-MAN21	Mannitol	25 mm PTFE	43	2.000	85.979
10/14/2020	FRV-Oct20-MAN22	Mannitol	25 mm PTFE	48	2.019	96.928
10/14/2020	FRV-Oct20-MAN23	Mannitol	25 mm PTFE	43	2.077	89.311
10/14/2020	FRV-Oct20-MAN24	Mannitol	25 mm PTFE	42	2.066	86.752
10/14/2020	FRV-Oct20-MAN25	Mannitol	25 mm PTFE	42	2.017	84.707
10/14/2020	FRV-Oct20-MAN26	Mannitol	25 mm PTFE	41	2.047	83.913
10/14/2020	FRV-Oct20-MAN27	Mannitol	25 mm PTFE	40	2.011	80.440
10/14/2020	FRV-Oct20-MAN28	Mannitol	25 mm PTFE	39	1.973	76.941
10/14/2020	FRV-Oct20-MAN29	Mannitol	25 mm PTFE	43	2.027	87.161
10/13/2020	FRV-Oct20-MANFB01	Mannitol	25 mm PTFE	0	0	0.000
10/13/2020	FRV-Oct20-MANFB02	Mannitol	25 mm PTFE	0	0	0.000
10/14/2020	FRV-Oct20-MANMB01	Mannitol	25 mm PTFE	0	0	0.000

Samples Submitted by: Ankit Sharma CIH LFOH
Phone: +1 203 751 0400, email: ankit.sharma @issehs.com

Amy Larson 10/27/20

AMY LARSON

Analytics Corporation
10329 Stony Run Lane
Ashland, Va 23005
Phone: (804) 365-3000 Fax: (804) 365-3002
AIHA-LAP, LLC Accreditation ID 100531

November 11, 2020

ANKIT SHARMA
ISS INTERNATIONAL SAFETY SYSTEMS INC
SUITE 104
13831 NORTHWEST FWY
HOUSTON, TX 77040

Laboratory Workorder ID: Y301103

Client Project ID:	ISS CLIENT-IOWA
Received:	October 27, 2020
Reported:	November 11, 2020

Attached are the results we obtained on the analysis of your samples submitted to Analytics. Any Chains-of-Custody associated by this sample group are enclosed. Air concentrations are calculated as a convenience to the client and the overall accuracy of this result depends on both the accuracy of the air volume and the amount found by analysis. Theoretical air volumes for passive monitors are calculated using the sampling time submitted and the manufacture's listed sampling rate for each compound. Results provided in this report relate only to the items tested.

For blanks and non-detects the results indicated with a '<' value represents the reporting limit for the analysis. Unless otherwise noted results are not corrected for blank values.

Unless the signature of the appropriate manager(s) appears on this report, this report should be considered PRELIMINARY and is subject to change.

We appreciate your confidence in allowing Analytics to be your testing laboratory. Any questions regarding this report can be addressed by calling our customer services department at (800) 888-8061.

Andrew L. Teague, CIH
Technical Director

Enclosures

Report ID: Y301103-202011114730

Analytics Corporation
10329 Stony Run Lane
Ashland, Va 23005
Phone: (804) 365-3000 Fax: (804) 365-3002
AIHA-LAP, LLC Accreditation ID 100531

Final Report

Work Order Y301103

ISS INTERNATIONAL SAFETY SYSTEMS INC
SUITE 104
13831 NORTHWEST FWY
HOUSTON, TX 77040

Customer: 42509720
Attention: ANKIT SHARMA
PO Number ANKIT SHARMA

Date Received: 10/27/20
Client Project ID ISS CLIENT-IOWA

Lab ID: Y301103001 Sample ID: FRV-OCT20-MANWS01 Media: Texwipe, Polyester Swab, TX7 Sample Date: 10/13/2020 Sampling Time:

Analyte	Method	Analysis Date	Volume		Reporting Limit	Front	Rear	Total	Concentration
Mannitol	IH IC 021	11/10/20	100	cm2	10.0 ng			835 ng	8.35 ng/cm2

Lab ID: Y301103002 Sample ID: FRV-OCT20-MANWS02 Media: Texwipe, Polyester Swab, TX7 Sample Date: 10/13/2020 Sampling Time:

Analyte	Method	Analysis Date	Volume		Reporting Limit	Front	Rear	Total	Concentration
Mannitol	IH IC 021	11/10/20	100	cm2	10.0 ng			4110 ng	41.1 ng/cm2

Lab ID: Y301103003 Sample ID: FRV-OCT20-MANWS03 Media: Texwipe, Polyester Swab, TX7 Sample Date: 10/13/2020 Sampling Time:

Analyte	Method	Analysis Date	Volume		Reporting Limit	Front	Rear	Total	Concentration
Mannitol	IH IC 021	11/10/20	100	cm2	10.0 ng			8320 ng	83.2 ng/cm2

Lab ID: Y301103004 Sample ID: FRV-OCT20-MANWS04 Media: Texwipe, Polyester Swab, TX7 Sample Date: 10/13/2020 Sampling Time:

Analyte	Method	Analysis Date	Volume		Reporting Limit	Front	Rear	Total	Concentration

Analytics Corporation
10329 Stony Run Lane
Ashland, Va 23005
Phone: (804) 365-3000 Fax: (804) 365-3002
AIHA-LAP, LLC Accreditation ID 100531

Final Report

Work Order Y301103

Lab ID: Y301103004 Sample ID: FRV-OCT20-MANWS04 Media: Texwipe, Polyester Swab, TX7 Sample Date: 10/13/2020 Sampling Time:

Analyte	Method	Analysis Date	Volume		Reporting Limit	Front	Rear	Total	Concentration
Mannitol	IH IC 021	11/10/20	100	cm2	10.0 ng			9220 ng	92.2 ng/cm2

Lab ID: Y301103005 Sample ID: FRV-OCT20-MANWS05 Media: Texwipe, Polyester Swab, TX7 Sample Date: 10/13/2020 Sampling Time:

Analyte	Method	Analysis Date	Volume		Reporting Limit	Front	Rear	Total	Concentration
Mannitol	IH IC 021	11/10/20	100	cm2	10.0 ng			2220 ng	22.2 ng/cm2

Lab ID: Y301103006 Sample ID: FRV-OCT20-MANWS06 Media: Texwipe, Polyester Swab, TX7 Sample Date: 10/13/2020 Sampling Time:

Analyte	Method	Analysis Date	Volume		Reporting Limit	Front	Rear	Total	Concentration
Mannitol	IH IC 021	11/10/20	100	cm2	10.0 ng			1570 ng	15.7 ng/cm2

Lab ID: Y301103007 Sample ID: FRV-OCT20-MANWS07 Media: Texwipe, Polyester Swab, TX7 Sample Date: 10/13/2020 Sampling Time:

Analyte	Method	Analysis Date	Volume		Reporting Limit	Front	Rear	Total	Concentration
Mannitol	IH IC 021	11/10/20	100	cm2	10.0 ng			2040 ng	20.4 ng/cm2

Analytics Corporation
10329 Stony Run Lane
Ashland, Va 23005
Phone: (804) 365-3000 Fax: (804) 365-3002
AIHA-LAP, LLC Accreditation ID 100531

Final Report

Work Order Y301103

Lab ID: Y301103008 Sample ID: FRV-OCT20-MANWS08 Media: Texwipe, Polyester Swab, TX7 Sample Date: 10/13/2020 Sampling Time:

Analyte	Method	Analysis Date	Volume		Reporting Limit	Front	Rear	Total	Concentration
Mannitol	IH IC 021	11/10/20	100	cm2	10.0 ng			< 10 ng	< 0.1 ng/cm2

Lab ID: Y301103009 Sample ID: FRV-OCT20-MANWS09 Media: Texwipe, Polyester Swab, TX7 Sample Date: 10/13/2020 Sampling Time:

Analyte	Method	Analysis Date	Volume		Reporting Limit	Front	Rear	Total	Concentration
Mannitol	IH IC 021	11/10/20	100	cm2	10.0 ng			1200 ng	12.0 ng/cm2

Lab ID: Y301103010 Sample ID: FRV-OCT20-MANWS10 Media: Texwipe, Polyester Swab, TX7 Sample Date: 10/13/2020 Sampling Time:

Analyte	Method	Analysis Date	Volume		Reporting Limit	Front	Rear	Total	Concentration
Mannitol	IH IC 021	11/10/20	100	cm2	10.0 ng			6110 ng	61.1 ng/cm2

Lab ID: Y301103011 Sample ID: FRV-OCT20-MANWS11 Media: Texwipe, Polyester Swab, TX7 Sample Date: 10/13/2020 Sampling Time:

Analyte	Method	Analysis Date	Volume		Reporting Limit	Front	Rear	Total	Concentration
Mannitol	IH IC 021	11/10/20	100	cm2	10.0 ng			35400 ng	354 ng/cm2

Analytics Corporation
10329 Stony Run Lane
Ashland, Va 23005
Phone: (804) 365-3000 Fax: (804) 365-3002
AIHA-LAP, LLC Accreditation ID 100531

Final Report

Work Order Y301103

Lab ID: Y301103012 Sample ID: FRV-OCT20-MANWS12 Media: Texwipe, Polyester Swab, TX7 Sample Date: 10/13/2020 Sampling Time:

Analyte	Method	Analysis Date	Volume		Reporting Limit	Front	Rear	Total	Concentration
Mannitol	IH IC 021	11/10/20	100	cm2	10.0 ng			3960 ng	39.6 ng/cm2

Lab ID: Y301103013 Sample ID: FRV-OCT20-MANWS13 Media: Texwipe, Polyester Swab, TX7 Sample Date: 10/13/2020 Sampling Time:

Analyte	Method	Analysis Date	Volume		Reporting Limit	Front	Rear	Total	Concentration
Mannitol	IH IC 021	11/10/20	100	cm2	10.0 ng			15820 ng	158.2 ng/cm2

Lab ID: Y301103014 Sample ID: FRV-OCT20-MANWS14 Media: Texwipe, Polyester Swab, TX7 Sample Date: 10/13/2020 Sampling Time:

Analyte	Method	Analysis Date	Volume		Reporting Limit	Front	Rear	Total	Concentration
Mannitol	IH IC 021	11/10/20	100	cm2	10.0 ng			30600 ng	306 ng/cm2

Lab ID: Y301103015 Sample ID: FRV-OCT20-MANWS15 Media: Texwipe, Polyester Swab, TX7 Sample Date: 10/13/2020 Sampling Time:

Analyte	Method	Analysis Date	Volume		Reporting Limit	Front	Rear	Total	Concentration
Mannitol	IH IC 021	11/10/20	100	cm2	10.0 ng			2610 ng	26.1 ng/cm2

Analytics Corporation
10329 Stony Run Lane
Ashland, Va 23005
Phone: (804) 365-3000 Fax: (804) 365-3002
AIHA-LAP, LLC Accreditation ID 100531

Final Report

Work Order Y301103

Lab ID: Y301103016 Sample ID: FRV-OCT20-MANWS16 Media: Texwipe, Polyester Swab, TX7 Sample Date: 10/13/2020 Sampling Time:

Analyte	Method	Analysis Date	Volume		Reporting Limit	Front	Rear	Total	Concentration
Mannitol	IH IC 021	11/10/20	100	cm2	10.0 ng			1460 ng	14.6 ng/cm2

Lab ID: Y301103017 Sample ID: FRV-OCT20-MANWS17 Media: Texwipe, Polyester Swab, TX7 Sample Date: 10/13/2020 Sampling Time:

Analyte	Method	Analysis Date	Volume		Reporting Limit	Front	Rear	Total	Concentration
Mannitol	IH IC 021	11/10/20	100	cm2	10.0 ng			132 ng	1.32 ng/cm2

Lab ID: Y301103018 Sample ID: FRV-OCT20-MANWS18 Media: Texwipe, Polyester Swab, TX7 Sample Date: 10/13/2020 Sampling Time:

Analyte	Method	Analysis Date	Volume		Reporting Limit	Front	Rear	Total	Concentration
Mannitol	IH IC 021	11/10/20	100	cm2	10.0 ng			406 ng	4.06 ng/cm2

Lab ID: Y301103019 Sample ID: FRV-OCT20-MANWS19 Media: Texwipe, Polyester Swab, TX7 Sample Date: 10/13/2020 Sampling Time:

Analyte	Method	Analysis Date	Volume		Reporting Limit	Front	Rear	Total	Concentration
Mannitol	IH IC 021	11/10/20	100	cm2	10.0 ng			7200 ng	72.0 ng/cm2

Analytics Corporation
10329 Stony Run Lane
Ashland, Va 23005
Phone: (804) 365-3000 Fax: (804) 365-3002
AIHA-LAP, LLC Accreditation ID 100531

Final Report

Work Order Y301103

Lab ID: Y301103020 Sample ID: FRV-OCT20-MANWS20 Media: Texwipe, Polyester Swab, TX7 Sample Date: 10/13/2020 Sampling Time:

Analyte	Method	Analysis Date	Volume		Reporting Limit	Front	Rear	Total	Concentration
Mannitol	IH IC 021	11/10/20	100	cm2	10.0 ng			4800 ng	48.0 ng/cm2

Lab ID: Y301103021 Sample ID: FRV-OCT20-MANWS21 Media: Texwipe, Polyester Swab, TX7 Sample Date: 10/13/2020 Sampling Time:

Analyte	Method	Analysis Date	Volume		Reporting Limit	Front	Rear	Total	Concentration
Mannitol	IH IC 021	11/10/20	100	cm2	10.0 ng			< 10 ng	< 0.10 ng/cm2

Lab ID: Y301103022 Sample ID: FRV-OCT20-MANWS22 Media: Texwipe, Polyester Swab, TX7 Sample Date: 10/13/2020 Sampling Time:

Analyte	Method	Analysis Date	Volume		Reporting Limit	Front	Rear	Total	Concentration
Mannitol	IH IC 021	11/10/20	100	cm2	10.0 ng			6680 ng	66.8 ng/cm2

Lab ID: Y301103023 Sample ID: FRV-OCT20-MANWS23 Media: Texwipe, Polyester Swab, TX7 Sample Date: 10/13/2020 Sampling Time:

Analyte	Method	Analysis Date	Volume		Reporting Limit	Front	Rear	Total	Concentration
Mannitol	IH IC 021	11/10/20	100	cm2	10.0 ng			604 ng	6.04 ng/cm2

Analytics Corporation
10329 Stony Run Lane
Ashland, Va 23005
Phone: (804) 365-3000 Fax: (804) 365-3002
AIHA-LAP, LLC Accreditation ID 100531

Final Report

Work Order Y301103

Lab ID: Y301103024 Sample ID: FRV-OCT20-MANWS24 Media: Texwipe, Polyester Swab, TX7 Sample Date: 10/13/2020 Sampling Time:

Analyte	Method	Analysis Date	Volume		Reporting Limit	Front	Rear	Total	Concentration
Mannitol	IH IC 021	11/10/20	100	cm2	10.0 ng			3790 ng	37.9 ng/cm2

Lab ID: Y301103025 Sample ID: FRV-OCT20-MANWS25 Media: Texwipe, Polyester Swab, TX7 Sample Date: 10/13/2020 Sampling Time:

Analyte	Method	Analysis Date	Volume		Reporting Limit	Front	Rear	Total	Concentration
Mannitol	IH IC 021	11/10/20	100	cm2	10.0 ng			2530 ng	25.3 ng/cm2

Lab ID: Y301103026 Sample ID: FRV-OCT20-MANWS26 Media: Texwipe, Polyester Swab, TX7 Sample Date: 10/13/2020 Sampling Time:

Analyte	Method	Analysis Date	Volume		Reporting Limit	Front	Rear	Total	Concentration
Mannitol	IH IC 021	11/10/20	100	cm2	10.0 ng			1590 ng	15.9 ng/cm2

Lab ID: Y301103027 Sample ID: FRV-OCT20-MANWS27 Media: Texwipe, Polyester Swab, TX7 Sample Date: 10/13/2020 Sampling Time:

Analyte	Method	Analysis Date	Volume		Reporting Limit	Front	Rear	Total	Concentration
Mannitol	IH IC 021	11/10/20	100	cm2	10.0 ng			506 ng	5.06 ng/cm2

ANALYTICS

Analytics Corporation
10329 Stony Run Lane
Ashland, Va 23005
Phone: (804) 365-3000 Fax: (804) 365-3002
AIHA-LAP, LLC Accreditation ID 100531

Final Report

Work Order Y301103

Lab ID: Y301103028 Sample ID: FRV-OCT20-MANWS28 Media: Texwipe, Polyester Swab, TX7 Sample Date: 10/13/2020 Sampling Time:

Analyte	Method	Analysis Date	Volume		Reporting Limit	Front	Rear	Total	Concentration
Mannitol	IH IC 021	11/10/20	100	cm2	10.0 ng			1240 ng	12.4 ng/cm2

Lab ID: Y301103029 Sample ID: FRV-OCT20-MANWS29 Media: Texwipe, Polyester Swab, TX7 Sample Date: 10/13/2020 Sampling Time:

Analyte	Method	Analysis Date	Volume		Reporting Limit	Front	Rear	Total	Concentration
Mannitol	IH IC 021	11/10/20	100	cm2	10.0 ng			68.7 ng	0.687 ng/cm2

Lab ID: Y301103030 Sample ID: FRV-OCT20-MANWS30 Media: Texwipe, Polyester Swab, TX7 Sample Date: 10/13/2020 Sampling Time:

Analyte	Method	Analysis Date	Volume		Reporting Limit	Front	Rear	Total	Concentration
Mannitol	IH IC 021	11/10/20	100	cm2	10.0 ng			171000 ng	1710 ng/cm2

Lab ID: Y301103031 Sample ID: FRV-OCT20-MANWS31 Media: Texwipe, Polyester Swab, TX7 Sample Date: 10/13/2020 Sampling Time:

Analyte	Method	Analysis Date	Volume		Reporting Limit	Front	Rear	Total	Concentration
Mannitol	IH IC 021	11/10/20	100	cm2	10.0 ng			879 ng	8.79 ng/cm2

ANALYTICS

Analytics Corporation
10329 Stony Run Lane
Ashland, Va 23005
Phone: (804) 365-3000 Fax: (804) 365-3002
AIHA-LAP, LLC Accreditation ID 100531

Final Report

Work Order Y301103

Lab ID: Y301103032 Sample ID: FRV-OCT20-MANWSFB01 Media: Texwipe, Polyester Swab, TX7 Sample Date: 10/13/2020 Sampling Time:

Analyte	Method	Analysis Date	Volume		Reporting Limit	Front	Rear	Total	Concentration
Mannitol	IH IC 021	11/10/20	NA	cm2	10.0 ng			< 10 ng	--

Lab ID: Y301103033 Sample ID: FRV-OCT20-MANWSFB02 Media: Texwipe, Polyester Swab, TX7 Sample Date: 10/13/2020 Sampling Time:

Analyte	Method	Analysis Date	Volume		Reporting Limit	Front	Rear	Total	Concentration
Mannitol	IH IC 021	11/10/20	NA	cm2	10.0 ng			< 10 ng	--

Lab ID: Y301103034 Sample ID: FRV-OCT20-MANWSFB03 Media: Texwipe, Polyester Swab, TX7 Sample Date: 10/13/2020 Sampling Time:

Analyte	Method	Analysis Date	Volume		Reporting Limit	Front	Rear	Total	Concentration
Mannitol	IH IC 021	11/10/20	NA	cm2	10.0 ng			< 10 ng	--

Lab ID: Y301103035 Sample ID: FRV-OCT20-MANWSMB01 Media: Texwipe, Polyester Swab, TX7 Sample Date: 10/13/2020 Sampling Time:

Analyte	Method	Analysis Date	Volume		Reporting Limit	Front	Rear	Total	Concentration
Mannitol	IH IC 021	11/10/20	NA	cm2	10.0 ng			< 10 ng	--

ANALYTICS

Analytics Corporation
10329 Stony Run Lane
Ashland, Va 23005
Phone: (804) 365-3000 Fax: (804) 365-3002
AIHA-LAP, LLC Accreditation ID 100531

Final Report

Work Order Y301103

General Laboratory Comments

Abbreviations:
ug = micrograms; mg=milligrams; g = grams, ppm=parts per million (volume), ppb = parts per billion (volume), mg/M3=milligrams per cubic meter of air, ug/M3=micrograms per cubic meter of air; Min=minutes, Qual=Qualifiers

Y301103

Chain of Custody from ISS Inc.

Client Project: **ISS Client -Iowa**

Project by: **International Safety Systems Inc.**

Invoice to/Bill To:
International Safety Systems Inc.

Send results to: ankit.sharma@issehs.com

NOTE: The samples are collected during engine parts handling likely contaminated with hexavalent chromium.

Date of Sampling	Sample ID	Analyte	Sampling Media	Area sample (cm^2)
10/13/2020	FRV-Oct20- MANWS01	Mannitol	TX 715 swabs (wet + dry)	100
10/13/2020	FRV-Oct20- MANWS02	Mannitol	TX 715 swabs (wet + dry)	100
10/13/2020	FRV-Oct20- MANWS03	Mannitol	TX 715 swabs (wet + dry)	100
10/13/2020	FRV-Oct20- MANWS04	Mannitol	TX 715 swabs (wet + dry)	100
10/13/2020	FRV-Oct20- MANWS05	Mannitol	TX 715 swabs (wet + dry)	100
10/13/2020	FRV-Oct20- MANWS06	Mannitol	TX 715 swabs (wet + dry)	100
10/13/2020	FRV-Oct20- MANWS07	Mannitol	TX 715 swabs (wet + dry)	100
10/13/2020	FRV-Oct20- MANWS08	Mannitol	TX 715 swabs (wet + dry)	100
10/13/2020	FRV-Oct20- MANWS09	Mannitol	TX 715 swabs (wet + dry)	100
10/13/2020	FRV-Oct20- MANWS10	Mannitol	TX 715 swabs (wet + dry)	100
10/13/2020	FRV-Oct20- MANWS11	Mannitol	TX 715 swabs (wet + dry)	100
10/13/2020	FRV-Oct20- MANWS12	Mannitol	TX 715 swabs (wet + dry)	100
10/13/2020	FRV-Oct20- MANWS13	Mannitol	TX 715 swabs (wet + dry)	100
10/13/2020	FRV-Oct20- MANWS14	Mannitol	TX 715 swabs (wet + dry)	100
10/13/2020	FRV-Oct20- MANWS15	Mannitol	TX 715 swabs (wet + dry)	100
10/13/2020	FRV-Oct20- MANWS16	Mannitol	TX 715 swabs (wet + dry)	100
10/13/2020	FRV-Oct20- MANWS17	Mannitol	TX 715 swabs (wet + dry)	100
10/13/2020	FRV-Oct20- MANWS18	Mannitol	TX 715 swabs (wet + dry)	100
10/13/2020	FRV-Oct20- MANWS19	Mannitol	TX 715 swabs (wet + dry)	100
10/13/2020	FRV-Oct20- MANWS20	Mannitol	TX 715 swabs (wet + dry)	100
10/13/2020	FRV-Oct20- MANWS21	Mannitol	TX 715 swabs (wet + dry)	100
10/13/2020	FRV-Oct20- MANWS22	Mannitol	TX 715 swabs (wet + dry)	100
10/13/2020	FRV-Oct20- MANWS23	Mannitol	TX 715 swabs (wet + dry)	100
10/13/2020	FRV-Oct20- MANWS24	Mannitol	TX 715 swabs (wet + dry)	100
10/13/2020	FRV-Oct20- MANWS25	Mannitol	TX 715 swabs (wet + dry)	100
10/13/2020	FRV-Oct20- MANWS26	Mannitol	TX 715 swabs (wet + dry)	100
10/13/2020	FRV-Oct20- MANWS27	Mannitol	TX 715 swabs (wet + dry)	100
10/13/2020	FRV-Oct20- MANWS28	Mannitol	TX 715 swabs (wet + dry)	100
10/13/2020	FRV-Oct20- MANWS29	Mannitol	TX 715 swabs (wet + dry)	100
10/13/2020	FRV-Oct20- MANWS30	Mannitol	TX 715 swabs (wet + dry)	100
10/13/2020	FRV-Oct20- MANWS31	Mannitol	TX 715 swabs (wet + dry)	100
10/13/2020	FRV-Oct20- MANWS FB01	Mannitol	TX 715 swabs (wet + dry)	NA

10/13/2020	FRV-Oct20- MANWS FB02	Mannitol	TX 715 swabs (wet + dry)	NA
10/13/2020	FRV-Oct20- MANWS FB03	Mannitol	TX 715 swabs (wet + dry)	NA
10/13/2020	FRV-Oct20- MANWS MB01	Mannitol	TX 715 swabs (wet + dry)	NA
Samples Submitted by: Ankit Sharma, CIH LFOH Phone: +1 203 751 0400, email: ankit.sharma@issehs.com				

Amy Larson 10/27/20

AMY LARSON

CIH Equipment Company, Inc.

An ISO 17025-2017 registered company

Certificate of Calibration

Reference No.:
35749-DCLM-4660

Instrument Identification

Manufacturer:	Bios International Corp	**Calibration Date:**	September 28, 2020
Model Number:	DCL-M	**Calibration Due Date:**	September 28, 2021
Serial Number:	4660	**Reference Number:**	35749-DCLM-4660
Service Order:	35749		

CIH Equipment Company Inc. certifies that the instrument listed above meets or exceeds manufacturing tolerance limits as stated in the referenced test procedure (unless otherwise noted). This instrument has been calibrated using standards with accuracies traceable to the National Institute of Standards and Technology.CIH Equipment Company Inc. calibration system is A2LA accredited to ISO/IEC 17025-2017, ANSI/NCSL Z540-1-1994.This report may not be reproduced, except in full, without the written approval CIH Equipment Company Inc. This calibration was done by comparing the unit under test to the listed calibration standards, there was no sampling used in this calibration. The results reported herein apply only to the calibration of the items described above and no limitations of use apply to the calibrated unit. A PASS (in tolerance) or FAIL (out of tolerance) result indicates all measured values fall within or outside unmodified limits. The statement of compliance does not take the reported measurement uncertainty into account.In addition, reported uncertainties do not include instabilities due to transportation, usage, passage of time etc.

Calibration Standards Used

Manufacturer	Description	Model	Serial Number	Certificate Number	Due Date
Bios	Piston Prover	220-H	110577	383571	4/9/2021
Bios	Piston Prover	220-M	127013	387142	4/30/2021

Certified By: ______________________ **Date:** Sep 28, 2020

Hashim Sweilem - Calibration Technician

1806 South Highland Ave • Clearwater, FL 33756-1762 • USA • PH: (727) 584-5063 • FX: (727) 581-5921Toll Free: (888) 873-2443
• Website: http://www.cihequipment.com

ROQUETTE

Certificate of Analysis

Please, note that this e-mail address is not a valid reply address and cannot be used for any answer. If you wish to contact Roquette, please use the usual e-mail address.

TO THE ATTENTION OF IMCD US LLC
PHARMACEUTICAL INGREDIENTS
20 ELM STREET
HARRINGTON PARK NJ07640-0000

CERTIFICATE OF ANALYSIS / COMPLIANCE
PRODUCT........ 450004 B PEARLITOL 50 C - MANNITOL EP-USP
CUSTOMER ...... IMCD/US/SOMERSET
(EMAIL CLIENT)
INVOICE. ...... KAM18P OF 19 JUN 19
NET WEIGHT..... 3,900 KG
ORDER.......... 19005010/2.000 OF 10 JUN 19
REGISTRATION NR W18237
BATCH NUMBER... KVYZM
MANUF&TESTED... 28 APRIL 2019
EXPIRY DATE 28 APR 2022

PH.EUR-USP/NF-JP
================
DESCRIPTION.... WHITE CRYSTALLINE POWDER
ODOURLESS, SWEET TASTE
MEANING TESTED = ANALYZED
MONITORED = MONITORING PLAN
THIS BATCH MEETS THE REQUIREMENTS OF CURRENT
PH.EUR-USP/NF-JP OFFICIAL MONOGRAPHS FOR MANNITOL.
MANUFACTURING SITE
ROQUETTE AMERICA INC, 1003 SOUTH 5TH ST, KEOKUK, IA 52632
USA ,IOWA/CRENSHAW THOMAS,19 JUNE 2019
MANAGER - QUALITY ASSURANCE

Certificate reprinted.
YOUR PRIVILEGED CONTACT BLOOD SALLIE

This document has been produced electronically though our validated IT system and is valid without a signature.

RESULTS of ANALYSIS
===================

GUARANTEED = COMPLIA E DATA

	RESULTS	STATUS	
APPEARANCE	CONFORMS	TESTED	
APPEARANCE IN SOLUTION	CONFORMS	TESTED	
LOSS ON DRYING	0.04	TESTED	%
INFRA-RED	CONFORMS	TESTED	
MELTING POINT	CONFORMS	MONITORED	
CONDUCTIVITY	0.7	TESTED	MICROS/C
REDUCING SUGARS	CONFORMS	TESTED	<0.1%
D-MANNITOL	99.1	TESTED	%
TOTAL IMPURITIES	0.9	TESTED	%
D-SORBITOL	0.9	TESTED	%
AMOUNT OF IMPURITIES B AND C	0.00	TESTED	%

UNSPECIFIED IMPURITIES	0.02	TESTED	%
PARTICLE-SIZE BY LASER		TESTED	
RESIDUE ON 250 MICRONS	0.1	TESTED	%
RESIDUE ON 100 MICRONS	19	TESTED	%
RESIDUE ON 20 MICRONS	73	TESTED	%
HEAVY METALS	CONFORMS	MONITORED	<5PPM
NICKEL	CONFORMS	MONITORED	<1PPM
TOTAL AEROBIC MICROBIAL COUNT	0	TESTED	/G
TOTAL YEASTS AND MOULDS COUNT	0	TESTED	/G
ESCHERICHIA COLI	CONFORMS	TESTED	ABS/10G
SALMONELLAE	CONFORMS	TESTED	ABS/10G

Institute for Briquetting and Agglomeration

2022 IBA CONFERENCE PAPERS

Paper Title:

Critical flow parameters of bulk solids: A review and study on the impact of particle size

Presenter:

Kurt Naugler

Company:

Jenike & Johanson

Critical flow parameters of bulk solids: A review and study on the impact of particle size

Author:

Kurt Naugler
Jenike & Johanson
(978) 649-3300
400 Business Park Drive
Tyngsboro, MA 01879

1 ABSTRACT

In any process that involves the storage, handling, or transfer of bulk solids, it is imperative to design equipment that meets the needs of both the process and the material. The intent of this paper is to review the flow properties of materials and how they can affect the effectiveness and efficiency of the agglomeration process followed by a study on the impact that different particle sizes can have on these properties. Common issues, such as arching and ratholing, arising from improperly designed systems will be discussed in addition to the material properties that must be considered in order to avoid these issues. Critical outlet dimensions and hopper angles are considered with a review of common hopper geometries that contribute to different acceptable design parameters. Following this review of common problems and corresponding material flow properties, a study on the impact of particle size relative to arching dimensions and wall friction angles is presented. Test results on identical materials, separated by particle size, will be reviewed with conclusions and recommendations on the impact of the results with respect to system design and the agglomeration process.

2 INTRODUCTION

When considering system design for bulk materials, engineers and designers are often focused on what they perceive as high impact portions of a process. These are generally the operations where material is changed in some way. Whether that is milling and crushing, mixing and blending, or agglomerating, a sole focus on these processes can lead to other portions of the system falling through the cracks in the course of the design. Equally as important as the processes that produce the desired end product are those portions of the system that feed, store and convey material between different process steps. A perfectly well-designed roller compaction system cannot be effective if material is not able to be feed into the system or if material plugs a chute intended to transport compacted material to a downstream process (Johanson, 1984).

While there are a number of components that are used to store and transport material, from silos and bins to chutes and conveyors, the design of each of these components should take into account both process requirements and material properties. An understanding of critical flow parameters for each material being handled is vital to ensuring that common flow problems do not impact the process or use of the handling system (Maynard, 2001). These flow properties that are critical to system design vary depending on the material and desired operating parameters but almost always include cohesive strength and wall friction.

At the intersection between the flow properties of a material being handled and the design of a vessel holding that material is the resulting flow pattern within the system. Within surge or storage vessels (bins, silos, hoppers, etc.), two main flow patterns can exist: funnel flow and mass flow. The flow pattern that occurs is a function of the bulk material as well as the equipment being used.

With either mass flow or funnel flow there are distinct issues that may arise during operation of a system designed to handle bulk solids. Two flow problems that may occur in a system include ratholing and arching. While both are a function of the cohesive strength of the material, ratholing is indirectly related to the wall friction of a material because, as will be described in more detail in the following sections, ratholing is impossible within a system that operates in mass flow.

In analyzing how to improve flow performance or avoid flow problems, adjusting the material is one lever that can be pulled. One of the common adjustments made to materials in an effort to improve flow properties is to increase the particle side of the material (Carson & Prescott, 1998). A study of historical test data from identical materials with varying particle sizes is presented as the penultimate section of this publication.

Prior to the study of particle size impact on critical flow properties, we examine the flow properties themselves and how they impact the flow patterns that can occur within bins and hoppers. Combining the flow properties and flow patterns, potential flow problems are examined with descriptions of the impact that they can have on critical processes such as agglomeration and briquetting.

3 CRITICAL MATERIAL FLOW PROPERTIES

As one designs a process for liquids or gasses, material properties are widely known and tabulated for use across industry. Whether water exists at sea level in a temperate climate or at the top of Mount Everest, the properties of that water can be accurately calculated and designed for. With bulk solids, material properties are not so easily obtained. Numerous interdependent factors can have an impact on how a certain material behaves (Carson, Purutyan, & Rotter, 2003). One can see these vastly differing properties when looking at beach sand. Compare the different behavior of this common bulk solid when it is dry to when it has a high moisture content. The most experienced structural engineer would struggle to build a sandcastle with dry beach sand, but even a toddler can accomplish this same task when provided with a higher moisture content sand.

Moisture content is just one of many factors that can impact how a bulk solid behaves within a system. The flow properties of a material can also be impacted by temperature, particle size and shape, time at rest, surrounding environment and even the equipment being used to handle the material. Just because one material has the same chemical composition as another material does not imply that the flow properties will be the same. For this reason, it is extremely important to fully understand the flow properties of the actual material this is going to be handled at an early stage in the system design process (Pittenger, 1995). The only way to gain this understanding of flow characteristics is to test the bulk properties on a sample of material at conditions representative of the final application.

Storage, transport, and feed systems vital to operation of agglomeration or other process equipment are impacted by different material flow properties depending on their function and desired operational state. Those properties that have the largest impact on the successful operation of this ancillary equipment are known as critical material flow properties. Two properties that are commonly defined as critical to the success of a system are cohesive strength and wall friction.

Cohesive Strength

Cohesive strength of a material can be traced back to soil mechanics where a sample of material is tested to determine its strength and load bearing capability then calculated. Deriving from soil mechanics where strength is used to ensure that material remains in one place, Dr Andrew Jenike's flow / no flow postulate on cohesive strength serves as the foundation to further study in the field of solids flow. He stated that when the stresses applied to a material exceed the strength of that material, flow will occur (Jenike, 1964). The strength in this relationship refers to the cohesive strength of a material.

Based on the direct relationship between a material's cohesive strength and the ability of a material to flow, it is clear that this property is vital to consider in system design. Cohesive strength refers to the ability of a material to support itself against external forces. It is a value that cannot be calculated from other material properties and must be determined through empirical means. It is also worth noting that cohesive strength, as well as most bulk solids properties, is a function of the consolidation load applied and resulting bulk density of the material. As principal compaction force increases, one can imagine that the strength of the material is likely to increase as well. As an example, the harder you pack a snowball, the stronger that snowball is likely to be.

One measure of cohesive strength is known as the unconfined yield strength of a material. This measure determines the load required to fracture a column of material unconfined on each side (Schulze, 2007). While this method can be used to measure the strength of very cohesive materials that are easily formed into self-supporting columns, it is difficult (and oftentimes impossible) to accurately measure unconfined yield strength of less cohesive materials through fracture of an unconfined sample. Think again about the example of dry and moist beach sand. The moist sand can be formed into a column to which force can then be applied and fracture force measured. If one attempted the same method with dry sand, it would be impossible to form a similar, self-supporting column of material and fracture strength would essentially be measured as zero.

The challenge of measuring cohesive strength for most materials was addressed with the development of test methods that can be used for a much wider range of materials. One such method is covered under ASTM D6128 and uses a device known as a Jenike Direct Shear Tester. This method measures the force required to shear a material across a fracture plane with known surface area under multiple consolidation loads. From these tests, a relationship between consolidation load and material cohesive strength can be determined. It is this relationship coupled with the forces applied to material within a system that is used to determine whether that material will flow (Craig & Hossfeld, 2002).

Wall Friction

Coefficient of stagnant and sliding friction are properties that are well taught and understood for two discrete solid objects sliding against one another. It is defined by the ratio of frictional force to the normal force being applied to the object and generally denoted by the Greek letter mu. Wall friction for bulk solids is a similar concept but is not as easily defined with one constant variable. Similar to cohesive strength, the force of friction from a bulk solid sliding across a wall surface is dependent on the consolidating load that has been applied to the material. It is also dependent on the material the bulk solid is sliding against as well as the surface finish of that material (Prescott & Ploof, 1995). Interestingly, for some bulk solids, a smoother surface may not always result in less friction between the solid and wall surface.

Due to the dependence on consolidation force and many interdependent material properties, the frictional properties of bulk solids are most easily determined through testing. Using the same Jenike Direct Shear Tester mechanism and a slightly different test setup, ASTM D6128 defines how to test bulk solids for wall friction. Instead of material shearing against itself in a known fracture plane as occurs in the cohesive strength test, material is sheared against a wall coupon. Due to the dependence of wall friction values on both the bulk solid being tested and the wall material used during the test, it is important that both of these materials are representative of what will be used in the system being designed (Carson, Del Cid, & McInerney, 2020).

4 FLOW PATTERNS

As material is discharged from a storage vessel such as a bin, silo or hopper, the manner in which the material flows can impact the success of the handling system as a whole. The two primary modes in which material can flow through a vessel are known as funnel flow and mass flow. Each flow pattern is shown in Figure A.

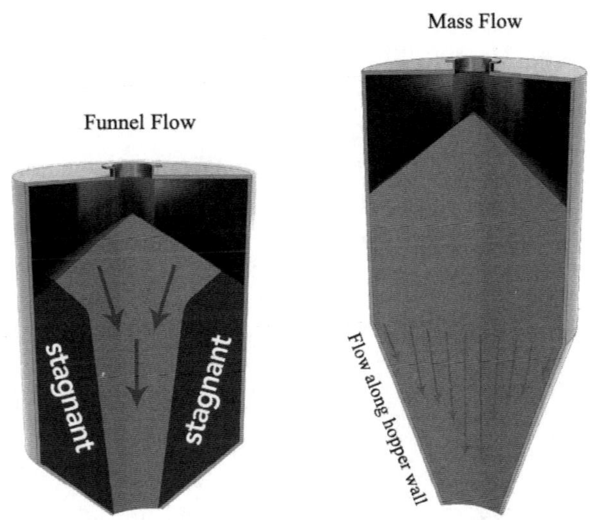

Figure A: Funnel and mass flow patterns

The flow pattern that occurs within a hopper is a function of the wall friction properties of the material with the specific wall surface that was used to construct the hopper wall. Funnel flow is the more common flow pattern that a material will operate in unless the system is specifically designed to operate in mass flow. Unless the wall angle and geometry that the hopper is designed for is able to overcome the frictional force between the bulk material and wall surface, funnel flow will result. For a system to operate in mass flow, the walls must be sufficiently steep and sufficiently non-frictional to allow for material to flow along the hopper walls. It follows naturally that the wall friction properties of a material are a key factor in determining the flow pattern of a material within a specific storge vessel design.

Funnel Flow

Funnel flow occurs when material is not able to overcome the frictional forces between the material being handled and the wall surface of the hopper. This results in a stagnant region of material and formation of an active flow channel that is narrower than the vessel geometry. Depending on the cohesive strength within the stagnant region, as the level of material within the active flow channel is drawn down, the stagnant material may or may not slide off into the flow channel. With materials that are at least somewhat cohesive, the stagnant regions will not discharge from the hopper and the associated usable capacity of the storage bin will be reduced to the volume of the active channel.

In addition to the potential of reduced live capacity, funnel flow results in a first-in-last-out flow sequence. The active flow channel and stagnant regions cause the material to flow out from top to bottom. This can cause issues with materials that are prone to caking, spoilage, oxidation or other forms of degradation over time. Finally, if the material being handled is prone to sifting, dusting or other forms of side-to-side segregation, a funnel flow pattern will result in increased impact of that segregation on downstream processes. This is due to discharge of material in the center of the vessel first followed at the end by the material from the stagnant regions at the periphery.

Due to the potential problems with funnel flow, there are limited materials that can successfully be stored and discharged from a funnel flow vessel. The requirements of a material to operate in funnel flow are that it is relatively coarse, free flowing, non-degrading, and not impacted by segregation.

Mass Flow

In mass flow, all material is in motion whenever any is withdrawn from the hopper. This means that there are no stagnant regions that are allowed to form. For this to occur, material must be able to slide along the walls of the hopper due to sufficiently steep walls and sufficiently low wall friction at the material and wall surface boundary. Depending on the level of friction at the walls, material discharge velocity may or may not be relatively consistent across the hopper. For discharge to be defined as operating in mass flow, it is not necessary that the velocity of all material is constant, only that there are no stagnant regions that form during discharge.

Mass flow results in a first-in-first-out flow sequence within the storage vessel and ensures that the usable capacity is equal to the full volume of the vessel (subtracting head space loss due to the angle of repose of the formed pile). The lack of stagnant regions means that the formation of a stable rathole, defined in the following section, is not possible when discharging in mass flow. In contrast to funnel flow accentuating the impact of side-to-side segregation within the storage bin, mass flow can be used to minimize these types of segregation. This is possible because when all material is in motion during discharge, the material in the center of the hopper and the material from the periphery are brought back together at the outlet. This leads to an approximate remixing of segregated material during discharge. (Note that mass flow should not be used to address segregation that results in top to bottom variations in the storage vessel.)

5 COMMON FLOW PROBLEMS

While there are a large number of problems that can occur in a system used to handle bulk solids, two high impact problems that are directly related to cohesive strength and flow pattern (and thus wall friction) include arching and ratholing. These flow problems are noted as high impact because they both can lead to flow stoppages and starve downstream processes of material. It is impossible to agglomerate or briquette if there is no material being fed into the equipment intended to form those agglomerates or briquettes. Alternatively, if these flow problems occur downstream of a piece of process equipment, there is the potential that material backs up into the equipment and causes damage or at the very least stops production. Additionally, any flow stoppage results in downtime where end product is not being produced and causes loss of time and revenue.

Arching

Arching, or bridging, occurs when material forms a stable arch typically over the outlet of a hopper. It is what occurs on the no flow side of the flow / no flow postulate. The strength of the material within a system is higher than the stress being applied to that material. The reason that arching typically occurs near the outlet of a storage vessel is that the outlet is the location within a system where there is the least stress available to overcome the strength of a material.

Figure B shows a cross section of what an arch may look like within a typical storage vessel as well as an example of an arch that formed in a cohesive powder. It can be seen that for cohesive materials, arching is possible in outlets that are fairly large in size respective to the average particle size of the material. The outlet shown is 8 inches in diameter and the average particle size of the material shown is on the order of 100-150 μm (0.004 – 0.006 inches).

Figure B: Typical arch or bridge at a hopper outlet

As a complete stoppage of flow, arching reduces the live capacity of the bin to essentially zero. The only material that flows out of the hopper is the material below the location where the arch forms. As noted above, this stoppage of flow can starve downstream processes of material or cause material to back up into upstream processes and equipment. Either of these consequences can have significant impact on the success of an entire material handling system.

Arching is overcome when the size of a hopper outlet is larger than the critical arching dimension of the material. The critical arching dimension is primarily a function of the material's cohesive strength and the geometry of the hopper. When a system is designed with an outlet larger than this critical dimension, arching is no longer a risk.

Ratholing

Ratholing, sometimes referred to as piping, is another flow problem that results in a no flow situation within a storage vessel. Ratholes differ from arches in that material is initially able to flow out of the hopper outlet, but the no flow occurs when the flow channel empties, and stagnant regions do not collapse or flow into the initial channel. As noted in the previous section, ratholing can only occur when operating in funnel flow because it requires stagnant material around the periphery of the hopper that does not exist in mass flow systems. A typical rathole geometry is shown in Figure C.

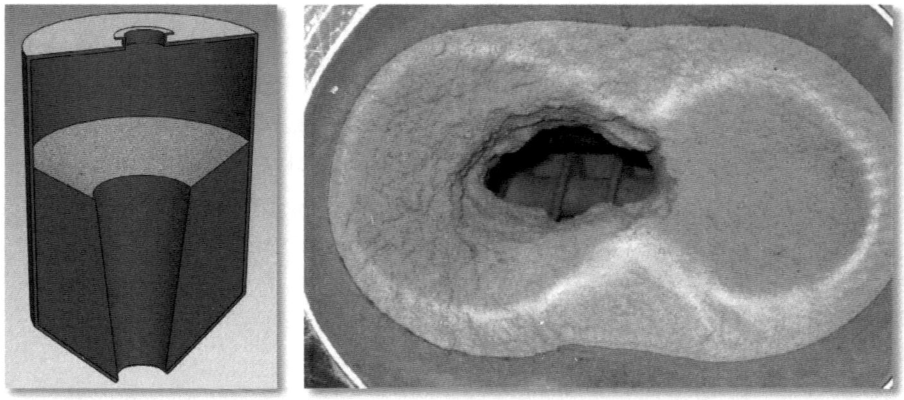

Figure C: Typical rathole within a storage vessel

While material initially flows from a vessel before the formation of a stable rathole, the usable capacity is reduced drastically. In general, the usable capacity becomes the effective volume of the flow channel which can be a low as 5-15% of the total volume of the storage vessel. In addition to the no flow issues described for arching, there is risk of flooding from fresh, aerated material being added to the system, and flooding or high, dynamic loads impacting the hopper and supporting structure from collapsing ratholes.

There are two typical approaches to avoiding problems associated with ratholing. The first is to avoid the possibility of ratholes forming by converting funnel flow to mass flow. This is achieved by either making hopper walls steeper or decreasing the wall friction value by changing either the properties of the handled material itself, or by changing the material or finish of the hopper wall surface. The second way is applicable only if the material meets the requirements outlined above for operating in funnel flow. Assuming a material is suitable for funnel flow operation, ratholing can be avoided by designing the outlet to be larger than the critical ratholing dimension. Similar to the critical arching dimension, the critical ratholing dimension is a measure of the material's cohesive strength. When a system is designed with an outlet larger than this critical dimension, ratholing is no longer a risk.

6 IMPACT OF PARTICLE SIZE ON FLOW PROPERTIES

Prior to looking at any potential relationships between a bulk material's flow properties and particle size, it is important to define the concept of particle size. On the surface, the particle size of a bulk solid appears to be an extremely simple concept. However, there are a number of factors that make particle size more complicated and difficult to define by a single value. For a vast majority of bulk solids, particle size is more accurately described by a distribution of particles of many different sizes. How that distribution is shaped, how wide it is, if it is skewed towards larger or smaller particles; these differences can have a large impact on how a material behaves within a system and cannot be determined by simply looking at a single value such as the average particle size.

There are also challenges associated with defining the size of individual particles with a single number. When measuring an elongated or fibrous material, the direction in which a measurement is taken can result in very different values. From those different values one must decide whether they will define that particle by the minimum dimension, by the maximum dimension or by some other specified value. It is then important when comparing for particle size, that the measurement method is consistent across each material. For bulk materials, a sieve analysis is a common particle size distribution measurement method that can utilize sieves defined by standards organizations such as ASTM.

While it is difficult to define particle size by a single value, it is often convenient or necessary. The values presented below, and referred to a material's particle size, are taken as the D50 value from each particle size distribution. The D50 value is calculated as the median particle size for a bulk material so 50% of particles are larger than this value and 50% of particles are smaller.

Background

As the average particle size of a bulk materials changes, the flow properties of that material are also expected to change. Flow properties are driven by how the particles interact with each other as well as with the boundary of the system, often the silo or hopper walls. The smaller the particles are in a specified volume; the more contact points exist between discrete particles and between the particles and hopper walls. With more contact points within the bulk material, one expects that cohesive strength would increase and with more contact points between the material and the wall surface, one expects that wall friction would increase as well.

This relationship is expected when comparing bulk materials, environments, processes, and equipment that are identical other than the particle size of the material. There are far too many external factors that can impact flow properties beyond particle size that make it impossible to build a direct relationship between particle size and flow properties that applies universally across different materials and processes. An attempt at a direct comparison between particle size and cohesive strength (shown as the critical rathole diameter) of 29 different materials is provided in Figure D. Materials studied include multiple grades of coal, sand, carbon black, limestone, coper ore and iron ore pellets.

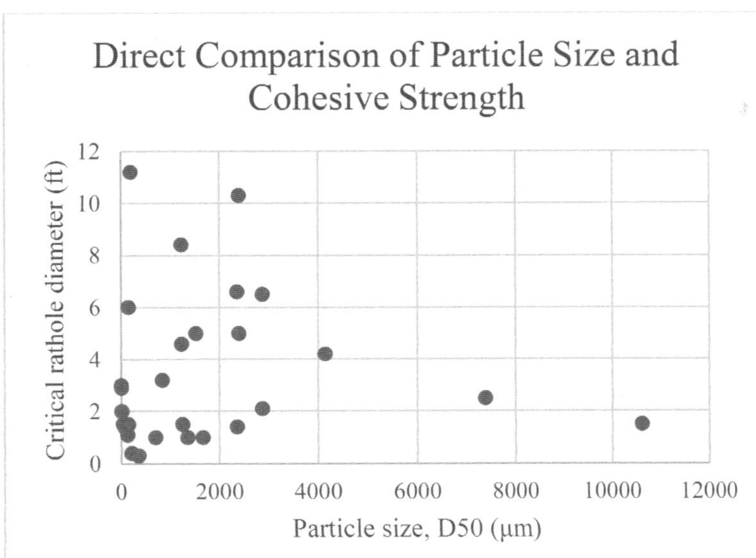

Figure D: Direct comparison of particle size and cohesive strength

It can be seen that there is no clear, definable relationship between particle size and critical rathole diameter across these different materials. There are fine powders that have both significantly lower and significantly higher cohesive strength than some of the very coarse materials examined. The remainder of this study examines potential relationships between different particle sizes of otherwise identical bulk materials and the flow properties of those materials.

To analyze the data across a wide spread of particle sizes and flow properties, each data point was normalized against the properties of the smallest particle size sample of each material type examined. The normalized data is described as the particle size distribution (PSD) ratio, critical arching diameter (BC) ratio, critical rathole diameter (DF) ratio, and wall friction ratio as calculated below:

$$PSD\ ratio = \frac{Sample\ D50}{D50\ of\ smallest\ identical\ material\ sample} \quad \text{(Equation 1)}$$

$$BC\ ratio = \frac{Sample\ BC}{BC\ of\ smallest\ identical\ material\ sample} \quad \text{(Equation 2)}$$

$$DF\ ratio = \frac{Sample\ DF}{DF\ of\ smallest\ identical\ material\ sample} \quad \text{(Equation 3)}$$

$$Wall\ friction\ ratio = \frac{Sample\ wall\ friction\ angle}{Wall\ friciton\ angle\ of\ smallest\ identical\ material\ sample} \quad \text{(Equation 4)}$$

It is worth noting that for the cohesive strength measures, a ratio of larger than 1 indicated that the sample was more cohesive than the smallest identical material sample. Conversely, a wall friction ratio of larger than 1 indicates that the sample was less frictional than the smallest identical material sample.

Relationship to Cohesive Strength

Figure E and Figure F provide charts of the impact of particle size on the normalized arching and ratholing diameters, respectively. The particle size ratio as calculated according to equation 1 is provided on the horizontal axis while the BC and DF ratios are provided on the vertical axis.

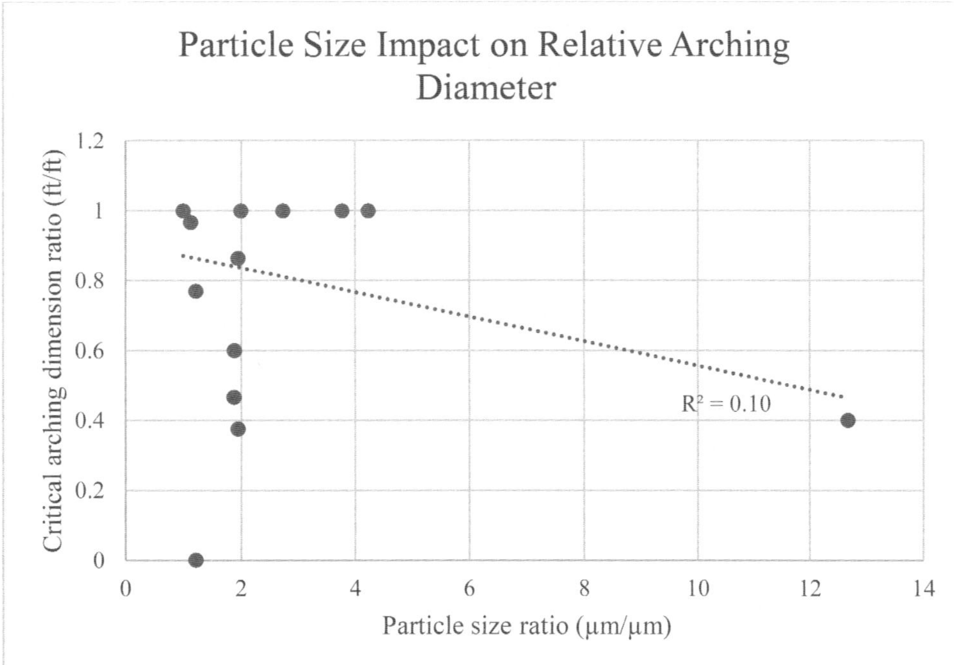

Figure E: Particle size impact on relative arching diameter

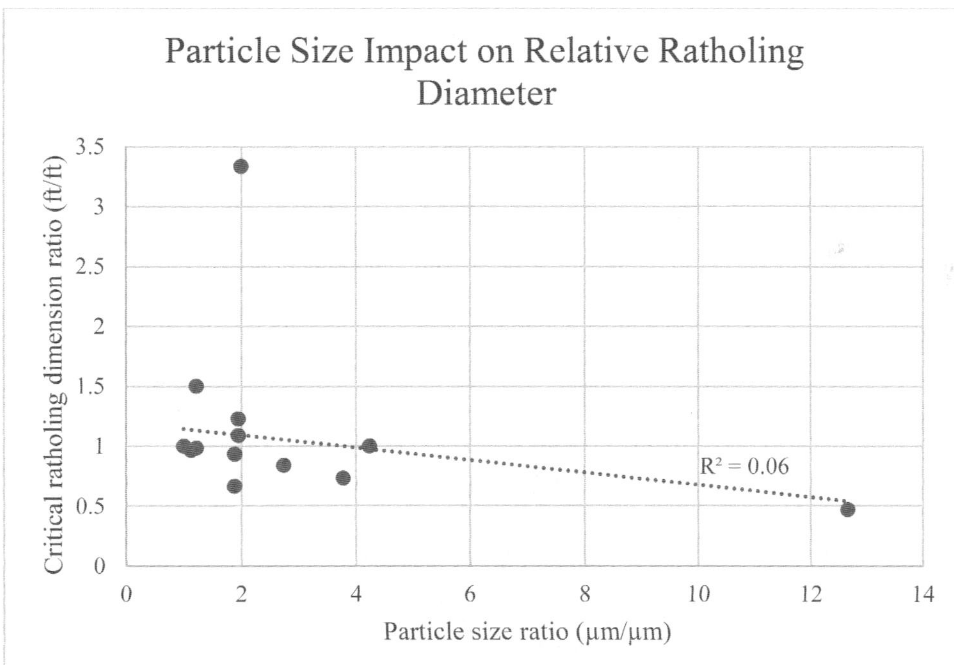

Figure F: Particle size impact on relative ratholing diameter

As hypothesized, each of these graphs show a negative relationship with arching and ratholing dimensions tending to decrease with increasing particle size. While this relationship appears to exist, the R^2 value for a linear relationship is extremely low. This suggests that although increasing particle size does typically result in lower cohesive strength, there does not appear to be a mathematical model that can be used to compute the magnitude of decreased strength based on the magnitude of shift in particle size alone. It appears that the magnitude of change in cohesive strength is material dependent.

Of the samples examined, 75% of materials showed a decrease or no change in the critical arching or ratholing diameters when particle size was increased. This suggests that for a majority of materials, cohesive strength can potentially be decreased by increasing particle size. This can be accomplished by adjusting milling or crushing processes or even more drastic changes can be accomplished though agglomerating or briquetting.

Relationship to Wall Friction Angles

Figure G provides a chart of the impact of particle size on the normalized wall angle required for mass flow. The particle size ratio as calculated according to equation 1 is provided on the horizontal axis while wall friction angle ratio is provided on the vertical axis.

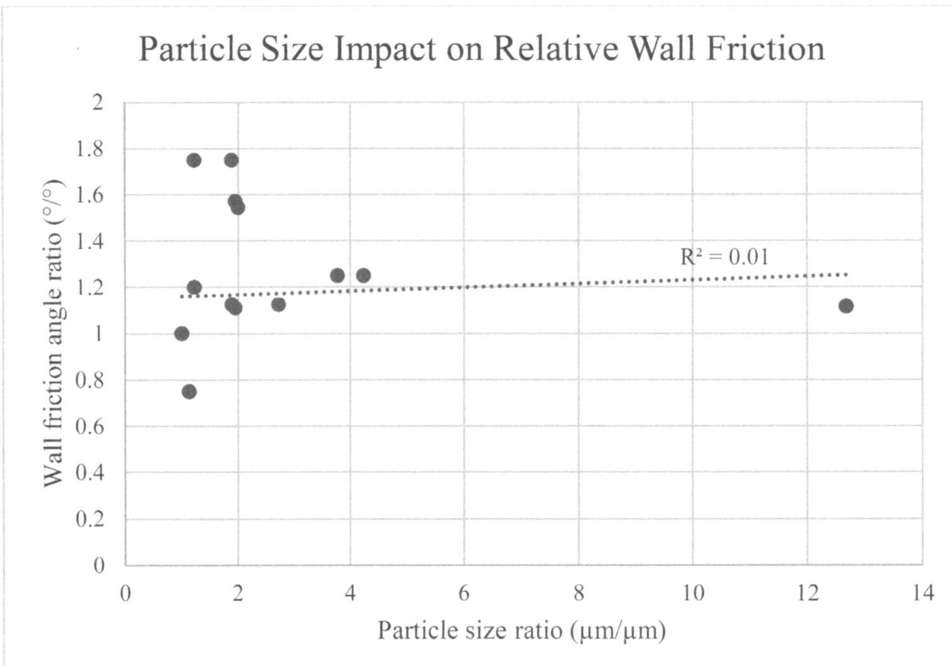

Figure G: Particle size impact on relative wall friction

Similar to the measures for cohesive strength, the wall friction angle ratio does not appear to have a mathematical relationship with relative particle size of the materials examined. Again, it does not appear possible to create a model to predict the increase in angle required for mass flow from the relative increase in particle size for a material. The amount that wall friction changes for the same relative increase in particle size appears to be material dependent.

While there is no strict relationship for predicting the magnitude of wall friction changes, 90% of the materials examined showed benefit in wall friction results from increasing particle size.

Importance of Flow Properties Testing

The fact that mathematical models cannot be created to determine magnitude of change in flow properties for materials based on particle size changes brings up the importance of material testing following any change to the material being handled. While a majority of materials examined showed that flow properties improved with increased median particle size, there were materials that showed an inverse reaction. Because of these outliers, it is a good idea when making any change to the material being handled by a system to test the flow properties of the new material. This is true even when increasing the particle size of the material being handled.

Physical flow properties testing is the only way to verify that a new material or a new system will operate as intended. It is best practice to test each material at each particle size distribution to be handled. However, the budget and risk tolerance of the project and impact of potential flow issues should also be considered. If only one size distribution per material can be tested, the relationships described above suggest that, generally, the more conservative approach would be to test the smallest size distribution of the material being handled as opposed to a larger size fraction.

7 CONCLUSIONS

Bulk materials can present unique challenges when designing handling systems. Flow properties such as cohesive strength and wall friction characteristics are important in determining how a specific material will interact with specific pieces of equipment. These properties are not only material specific but are also impacted by changes in the environment, handling system, and even changes to the material itself.

Flow properties have an impact on whether or not material is able to successfully flow through a system and the manner in which is flows: funnel flow or mass flow. Common flow problems of arching and ratholing can be avoided based on knowing the cohesive strength and wall friction properties of the material and ensuring that the system is designed to avoid these problems. Reducing the cohesive strength can help avoid arching and ratholing, while improving the wall friction can transform a funnel flow system to mass flow and avoid the potential of ratholing.

While a majority of flow properties examined improved with increased particle size of the material tested, the magnitude of improvement could not be modeled through historical test data. This means that increasing particle size is likely to improve flow performance, but flow properties testing is still required to determine the extent of that improvement and whether the newly sized material will flow successfully though a specific system design.

8 WORKS CITED

Carson, J., & Prescott, J. (1998). Effects of Surface Topography and Particle Size on Powder/Surface Friction Characteristics. *AIChE.* Miami.

Carson, J., Del Cid, L., & McInerney, J. (2020). Flow Measurements of Powders and Bulk Solids. In *Kirk-Othmer Encyclopedia of Chemical Technology* (pp. 1-23). John Wiley & Sons, Inc.

Carson, J., Purutyan, H., & Rotter, J. (2003). The Dangers of Relying on Wall Friction Values in Codes. *International Conference for Convying and Handling of Particle Solids, 4.* Budapest, Hungary.

Craig, D., & Hossfeld, R. (2002, September). Measuring Powder-Flow Properties. *Chemical Engineering*, 41-46.

Jenike, A. (1964, November). Storage and Flow of Solids. *University of Utah Engineering Experiment Station, Bulletin No. 123.*

Johanson, J. (1984). *Bulk Solids Handling*(4), 417-422.

Maynard, E. (2001, September). Designing Storage Bins for Bulk Solids: A Step-by-Step Procedure. *Chemical Processing, 64*(9), 4-8.

Pittenger, B. (1995, June). Survey Confirms: Testing Material Flow Properties Helps You Design Better Storage and Handling Systems. *Powder & Bulk Engineering, 9*(6), 23-35.

Prescott, J., & Ploof, D. (1995). Wall Friction: A Complex Variable in the Design of Bulk Solids Storage Systems. *AIChE.* Miami.

Schulze, D. (2007). *Powders and Bulk Solids: Behavior, Characterization, Storage and Flow* (Vol. 1). Berlin: Springer.

Institute for Briquetting and Agglomeration

2022 IBA CONFERENCE PAPERS

Paper Title:

Mechanisms of Polymeric Binders in the Production of Steelmaking By-Product Cold-bonded Agglomerates

Presenters and Company:

Julie Mortimer Veevers: BASF plc, Bradford, United Kingdom
Noelia Vega Aguirre: Arcelormittal Global R&D Asturias, Spain
José Luis García Cimadevilla: Arcelormittal Global R&D Asturias, Spain
Yanping Xiao: Tata Steel, R&D IJmuiden, The Netherlands
Frédéric Blaffart: CRM, Liege, Belgium

Mechanisms of Polymeric Binders in the Production of Steelmaking By-Product Cold-bonded Agglomerates

Julie Mortimer Veevers — BASF plc, Bradford, United Kingdom
Noelia Vega Aguirre — Arcelormittal Global R&D Asturias, Spain
José Luis García Cimadevilla — Arcelormittal Global R&D Asturias, Spain
Yanping Xiao — Tata Steel, R&D IJmuiden, The Netherlands
Frédéric Blaffart — CRM, Liege, Belgium

ABSTRACT

Polymeric binders can be used as binders in many agglomeration processes to improve the green strength and attrition qualities of briquettes in industrial fields such as steelmaking, coal, nickel, ferro-alloys, and recycling. Benefits of using such binders can be quantified via certain operational parameters such as recirculating load, cold handling properties, final briquette performance in the furnace and the impact on CO_2 footprint of the operation.

The aim of this work was to investigate the performance of organic binders by determining the mechanisms and interactions between the mineral surface and polymeric binder and the subsequent impact on down-stream performance. A batch of 100% Coarse BOF sludge (Recipe 1) as well as a blend of this by-product with oily mill-scales (Recipe 2) were used as test substrates and were sourced from one of ArcelorMittal's steel production facilities.

The down-stream performance was determined by a study of cold-agglomerate compression strength with time (ISO 4700), by the ISO T tumble test (ISO 3271), by the Reduction Disintegration test at 500°C (RDI - ISO 4696-1), and finally by custom blast furnace simulation tests carried out by Tata Steel which simulates agglomerate performance under a reductive atmosphere at higher temperatures. The interaction of the binder with the substrate was investigated by Scanning Electron Microscopy with Electron Probe Micro Analysis (SEM-EPMA) performed on cold-agglomerates which had been cured at room temperature as well as subjected to RDI conditions.

The results showed which of the polymer properties had greater or lesser impact on the cold-agglomerate quality in terms of cold cured properties as well as after exposure to reductive blast furnace conditions. The chemical composition of the polymeric binders was found to influence the optimum binder system for the steel mill residues. Mechanism theories for the optimized formulations were investigated through SEM-EPMA.

Key Words: Polymer, binder, cement, agglomeration, briquetting, extrusion, by-products, steel mill, blast furnace, cold curing

1. INTRODUCTION

Polymeric binders are becoming more recently accepted as agglomeration aids across a number of agglomeration technologies[1]. One such area where the use of binders are on the rise is the recycling of steel mill by-products such as sludges, dusts, slags and mill scales which are typically generated at a rate of 700kg for every tonne of steel[2]. Usually, materials such as molasses and lime, or cement are used to re-agglomerate the by-products and enable their recycling back into the process stream. However, key limitations to such binders are mainly in terms of handling large volumes, as well as reducing the quality of the final recycled agglomerates in terms of iron units. Additionally the carbon footprint of binders such as cement[3] is deleterious to the overall sustainability profile of the recycling operation.

Whilst the use of polymeric binders is known to show several advantages, selecting the optimum binder particularly for steel mill by-products is dependent on both the technical performance of the agglomerates in the downstream furnace processes (e.g. blast furnace) and the success of the agglomeration process itself with a controlled plasticity and stickiness, with a suitable curing evolution, and sufficient strength to allow the possibility for non-damaging handling at every step prior to introduction to the furnace operations.

The selection of organic polymers to provide a cost-viable proposition as a binder for agglomeration operations will significantly depends on the comprehensive understanding of the process and mineralogical variations inherent within the various steel mill by-products. The latter is particularly a challenge considering the multiplicity of the by-products generated by the iron makers . An understanding of the fundamentals of polymer binding mechanisms is essential, in order to take into account such multiplicity by optimally adapting the binder to the substrate to reach a sufficient quality for recycling back into the steel making process.

This paper discusses the use of polymeric binders to develop a cold-bonded, cement free agglomerate from recycling materials which are common to most steel making facilities, such that these agglomerates can be used to contribute towards the blast furnace burden in steel making and proposes the mechanisms that promote agglomerate strength and feasibility for recycling.

2. EXPERIMENTAL

2.1 Substrate Tested

In the experiments conducted, two substrates were investigated, one being comprised of 100% Coarse BOF sludge, and the other being comprised of 60% Coarse BOF sludge 40% oily mill-scales, the basic properties of which are tabulated below:

Table 1. Compositional Properties of Substrates Tested

	Coarse BOF Sludge	Oily Mill Scales
Moisture Content (%w/w)	9.2	3.94
C (%w/w)	2.83	0.32
S (%w/w)	0.24	0.10
Fe_{tot} (%w/w)	82.54	73.97

Fe_{metal} (%w/w)	69.85	0.27
FeO (%w/w)	7.62	60.31
Fe_2O_3 (%w/w)	9.68	38.34
Al_2O_3 (%w/w)	0.39	0.11
CaO (%w/w)	7.68	0.10
SiO_2 (%w/w)	0.37	0.10
MnO (%w/w)	0.16	0.55
ZnO (%w/w)	0.88	0.10

2.2 Binders Evaluated

Table 2. List of Binders Tested

Sample Label	Description
Alcotac® FE14	Modified polyacrylamide (PAM) based binder (BASF)
DP-OMC-1090	Linear polyacrylamide-based binder (BASF)
DP-OMC-1135 AP	Lower ashing version of a linear polyacrylamide-based binder (BASF)
Alcotac® FE-16	Modified polyacrylamide (PAM) based binder used for use in pelletisation processes in combination with sodium carbonate (BASF)
Alcotac® CB6	Linear polyacrylamide-based binder (BASF)
Ciment Fondu	High alumina cement (Imerys Secar 712)
Bentonite	Sodium bentonite (Imerys Ibeco Seal)
Cement	Ordinary Portland Cement (Local source)

2.3 Agglomeration Protocols

2.3.1 Briquetting

In order to assess preliminary binder dose and moisture requirements a KOMAREK model B220B roll press was used to agglomerate some batches of the Coarse BOF Sludge. Material from the feed hopper was supplied into a roll nip with a horizontal screw which was driven by a variable speed drive unit. A paddle mixer was utilized to agitate material into the horizontal screw at the feed inlet. The material is then compacted between two rolls which are cantilevered on the ends of shafts outside the bearing blocks. A fully adjustable hydraulic system provides the force holding the rolls together. This force is equal in magnitude to the roll separating force generated by the compacted material in roll nip. Gas filled accumulators in the hydraulic system act as pressured reservoirs and accumulator pre-charge pressure determines the hydraulic system stiffness. Material mixed with the binder under assessment was fed into the feed hopper. After the roll press was operating under stable conditions, briquettes were collected and stored under ambient conditions. The characterization of the samples was performed after sufficient maturation.

2.3.2 Extrusion

More extensive work on the Coarse BOF sludge and the blend with oily mill scales was performed using an extrusion process. The samples were agglomerated using extrusion with a stiff extruder Handle PZVM8e. All work reported herein was performed in CRM laboratories located in Liege, Belgium. The Coarse BOF sludge and binder blends were prepared and homogenized in a 5 L Eirich mixer using a mixing speed of 2000 rpm for 30 seconds after which water was added and an additional mixing step performed for 60 seconds. The mixture was then allowed to rest for 60 seconds prior to an additional mixing step of 30 seconds. The mixture was then introduced to an extruder equipped with a shearing die in order to mimic the de-airing associated with an industrial extruder prior to being re-introduced to the extruder with a regular extrusion die having four openings of 19mm in diameter. Vacuum was applied during this second stage. The extruded sample was then collected and stored under ambient conditions prior to further tests being performed.

2.4 Cold Tumble Test (ISO T)

The tumble strength (ISO 3271) is defined as the mechanical resistance of a lump or agglomerate when subjected to a tumble test in a rotating drum. For all tests due to limited sample size, after some correlation baselines had been established, 3kg (c.f. 15kg) of agglomerates were rotated using a drum of 1000mm x 500mm for a total of 200 revolutions. The agglomerates are then sieved with test sieves having apertures of 6.3mm and 0.5mm and the amount of material retained on each sieve being then reported in percentage weight. ISO-T is the large fraction (+6.3mm) and ISO-A is the fines fraction (-0.5mm). For the purposes of the tests a target of >75% +6.3mm and <6% -0.5mm was specified. This test was carried out on the agglomerates after a period of ambient curing of about one week, or until the agglomerates had reached ~1% w/w moisture content.

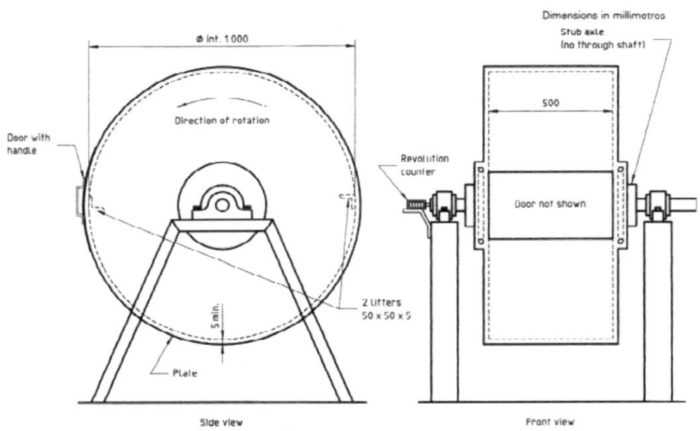

Figure 1. Diagram of Tumble Test Apparatus

2.5 Reduction Disintegration Test (RDI)

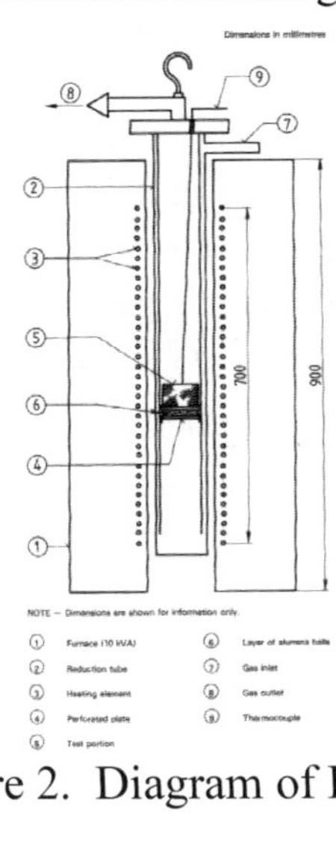

Figure 2. Diagram of RDI Test Apparatus

The RDI test (ISO 4696-1) provides a means of evaluating the degree of degradation observed when lumps or agglomerates are reduced with a mix of CO, CO_2, and Nitrogen (20%, 20%, 60%) under conditions typical in the low-temperature reduction zone of the blast furnace. A portion of agglomerates are exposed to static reduction in a fixed bed temperature of 500°C. The agglomerates are then cooled and tumbled. The percentage mass +6.3mm, +3.15mm and -0.5mm is then reported. For the purposes of the tests a target of 60% was +3.15mm was specified.

2.6 Scanning Electron Microscopy and Back Scatter Electron Imaging (SEM-BSE)

Samples of agglomerates, both cold-cured and after RDI exposure were submitted to BASF's Central Analytics department in Ludwigshafen, Germany. The principle of such a technique is that the surface of a material can be subjected to x-ray radiation, backscattered against the surface, and the kinetic energy of the resulting photo-emitted electrons are analysed and can also be detected by a scanning electron microscope to produce high resolution images of the elements present within the sample.

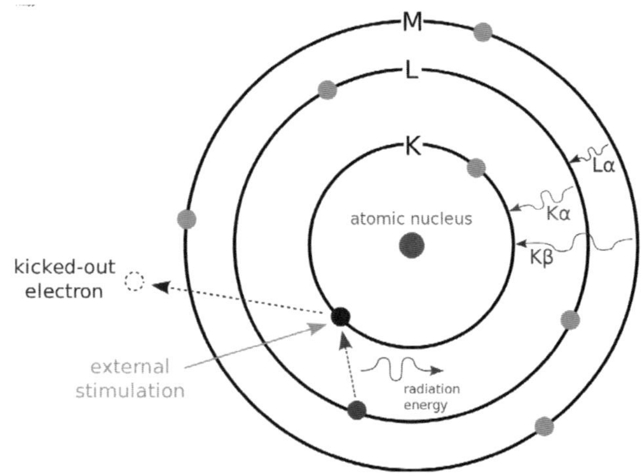

Figure 3. Schematic of Back-Scattered Electron Capture

A portion of the agglomerates were impregnated in resin, cross-sectioned, polished (dry polishing using silicon carbide) and were investigated in the SEM and imaged by BSE. In the BSE images, regions of higher density appear brighter (higher concentration/ higher atomic number /lower porosity).

The element distribution of the cross-sectioned agglomerates was measured by EDXS (Energy Dispersive X-Ray Spectroscopy, 20kV). Selected images are then reported as coloured elemental maps.

2.7 HOSIM Blast Furnace (BF) Simulation Tests

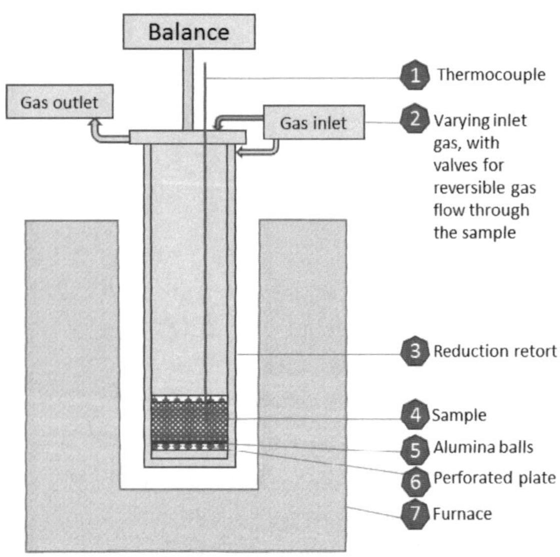

Figure 4. Diagram of HOSIM Test Apparatus

HOSIM tests were carried out at Tata's Metallurgical lab for ironmaking in Ijmuiden. The HOSIM test simulates the Blast Furnace process following the Rist-operating line. As shown in Figure 4, it consists of an electrically heated furnace, a reduction retort with a double wall, and a continuous weighing system. It is equipped with a programmed temperature and gas control, and the gas profile changes with the reduction progress which is monitored by the weight loss of the sample. The standard HOSIM test operates in the temperature range from 430 to 910 °C, and reaction gas contains CO, CO_2, H_2 and N_2. After reaction, the reacted sample is cooled under N_2 and tumbled. The percentage mass -3.15mm is reported as a quality measure for evaluation of the hot strength of the agglomerates.

3. RESULTS

3.1 Mechanical Strength Testing on Briquetted Agglomerates – Initial Screening of Conventional binders vs. Combinations with Polymeric Binders

Various combinations of high alumina cement, ordinary Portland cement with and without the addition of bentonite and polymeric binders were tested in collaboration with Euragglo, a well-recognized company in the business of cold-agglomeration. Generally speaking it was not possible to agglomerate the Coarse BOF sludge using purely cement or bentonite alone, either ordinary Portland cement or high alumina cement; **the use of polymeric binder was necessary to provide a briquette with suitable green strength and plasticity**. Doing so, the Coarse BOF sludge was briquetted at 5.6% moisture content. Compression strength was measured over time, as well as a drop test to determine the friability of the briquettes. Two drops at a height of 2 meters were performed, using a total of 5 briquettes per test. Results are reported in terms of percentage of fines generated below 10mm.

In some cases, additional water was added, as specified in the Binder Details column below:

Table 3. Physical Properties of Briquetted Agglomerates on Recipe 1 (100% BOF Sludge)

Binder Details	Average Strength (kg)				Drop Test < 10 mm fines generated (%)			
	Day 0	Day 1	Day 2	Day 7	Day 0	Day 1	Day 2	Day 7
4% cement Portland + 4% bentonite	28	41	42	95	35	25	16	12
7% cement Portland + 0.3% Alcotac® CB6	53	125	135	226	8	3	3	2
5% cement Portland + 0.3% Alcotac® CB6	44	107	125	217	2	2	2	2
3% cement Portland + 0.3% Alcotac® CB6	43	75	114	214	3	2	2	3
0.3% Alcotac® CB6	40	54	67	104	4	1	2	2
8% ciment fondu	35	205	263	-	63	6	6	-
7% ciment fondu + 0.3% Alcotac® CB6	56	163	199	-	25	2	3	-
7% ciment fondu + 0.3% Alcotac® CB6 + 2% water	50	209	201	-	12	2	3	-
5% ciment fondu +	52	163	203	-	12	2	1	-

0.3% Alcotac® CB6 + 1.5% water								
3% ciment fondu + 0.3% Alcotac® CB6 + 1.5% water	48	119	175	-	11	3	3	-

Table 3. Physical Properties of Briquetted Agglomerates on Recipe 1 (100% Coarse BOF Sludge)

BINDER DETAILS	Average Strength (kg)				Drop Test < 10 mm fines generated (%)			
	Day 0	Day 1	Day 2	Day 7	Day 0	Day 1	Day 2	Day 7
4% Portland Cement + 4% bentonite	28	41	42	95	35	25	16	12
7% Portland Cement + 0.3% Alcotac® CB6	53	125	135	226	8	3	3	2
5% Portland Cement + 0.3% Alcotac® CB6	44	107	125	217	2	2	2	2
3% Portland Cement + 0.3% Alcotac® CB6	43	75	114	214	3	2	2	3
0.3% Alcotac® CB6	40	54	67	104	4	1	2	2
8% ciment fondu	35	205	263	-	63	6	6	-
7% ciment fondu + 0.3% Alcotac® CB6 + 2% water	50	209	201	-	12	2	3	-
5% ciment fondu + 0.3% Alcotac® CB6 + 1.5% water	52	163	203	-	12	2	1	-
3% ciment fondu + 0.3% Alcotac® CB6 + 1.5% water	48	119	175	-	11	3	3	-

3.2 Mechanical Strength Testing on Extruded Briquettes produced with Organic Polymer Binders

3.2.1 Results for Recipe 1 (100% Coarse BOF sludge)

Considering that the organic binder is a key to the agglomeration success, further binder optimisation work was performed using extrusion as an agglomeration process. Extrusion was selected as an alternative to briquetting due to the potential benefit of the applied vacuum to improve contact between the particles of the substrate and, ultimately, the agglomerates quality. The Table 4 summarizes the recipes that meet the quality target, Table 5 summarizes the recipes that do not meet the target but that are not completely without merits. Table 6 shows the recipes of overwhelmingly insufficient quality.

As can be seen from Table 4 below, it is key to notice that some of the extruded briquettes prepared with organic binder Alcotac® FE14 **alone** were able to sustain acceptable levels of integrity after thermal treatment under ISO-4696 conditions in terms of the amount of agglomerates retained above 3.15mm after thermal reduction (target >60%). In order to understand the mechanisms further, some of the produced agglomerates were analyzed further using SEM-BSE imaging which is detailed in the next section.

Table 4. Physical Properties of Extruded Pellets with Recipe 1 (100% Coarse BOF Sludge) Achieving RDI target of ~60%

BINDER	RDI w/w% > 6.3 mm	RDI w/w% > 3.15 mm	RDI w/w% < 0.5 mm	ISO T w/w% > 6.3 mm	ISO A w/w% < 0.5 mm
5% Portland Cement + DP-MH-1025 + 1% Alcotac® FE14	84.8	84.8	14.7	87.5	10.7
0.75% Alcotac® FE14 & 1 % bentonite	70.7	70.7	25.4	50.5	40.9
1% Alcotac® FE14	60.5	60.5	33.9	80.4	17.3
0.75% Alcotac® FE14 & 1 % bentonite	60.5	60.5	33.5	57.0	31.3
1% DP-OMC-1090	60.4	60.4	33.7	70.0	23.3

Table 5. Physical Properties of Extruded Pellets with Recipe 1 (100% Coarse BOF Sludge) Achieving Average Results w.r.t RDI Target

BINDER	RDI w/w% > 6.3 mm	RDI w/w% > 3.15 mm	RDI w/w% < 0.5 mm	ISO T w/w% > 6.3 mm	ISO A w/w% < 0.5 mm
0.75 % Alcotac® FE14	58.9	58.9	27.0	69.6	26.6
1% Alcotac® FE14 + 1 % bentonite	57.8	57.8	36.8	67.4	30.5
1% DP-OMC-1090	56.2	56.2	36.7	73.0	22.9
5% high alumina cement + DP-MH-1025 + 1% Alcotac® FE14	55.2	55.3	38.2	72.9	23.7
1% Alcotac® FE14 + 0.7 % bentonite	53.9	53.9	39.7	74.1	23
1% Alcotac® FE14 + 0.25% bentonite	53.5	53.5	39.8	76.3	20.9
1% Alcotac® FE14 + 0.5% bentonite	53.0	53.0	40.4	75.3	22
1% Alcotac® CB6	47.1	47.1	44.9	72.1	24.5
1% DP OMC 1135 AP	46.8	46.8	48.7	72.4	23.9
3% bentonite	46.5	45.7	45.9	0.1	83.2
0.75% Alcotac® FE14 & 3% high alumina cement	42.8	43.4	47.1	16.2	57.9
0.75% Alcotac® FE14	42.8	42.9	46.9	65.8	28.7

Table 6. Physical Properties of Extruded Pellets with Recipe 1 (100% Coarse BOF Sludge) Achieving Poor Results w.r.t RDI Target

BINDER	RDI w/w% > 6.3 mm	RDI w/w% > 3.15 mm	RDI w/w% < 0.5 mm	ISO T w/w% > 6.3 mm	ISO A w/w% < 0.5 mm
0.75% FE14 & 5 % high alumina cement	16.7	17.9	65.8	0.0	99.9
5% Portland Cement + DP-MH-1025 + 1% Alcotac® FE14	13.1	13.5	70.7	56.8	33.5
1% Alcotac® FE-16	10.7	12.67	69.8	25.1	49.4
0.75% Alcotac® FE14 & 1 % high alumina cement	0.71	1.2	78.3	17.6	45.3

3.2.2 Results for Recipe 2 (60% Coarse BOF sludge + 40% Oily Mill Scales)

The extrusion method was similarly applied was also used to evaluate binder systems on the Recipe 2 substrate. Table 7 summarises the recipes that meet the quality target. Again, several recipes produced with polymer binder **alone** allowed the production of agglomerates of good quality.

Table 7. Physical Properties of Extruded Pellets with Recipe 2 (60% Coarse BOF Sludge + 40% Oily Mill Scales

BINDER	RDI w/w% > 6.3 mm	RDI w/w% > 3.15 mm	RDI w/w% < 0.5 mm	ISO T w/w% > 6.3 mm	ISO A w/w% < 0.5 mm
5% ciment fondu + DP-MH-1025 + 1% Alcotac® FE14	77.4	77.4	20.7	74.4	19.9
1% Alcotac® FE14	71.1	71.1	26.5	75.0	22.9
1% Alcotac® CB6	65.2	66.2	31.4	67.4	20.6
1% DP-OMC-1135 AP	64.3	64.3	32.9	76.2	22.1
1% DP-OMC-1090	63.24	63.2	34.35	75.2	23.1
0.75 % Alcotac® FE14	61.3	61.3	35.3	57.5	27.7
1% Alcotac® FE14 + 1% bentonite	56.7	56.7	39.4	66.0	30.6
1% Alcotac® FE14 + 0.25% bentonite	56.2	56.2	39.7	74.7	22.9

3.3 SEM-BSE Imaging on Recipe One Agglomerates prepared with Polymeric Binders

One question of interest is to understand the polymer induced binding mechanism that provide a mechanical strength to the agglomerate even after a thermal treatment under reducing conditions. In order to investigate at which particular sites bonding is occurring between the substrates and chemical binder, SEM-BSE tests were carried out on a selection of the samples which had been considered to be different in terms of mechanical strength as detailed below, selected from Tables 4 - 6.

Table 8. Recipe 1 (100% Coarse BOF Sludge) Agglomerates analysed with SEM-BSE

Sample Label	Binder Used	Agglomerate Properties
2021.05.27 EXT03	1% Alcotac® FE14	Passes RDI and ISO T testing
2021.06.09 EXT03	1% DP-OMC-1135 AP	Passes ISO T but fails RDI
2021.06.09 EXT02	1% Alcotac® FE-16	Fails both RDI and ISO T tests

In all cases agglomerates were analysed that had been cured at room temperature, and after exposure to the RDI test (ISO 4696-1) conditions. A binderless sample was also analysed for reference purposes.

A portion of the agglomerates were impregnated in resin, cross-sectioned, polished (dry polishing using silicon carbide) and were investigated in the SEM and imaged by BSE. In the BSE images, regions of higher density appear brighter (higher concentration/ higher atomic number /lower porosity).

The element distribution of the cross-sectioned agglomerates was measured by EDXS (Energy Dispersive X-Ray Spectroscopy, 20kV). Selected images are displayed in the following charts as coloured elemental maps showing the distribution of C, O, Ca and Fe throughout the cold-bonded agglomerates. For each of the separate images (O, Ca, Fe) the same area (region) of the agglomerate is shown.

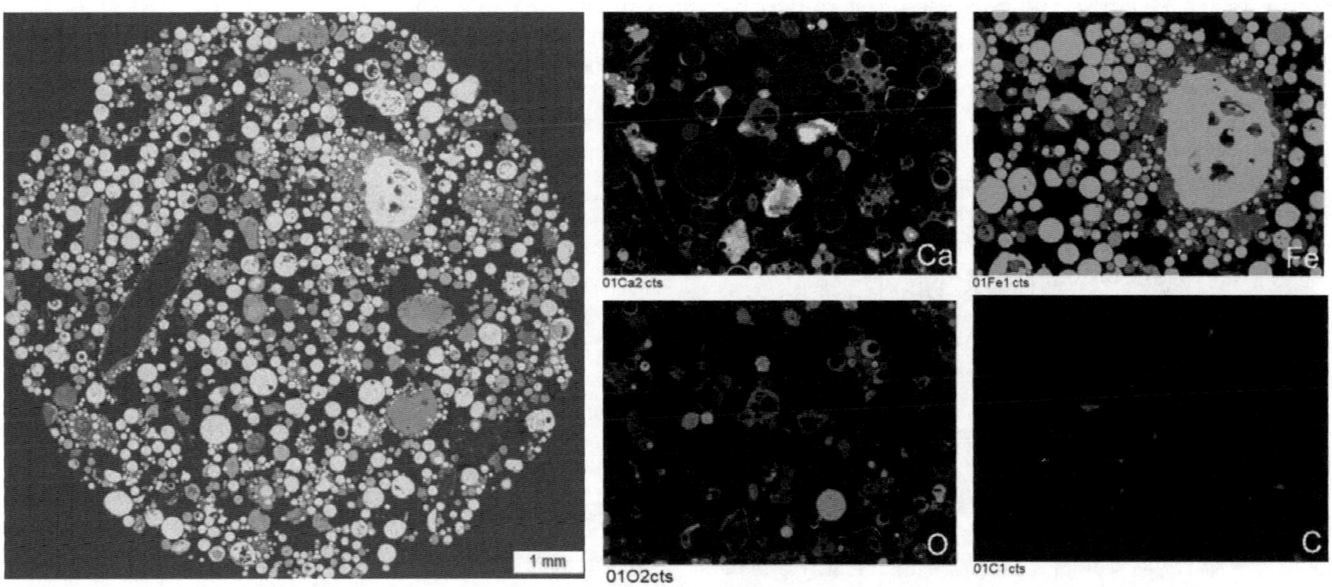

Figure 5: SEM-BSE Analysis – BINDERLESS AGGLOMERATE

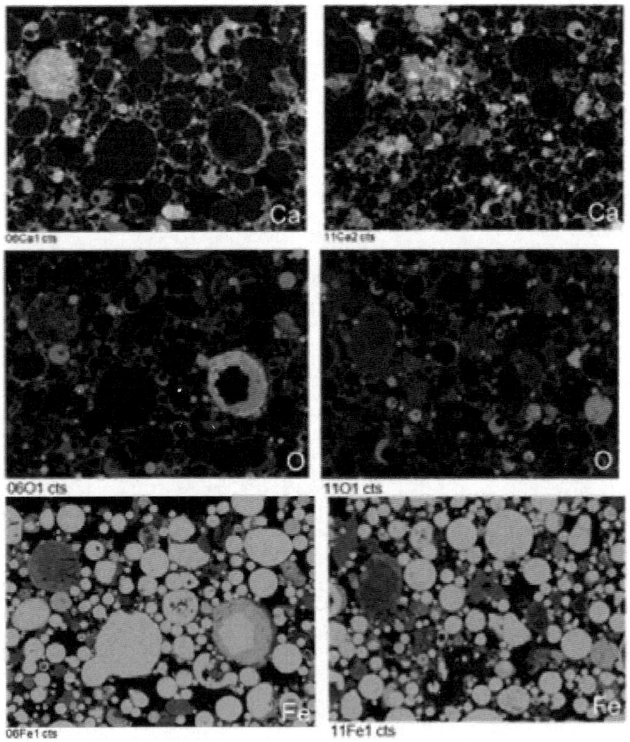

Figure 6: SEM-BSE Analysis – Cold-Bonded Agglomerate with 1% Alcotac® FE14 (cold-cured Left-Hand Images, and after RDI testing Right-Hand Images)

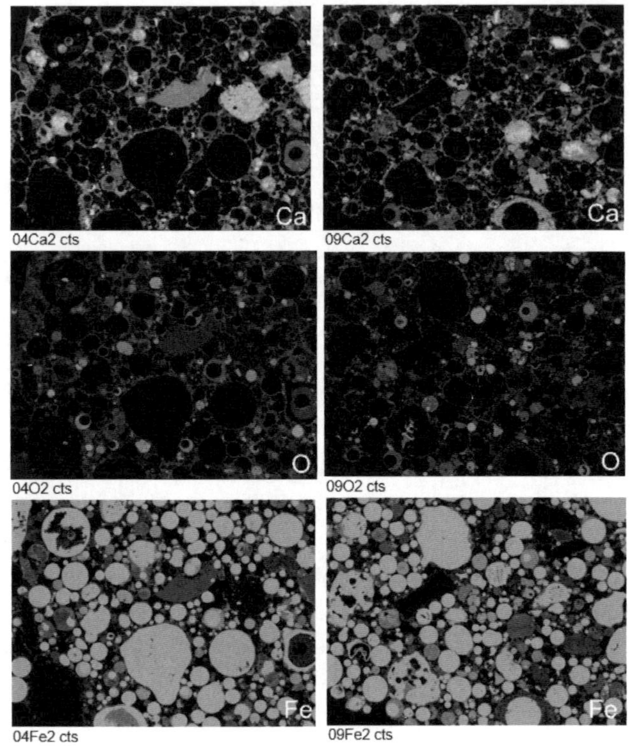

Figure 7: SEM-BSE Analysis – Cold-Bonded Agglomerate with 1% DP-OMC-1135 AP (cold-cured Left-Hand Images, and after RDI testing Right-Hand Images)

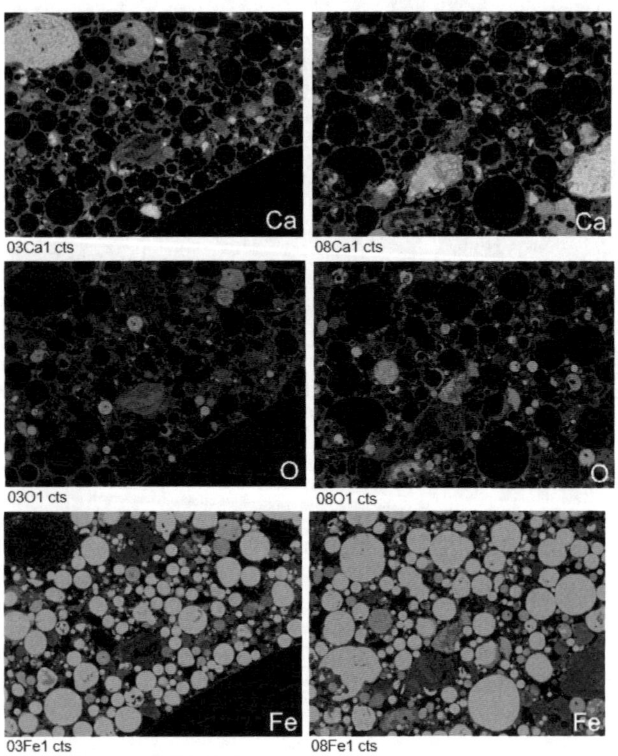

Figure 8: SEM-BSE Analysis – Cold-Bonded Agglomerate with 1% Alcotac® FE-16 (cold-cured Left-Hand Images, and after RDI testing Right-Hand Images)

As displayed in Figures 5 to 8 above, it can be seen that in the agglomerate which contained no binder, the particles and associated ions are dispersed very uniformly, i.e., plenty of interstitial spaces seem to be present. In the agglomerates whereby Alcotac® FE14 was used, both the calcium and oxygen ions are dispersed far more prevalently throughout the interstitial Fe-rich matrix. The SEM-BSE analysis was repeated on other samples. So far, many of the observations regarding calclium and oxygen when using Alcotac® FE14 apply also for the other binder systems considered: Alcotac® FE-16, and DP-OMC-1135 AP. As the sodium/calcium exchange mechanism (explained later in Section 3.4) was thought to be of significance, Alcotac® FE-16 was also submitted for SEM-BSE analysis, and this is a binder using Alcotac® FE14 as the base polymer which is then blended with sodium carbonate, as is commonly required for typical application in iron ore pelletisation.

3.4 Proposed Mechanism of Polymeric Binder via Calcium and Oxygen Dispersion

The SEM images of extruded agglomerates in the previous section show that the segregated Ca atoms are redistributed in-between the particles when in the presence of the polymeric binder. SEM image of the agglomerates after RDI test shows that the Ca atoms remains distributed in-between the particles. The quality of the low temperature binding effect and the high temperature binding effect could both be related to the action of the polymeric binder, revealed by the redistribution of the cations. The calcium redistribution is explained by the affinity of the polymer binder with cations such as Ca^{2+} as depicted in Figure 7 below.

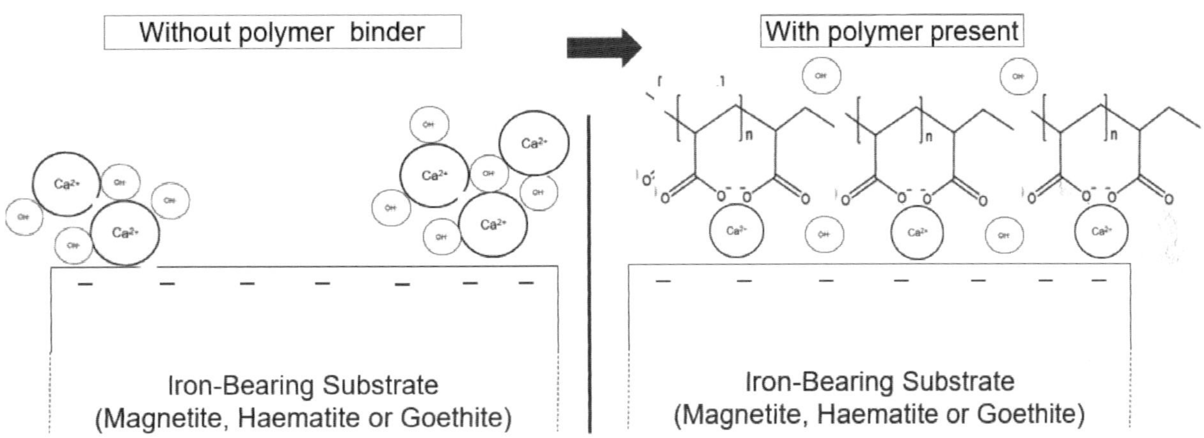

Figure 9: Proposed Mechanism of Calcium and Oxygen Dispersion through the Interstitial Surface

3.5 Reduction Degradation of the Agglomerates under Blast Furnace Simulation Conditions

Low temperature reduction degradation is unfavorable in BF ironmaking. In BF ironmaking, the reduction degradation of sinter and pellets is mainly triggered by the haematite to magnetite transition[5]. Usually a high reduction degradation index indicates a high level of disintegration or un-sintered individual particles.

In the present study, interrupted HOSIM tests have been conducted to evaluate the reduction degradation behavior at a characteristic temperature range from 430 °C - 600 °C, which is usually considered to be the sensitive temperature region for the reduction degradation of sinter and pellets. In the test, a standard time-temperature profile is applied, and the gas composition is adjusted according to the reaction progress of the sample. After the test, the agglomerates are cooled, tumbled and sieved. The percentage mass of less than 3.15mm is defined as one of the major KPI's to dictate agglomerate quality. For the cold bonded agglomerates less than 35% was set as the research target. Figure 8 below illustrates the reduction degradation index of the cold bonded agglomerates, and its relation to the ISO tumble index. It shows that the hot strength is relatively low, and the higher tumble index usually leads to lower reduction degradation. For 100% Coarse BOF sludge, the Alcotac® FE14 binder gives the highest cold and hot strength of the agglomerate.

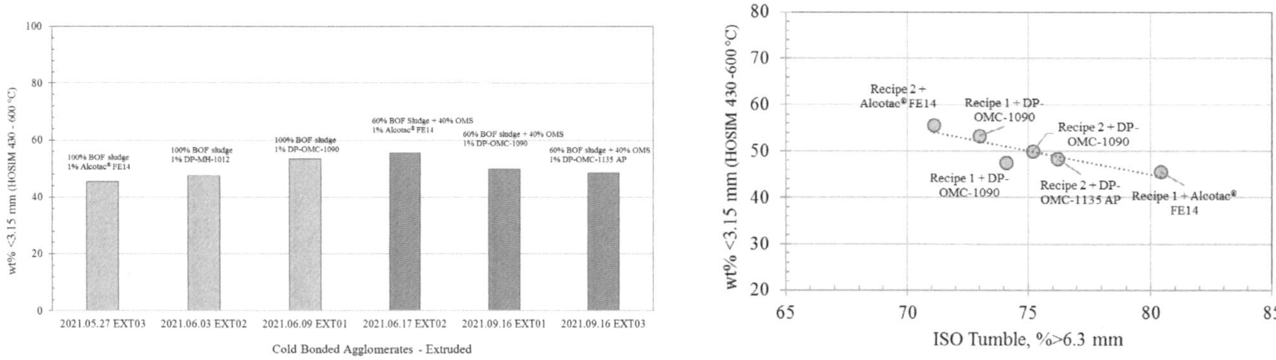

Figure 10: HOSIM Test Results for Reduction Degradation and the correlation to ISO T Tumble Strength

The HOSIM reduction degradation test quantifies the dust generating tendency in the BF upper shaft, and the ISO tumbler index measures the fines generation resistance during agglomerates handling and transportation. The thermal behavior of the polymer bonding phases plays a vital role in controlling the hot strength of the agglomerates. For the application of the cold bonded briquettes, the high temperature metallurgical behavior of the cold bonded agglomerates will be further investigated. The charging rate of the agglomerates into BF will be evaluated based on the physical and metallurgical quality, in combination with the properties of other BF burden components, to minimize the dust generation for stable Blast Furnace operation.

4. DISCUSSION AND CONCLUSIONS

Various binder systems have been tested, on substrates of BOF coarse sludge and mill scales. The best results observed have been achieved with the use of Alcotac® FE14 at a dose rate of 1% w/w. Further optimization is expected in terms of cold tumble and RDI, however this binder should be used as a reference for all binder developments going forwards, to further improve on these two critical parameters.

The present results showed primarily that the polymer binder alone is sufficient to produce agglomerates that maintain mechanical stability at high temperature (i.e., under RDI and HOSIM test conditions). A correlation of the HOSIM results to the ISO T tumble test was observed, indicating that the bonding effect coming from the binders is non-reversible. In addition, there were no apparent observable differences between the SEM-BSE analyses performed on the "green" or cold-cured agglomerates as compared to the cold-agglomerates which had been exposed to RDI conditions.

From looking at the SEM-BSE analyses it can be concluded that wherever a polyacrylamide type binder is used, there is a level of dispersion with calcium and oxygen which seems to contribute towards both the cold and the hot strength of the cold-agglomerates. Additionally it was observed that while the Ca-O dispersion is initiated with the polymer chemistry, simply adding in additional sodium to the interstitial matrix is insufficient to impart any additional strength, in fact it is deleterious to the final strength when introduced in the form of sodium carbonate with reference to the inferior RDI and ISO T results obtained when using Alcotac® FE-16 as a binder. It is apparent that the use of the binders detailed above all contribute to some extent towards the postulated Ca-O dispersion mechanism however the degree to which this influences final strength characteristics cannot yet be fully defined.

It is known that polyacrylamide adsorption is influenced by the nature of the mineral surface, as well as the chemical nature of the polymer, i.e. charge density. It was observed that using the non-ionic binder DP-OMC-1135 AP displayed the Ca-Na-O dispersion effect indicating that hydrogen bonding coming from the amide group on the polymer backbone is the driving force in this case, however this alone is not enough to obtain a sufficiently strong agglomerate after heating, given that these agglomerates passed the ISO T testing but failed the RDI tests. It is therefore fair to conclude that the additional agglomerate strength observed with Alcotac® FE14 arises not only from the hydrogen bonding coming from the polymer backbone but also from the sodium acrylate anionic functional groups present within this particular polymer, potentially due to salt linkages between the carboxyl groups and the metal ions present within the Recipe 1 and Recipe 2 blends. It could be further postulated that the improvements to agglomerate strength arises where higher levels of Fe_2O_3 are present in the recycling blend and that this is advantageous considering the known affiliation of polyacrylamides to oxide minerals[4].

Adsorption isotherms to determine the degree of polymer adsorption[4] can also be considered as a way forward for further investigation in conjunction with subsequent SEM-BSE analyses. The analysis should also extend into other binder systems to try and understand further how the role of different binder chemistries affects the resulting ionic bonding within the interstitial matrix of the agglomerates produced.

A mechanism for Na-Ca-O dispersion is proposed, and it would lead to the recommendation to assess new polymers with additional anionic sodium moieties on the backbone in order to ascertain whether fines generation after RDI exposure can be improved beyond what has already been observed.

Acknowledgements

John Bellwood, BASF plc, UNITED KINGDOM
Beate Fröhling, BASF SE, Ludwigshafen, GERMANY
Pascal Hervieu, Euragglo, Quiévrechain, FRANCE
Sylvain Chevron, Euragglo, Quiévrechain, FRANCE
COACH Project, Research Fund for Coal and Steel (RFCS), European Commission

5. REFERENCES

[1] https://www.researchgate.net/publication/360511775_Using_of_Adhesives_and_Binders_for_Agglomeration_of_Particle_Waste_Resources/link/627b1502b1ad9f66c8b3d23d/download

[2] https://www.researchgate.net/publication/327633282_By-products_and_waste_materials_in_steelmaking/link/5b9a9a4c92851ca9ed049bee/download

[3] https://link.springer.com/article/10.1617/s11527-013-0114-5

[4] Adsorption of Polyacrylamide on Oxide Minerals, Lee & Somasundaran, Langmuir 1989, 5, 854

[5] Influence of sintering conditions on the reduction behaviour of pure hematite compacts
K.Higuchi, R.H.Heerema

[6] Comparison of adsorption affinity of ionic polyacrylamide for the surfaces of selected metal oxides
Małgorzata Wiśniewska, Stanisław Chibowski, Teresa Urban

Institute for
Briquetting and
Agglomeration

2022 IBA CONFERENCE PAPERS

Paper Title:
Polymeric Binders for Agglomeration in Ferrous Metallurgy

Presenters:
Willy Cilengi and Dr. Aitber Bizhanov

Company:
Ex-BASF and J.C.Steele & Sons,Inc.

Polymeric Binders for Agglomeration in Ferrous Metallurgy

Willy Cilengi*; Dr Aitber Bizhanov**

*Ex-BASF, Box 2801 Halfway House, South Africa 1685, wcilengi@gmail.com. (Retired in 2021)
**J.C.Steele&Sons,Inc., 710 South Mulberry Street, Statesville, NC 28677 USA. abizhanov@jcsteele.com

Introduction

Agglomeration of natural and anthropogenic iron-containing fine raw materials plays a very important role in ferrous metallurgy, allowing the recycling of significant volumes of sludge and dust, which otherwise could lead to a significant negative impact on the environment and to the ineffective use of large areas for their disposal [1]. The most widely used industrial agglomeration technologies in ferrous metallurgy are sinter production, pelletizing and briquetting.

In two of these technologies, bonding materials play a significant role - in pelletizing and in briquetting. Bentonite is the main binder used in pelletizing. Starch and other materials such as molasses, hydrocarbons, coal and lignosulfonates may not be attractive to the indurated pellet market, which requires a stable, high-volume binder supply [2].

A wide variety of different binders (inorganic and organic) are used in briquetting. The type of inorganic binder used is largely determined by the briquetting method. Currently, the most widespread are the following main industrial briquetting technologies - roller briquetting, vibrocompression and stiff vacuum extrusion. (Figure 1). Large values of the applied pressure in roller briquetting make it difficult to use hydrated binders (cement) due to the limitations on the moisture content of the briquetted mass (no more than 5%); vibrocompression is possible only with the use of a binder showing thixotropic properties (cement); stiff vacuum extrusion allows to agglomerate wet masses (12-16%), allowing the use of hydrated binders.

The use of organic binders also has its limitations in combination with roll briquetting due to the possibility of its extrusion during pressing; there are practically no restrictions on the use of organic binders when using stiff extrusion.

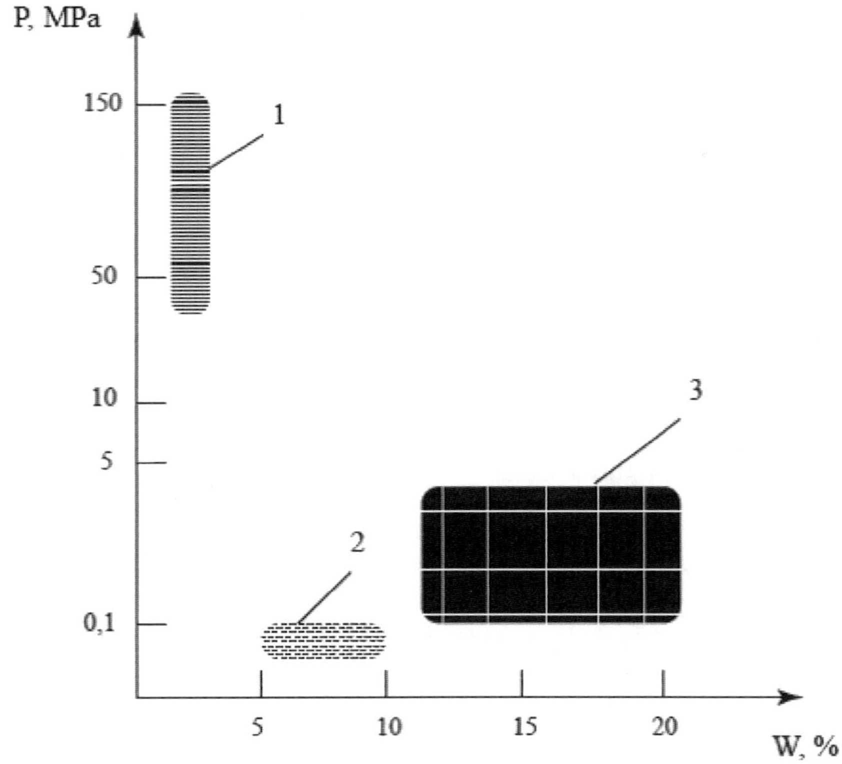

Figure 1 Comparison of technologies of briquetting according to the parameters of briquetting (applied pressure P and moisture content of the charge W). 1 - roller pressing, 2 - vibropressing, 3 – stiff vacuum extrusion

A significant drawback of most inorganic binders is that achieving the required levels of mechanical and so-called "hot" strength (the ability to maintain integrity before melting in a metallurgical furnace) requires a significant consumption of such binders. Therefore, for example, the minimum required amount of cement for the production of blast furnace and ferroalloy briquettes is rarely below 6-7%, and when using vibration compression it exceeds 10-12% of the briquette mass.

The use of polymeric BASF binders makes it possible to achieve the properties of agglomerated products required by metallurgists at a significantly lower consumption, which, as a rule, does not exceed 1% of the briquette mass. It is clear that with the same number of briquettes on the inorganic binder and on the organic BASF binder in the furnace charge, a noticeably larger amount of the leading element enters the metallurgical furnace when using BASF binders.

Comparison of other organic and inorganic binders is given in Table 1.

Table 1 Organic and Inorganic Binders comparison

BINDER TYPE	**POSITIVE FEATURES**	**DRAW-BACKS**
Bentonite	Green strength	High volumes needed. Calorific Value reduction and global ore quality is on the decline
Polyvinyl Alcohol	Waterproof when cured	Capex & Opex to run boiler as well as excessive fines produced during briquetting processes
Polymers	Strength & Waterproofing	Expensive per kilogram although cost of operation are comparable
Molasses + Lime	Cured strength	High volumes needed and can produce excessive fines.

In 1980's – 90's, Allied Colloids published patents on polyacrylamide (PAM) as organic binders. Allied Colloids evolved to become part of BASF through CIBA Holding AG acquisitions in 2009. Two main product types were developed:

- Carboxy methyl cellulose (CMC) polymers
- Anionic polyacrylamides – Alcotac® product range.

Since then BASF developed and implements effective solutions using a number of original organic polymer binders. Currently, BASF's collection of such binders includes the following grades (Table 2):

Table 2 BASF binders for agglomeration

Alcotac® Series	Application Areas	Chemical Nature
Alcotac® CB8, CB11	Nickel, Coal agglomeration	Polyacrylate, aqueous solution
Alcotac® FE14	e.g. coal, ferro-alloys, and mixed fines agglomeration	Anionic polyacrylamide
Alcotac® FE16	Iron ore pelletization	Anionic polyacrylamide blend
Alcotac® CS, CS-A	Iron ore pelletization	Modified anionic polyacrylamide blend

1. BASF solutions for Pelletizing

Bentonite as a binder makes it possible to achieve high strength of iron ore pellets due to the increased concentration of silica. However, increased concentration of bentonite dilutes the concentrate and increases the cost of hot metal production. Traditional organic binders (carboxymethylcellulose or polyacrylamides) improve the quality of the charge while decreasing the strength of the raw pellets. The mechanical properties of raw pellets achieved with bentonite have so far not been achieved with organic binders.

Over the past few years, BASF has carried out a large amount of research and made many attempts to develop new chemistry that could significantly improve the performance of organic polymers when using them. The result of these studies was the development of a new organic binder Alcotac® CS, with the help of which it is possible to replace a significant proportion of bentonite in the industrial pelletizing process of iron ore or laterite. Among its other advantages, Alcotac® CS is the only product on the market that effectively operates in conditions of high Ca and Mg salt content in the pelletizer feed.

The utilization of Alcotac® CS increases the mechanical strength of the pellets in a ratio between 2.6 and 4.2 times higher than the strength obtained with Standard HPAM binder (Alcotac® FE16, conventional partially hydrolyzed polyacrylamide). The increase in the mechanical strength of the pellets with the addition of Alcotac® CS in comparison with Standard Hydrolyzed Polyacrylamide HPAM and bentonite is illustrated in Figure 2, [3].

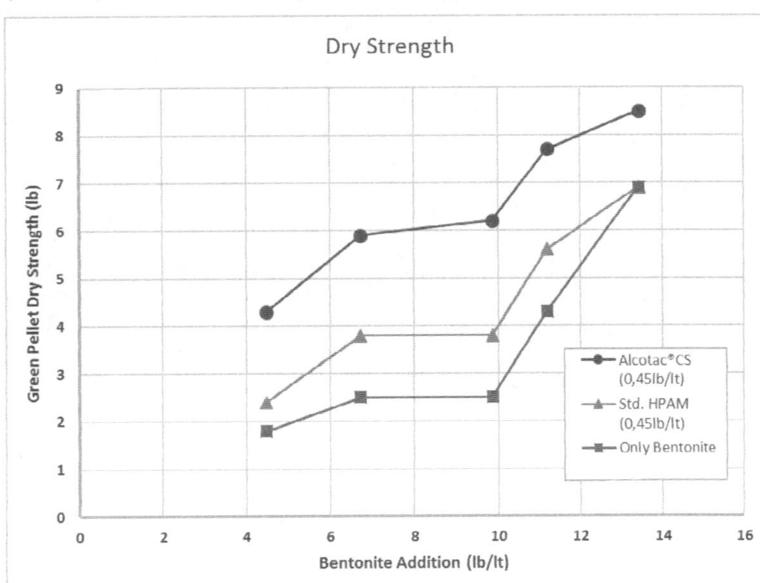

Figure 2 Dry strength of pellets obtained from agglomeration experiments [3].

The floc-type structure is also obtained like in the case of Standard HPAM. However, from the fluorescence images (right side), the degree of adsorption of the Alcotac® CS molecules are much higher than Standard HPAM and it is not only limited to the outer areas of the floc but it is found in the entire the surface of the bentonite. This unique high level of adsorption is congruent with the SEM structures and serves as a hypothesis to explain the superior mechanical properties of the pellets produced with Alcotac® CS and bentonite (Figure 3, [3]).

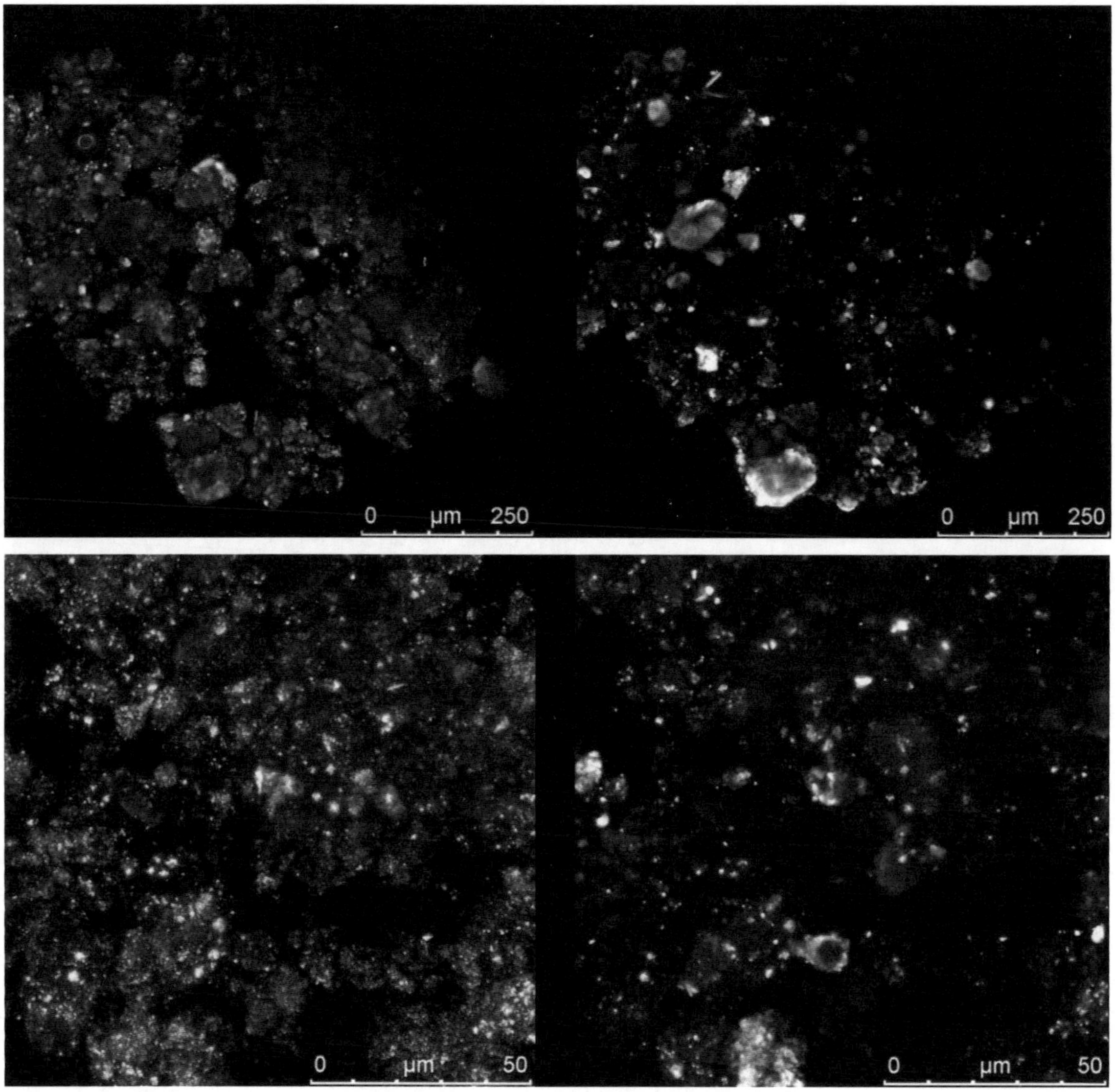

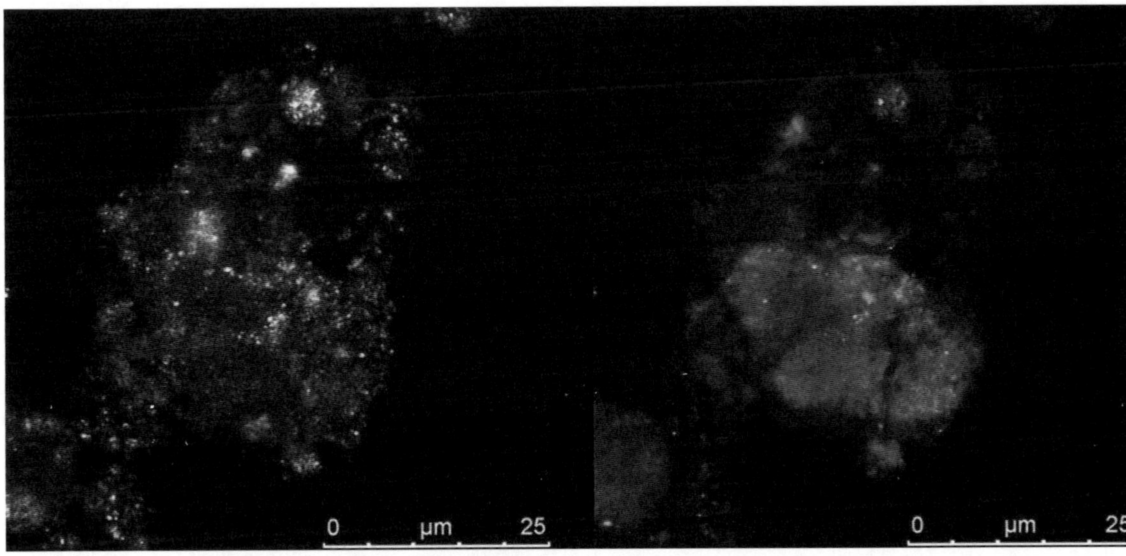

Figure 3. Confocal Laser Scanning Microscopy (CLSM) images of bentonite suspension with Alcotac® CS polymer binder added. Left: reflected light. Right: emitted fluorescence.

2. BASF solutions for Ironmaking Applications

2.1. Study Case 1

The research results have shown the high efficiency of using a BASF binder for agglomeration of iron-containing materials in relation to blast furnace (BF) production. The content of BASF binder in briquettes is 0.3% by weight. On a laboratory extruder, three BASF binders (Alcotac® CB6, Alcotac® CS and Alcotac® FE14) were used for briquetting iron ore concentrate. Bentonite (2% mass) was also added when using CS. Figure 4 shows the process of making extruded briquettes (BREX, [4]) with Alcotac® CB6 (0.3%) and the finished samples. The mechanical strength of the BREX with Alcotac® CB6 and Alcotac® FE14 reached 12-15 MPa, with Alcotac® CS - 20 MPa.

Figure 4 Experimental BREX production and finished samples

Figure 5 shows the BREX on the three mentioned binders after holding at 900 °C in the furnace. As can be seen, all the samples showed high heat resistance.

Figure 5 BREX after 5 minutes exposure at T = 900 °C

Results of the mineralogical analysis of raw and reduced at 1100 °C samples of BREX are presented in Figure 6. The analysis of mineral phases in polished sections was carried out on an automated instrumental complex MLA 650 (FEI Company), including a FEI Quanta 650 SEM scanning electron microscope equipped with an X-ray spectral microanalysis system with two detectors. The main mineral phases were determined by X-ray diffraction analysis using the analytical complex ARL 9900 Workstation IP3600 (combined design "X-ray fluorescence spectrometer with top tube position + θ-θ diffractometer").

Figure 6 Mineralogical analysis data of raw and reduced BREX sample with Alcotac®CB6. Left - raw BREX (1-iron, 2-magnetite, 3-calcium ferrite, 4-SiO_2, 5-CaO, 6-tridymite, 7-carbon); on the right - reduced briquette at a temperature of 1100 °C (1,2 - iron, 3,5 - Hematite, 4 - magnetite, 6,7 – olivine)

The Figure 7 shows that in the reduced sample, the integrity of the BREX is ensured by the formation of iron-silicate structures and a metallic framework.

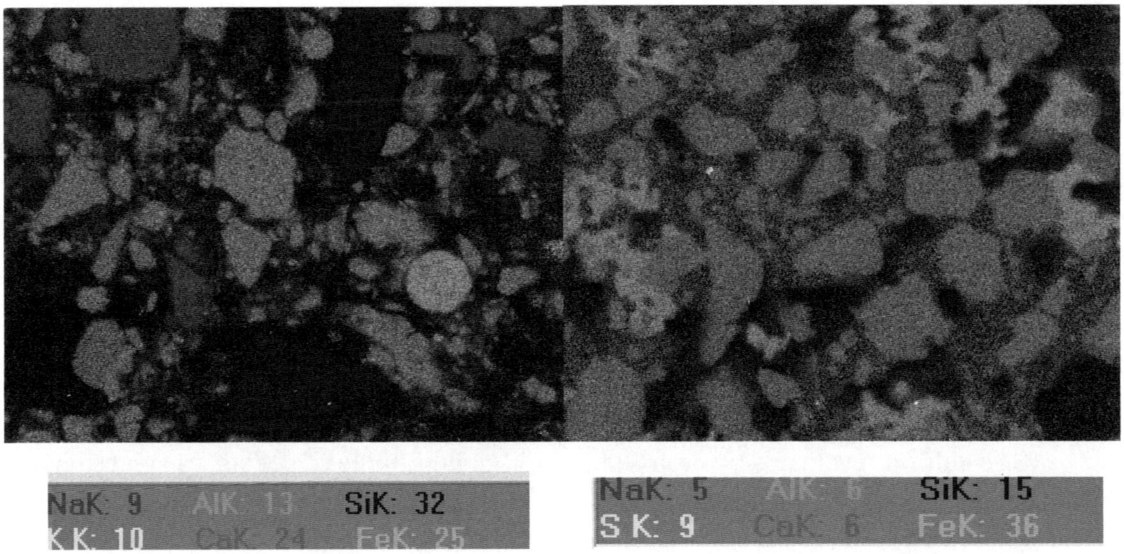

Figure 7 Raw (left) and reduced samples. Image combined in the characteristic radiation of the elements

It is known that the system CaO-FeO-SiO_2 has a eutectic (25% $CaO \cdot SiO_2$ and 75% $FeO \cdot SiO_2$) with a crystallization temperature of 1030 °C (Figure 8). There are also fields with a crystallization temperature close to 1150 °C.

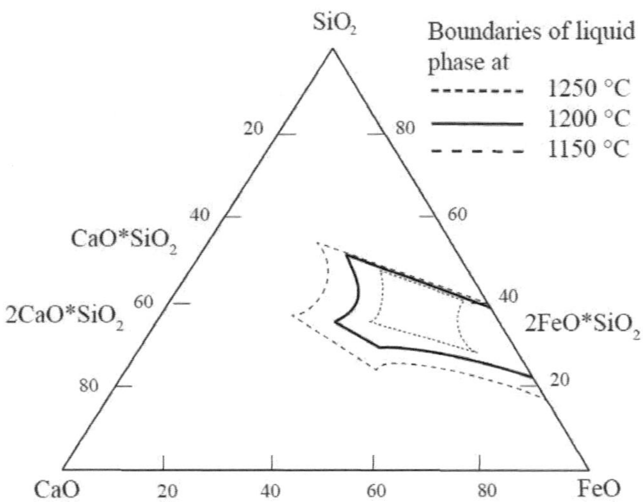

Figure 8 Phase diagram of CaO- FeO- SiO_2

Apparently, because of the limited time in the furnace at a temperature of 1150°C and above, the iron-silicate phase does not reach a liquidus temperature and remained in a plastic condition without violating the integrity of the briquette in the already established frame of metallic iron with a melting point above 1500°C.

Thus, the BASF polymer binder contributes to the preservation of the integrity of blast furnace BREX up to the moment of action of the following strengthening mechanisms - metallization and the formation of iron-silicate bonds.

2.2 Study Case 2

Due to the possibility of closing the sinter plant as part of a steel plant, a study was conducted on the feasibility of operating local blast furnaces on pellets and briquettes. In particular, the metallurgical properties of the BREX bonded by BASF Alcotac® CB6 polymer binder were studied. A minimum of 1% sodium bentonite addition was required as a plasticizer/extrusion aid. The BREX had a circular cross section of 2.5 mm in diameter and 1.5-2.0 mm in length. The average moisture content of the freshly formed BREX was 11%. The vacuum level in the working chamber of the extruder was maintained at 38-48 mm Hg. The BREX remained somewhat elastic during the testing period (up to four days).

Strength was evaluated by drop test. A 460-gram sample of pellets was placed in a sealed 25mm square plastic bag and dropped from two meters onto a steel plate five times. Then the fallen sample was sieved and the mass fraction of particles with sizes less than 5.00 mm was determined. Table 3 shows the results of the drop testing of BREX after 24 hours and four days of strengthening. Figure_ shows negligible amount of fines generated after drop testing.

Figure 9 Drop testing of experimental BREX results (left – fines generated; right – dropped samples)

Table 3 Physical-mechanical properties of BREX

Property	BREX #1	BREX #2
Wet Base Moisture (WBM), %	12.3	11.6
Density, kg/m^3	2.60	2.90
Drop strength (green), %	0.9	0.8
Compressive strength 24 hours (MPa)	1.1	1.3
Compressive strength 4 days (MPa)	1.7	2.4

These samples were also heated to 900°C, returned to ambient conditions and then observed for general appearance and integrity (Figure 10). Good thermal shock stability was demonstrated.

Figure 10 Appearance of experimental BREX (left – raw; right – partially reduced) after heating to 900°C

Tumble testing in accordance with ISO 3271: 2015 showed that the average impact strength (tumble index, TI) of BREX is not less than 85%, and abrasion resistance (abrasion index, AI) - not more than 12.3% (Table 4).

Table 4 Tumble testing results

Initial briquette weight	m_0	**grams**	15012
+ 6.30 мм	m_1	**grams**	12917
+ 500 microns	m_2	**grams**	239
- 500 microns	m_3	**grams**	1690
m_0-m_1-m_2-m_3	**d**	**grams**	166
d/m_0	**D**	%	1.1
(m_1/m_0)	**TI**	%	86.0
$(m_0-m_1-m_2)/m_0$	**AI**		12.4
		TI	86.2
		AI	12.3

The tumble test results show that the BASF binder is capable of imparting the required impact strength and abrasion resistance to blast furnace briquettes.

2.3. Study Case 3

A ferro-minerals trading company with access to over 35 million tons of low-grade magnetite (~ 53% Fe) and planning to build a processing plant to upgrade to an Fe content of over 63% has studied the agglomeration process (extrusion) using organic binders.

The material with a moisture content of 0.9% WBM was wetted to 8.5% WBM. Alcotac® FE14 and Alcotac® CB6 were selected for the tests. The mixer was charged with 12 kg of finely dispersed magnetite. While mixing, 1 kg of water was added and mixed for 3 minutes. Then 72 g of Alcotac® FE14 was added and mixed for 3 minutes. The mixture was then extruded as 18 mm diameter BREX, which were then placed in a drum that rotated 10 times for 30 seconds. Thereafter, the BREX were fired at 250 °C for 3 minutes. A batch of 12 kg was repeated 5 times.

The rate of strength gain of the BREX is from 297 N for green briquettes to 383 N after a day of aging, 652 N after three days and 1112 N after a week. After three minutes of firing at a temperature of 250 C, the strength increased to 1230 N.

Another sample on which Alcotac® CB6 was tested (0.60 % and addition of bentonite at 1 %). The green strength of the sample - 352.2 N and after 20 minutes in muffle furnace at 1100 °C strength increased to value 3214.4 N.

Figure 11 shows the green and fired samples. The samples do not blister or crack but remain in good condition.

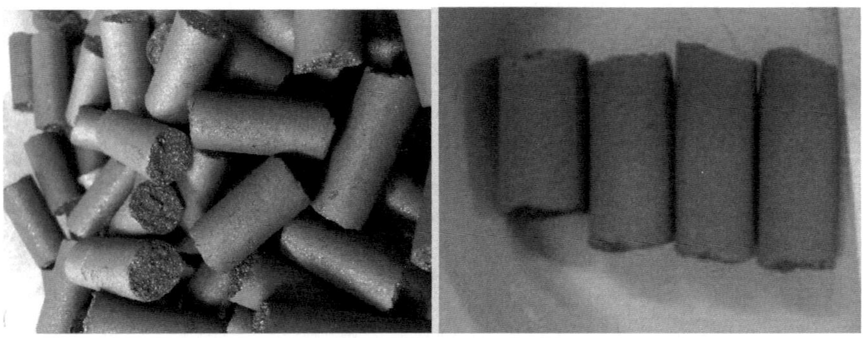

Figure 11 Green (left) and fired Magnetite BREX

3. BASF solutions for Ferroalloys Production

3.1 Study Case 4

Another study for the benefit of a mining trading company was carried out using a BASF binder for extrusion agglomeration of chrome-containing fines. The material was successfully extruded using the BASF Alcotac® FE14 at 0.2% w/w dosage and 18.3% w/w moisture. The BREX produced showed good green and dry compression strength. The hot test consisted in introducing BREX into the muffle oven at 1200 °C for 15 minutes. The BREX came out of the oven glowing, intact and stable.

The rate of compressive strength gain of the BREX is from 279 N for green briquettes to 311 N after a day of aging, 529 N after three days and 913 N after a week. Compressive strength after 2 weeks reached values of 1128 N and 1837 N after three weeks hardening. After only three minutes of firing at 250 °C, the strength of green BREX increased to 1230 N. A quick hot test performed on BREX at 1200 °C after Day 14 in a muffle oven showed BREX glowing, stable and intact. The compressive strength of the BREX extracted from the furnace was 2526.44 N.

The 12 figure shows the appearance of briquettes when tested for thermal stability and immediately after being removed from the oven.

Figure 12 Appearance of the BREX during thermal stability testing (left) and after extraction from the furnace

Cured BREX were placed in water in a beaker for 24 hours. They were removed from water, weighed again and showed no mass increase or loss.

Conclusions

The study cases as elaborated above have demonstrated the possibility for efficient usage of the BASF organic binders in the ferrous metallurgy. The usage of BASF organic binders can be combined or complimented with inorganic binders such as sodium bentonite or other materials to increase thermal stability and to improve the behavior in the furnace (slagging and easing of different metallization phases). The low dosage of BASF organic binders required in the ferrous material, increase the charge of desired material into the furnace, which indicates there is an economic benefit to be obtained.

References

1. A. Bizhanov, V. Chizhikova Agglomeration in Metallurgy. Springer, Berlin, 2020, p 454

2. T. C. Eisele, S. K. Kawatra A Review of Binders in Iron Ore Pelletization. Mineral Processing & Extractive Metall. Rev., 24: 1-90, 2003

3. A. Villanueva, S. Hoff, A. Michailovski: Novel Binder Technology from BASF: Study of Bentonite Modification. SME Annual Meeting Feb. 25-28, 2018, Minneapolis, MN

4. BREX. Certificate of trademark (service mark) No. 498006, application No. 2012706053 of 02.03.2012. Right holder AM Bizhanov. (in Russian)

Institute for Briquetting and Agglomeration

2022 IBA CONFERENCE PAPERS

Paper Title:

Using Automotive Paint Sludge as a Binder for Pelletizing Magnetite Ore

Presenters:

Dr. Victoria Vaccarezza and Dr. Corby Anderson

Company:

Kroll Institute for Extractive Metallurgy

Center for Resource Recovery and Recycling Colorado School of Mines

Using Automotive Paint Sludge as a Binder for Pelletizing Magnetite Ore

Dr. Victoria Vaccarezza and Dr. Corby Anderson

Kroll Institute for Extractive Metallurgy

Center for Resource Recovery and Recycling
Colorado School of Mines

ABSTRACT

Due to environmental and economic concerns, there has been a large push to investigate recycling applications for automotive paint sludge. Automotive paint sludge is considered a nuisance and hazardous waste material within the automotive industry around the world. The focus of this project was to investigate and develop a recycling application that would employ the use of the automotive paint sludge material as received. The paint sludge was used as a binder for iron ore pellets, typically used for iron- and steelmaking. The development of the type of recycling application conducted during this project was aided by a review of different binders used in iron ore pellets, as well as the various techniques used to recycle automotive paint sludge materials.

Two different paint sludge samples were characterized for their organic and inorganic components. It was then determined to be a possible substitute for the standard iron ore pellet binder: bentonite clay. Unlike bentonite, paint sludge has half the concentration of silica and alumina, which are detriments in the ironmaking process. Iron ore pellets were made using magnetite ore, 1.0 – 3.0 wt.% limestone, 0.0 – 1.0 wt.% bentonite, and 0.0 – 1.0 wt.% paint sludge from two different paint shops. The pellet recipes were evaluated via a statistical analysis software where low, middle and high material weight percentages were output to ensure optimized results. The iron ore pellets with paint sludge material as a binder were then tested for their standard physical and chemical properties to make sure they were comparable to pellets made with bentonite clay.

It was concluded via the physical and chemical property tests that iron ore pellet made with paint sludge material with this patent pending technology were just as capable of withstanding typical transportation and handling used in the iron- and steelmaking industries.

INTRODUCTION

Automotive paint sludge is a by-product of overspray in the painting booths. Paint sludge is either water-based or solvent-based, however, both types contain a combination of inorganic and organic material. The designation of waterborne or solvent-based depends on the type of paint material, i.e., if the paint is contained in a water base, it is waterborne. Both types of paint sludge consist of uncured polymer resins, metal-containing pigments, curing agents, flotation agents, detackifiers and water. Waterborne paint sludge has been promoted as the environmentally friendly option in comparison, but the entire vehicle painting process does still rely on organic materials. It is for this reason the generation of automotive paint sludge, regardless of its base, is considered one of the largest contributors of hazardous waste in the automotive industry [1].

However, the new millennia also brought new environmental concerns across all industries, as well as increases in fees for the storage of hazardous material. In response, the automotive industry has become the leader in promoting zero waste [2]. This has also led many, if not all, automotive companies to seek other techniques for recycling their paint sludge. Previous research methods include attempting to extract valuable metals or utilizing it for construction materials.

Iron ore pellets are used in the steel making process with bentonite clay as the current industry standard binder. This investigation seeks to develop comparable iron ore pellets with a paint sludge binder by employing similar testing techniques used for traditional iron ore pellets.

In addition to the experimental results presented, the implications of these results will be discussed as they relate to the two major ironmaking methods: blast furnace and direct reduction. The blast furnace is considered an indirect reduction of iron in combination with a converter, while direct reduction produces direct reduced iron (DRI) [5] It is critical to examine how the use of a different iron ore pellet binder affects the ironmaking process in both the blast furnace and direct reduction processes since each has differences in feed requirements and allowances.

MATERIALS AND METHODS

A 2^n half-factorial design was chosen for this project due to insufficient raw materials for the experiments. "n" is the number of controllable factors included in the experiment by the user. The controllable factors included weight percent addition of paint sludge, weight percent addition of bentonite, weight percent addition of limestone, temperature of induration and time of induration. The values of each factor were chosen based on current industry values, the literature review as well as the project's experimental need. Inputting the information into Stat-Ease, the following DOE was produced shown in Table 1.

Table 1. Design of experiments for iron ore pellets with paint sludge binder.

	Factor 1: Temperature (Celsius)	Factor 2: Paint Sludge addition (wt. %)	Factor 3: Bentonite addition (wt. %)	Factor 4: Limestone addition (wt. %)	Factor 5: Induration Time (minutes)
High	1150	1.0	1.0	3.0	90
Mid	1010	0.5	0.5	1.5	60
Low	870	0.0	0.0	0.0	30

Table 2. Half- Factorial Design Order for Batch 1 of Paint Sludge.

Run	Factor 1: Temperature (Celsius)	Factor 2: Paint Sludge addition (wt. %)	Factor 3: Bentonite addition (wt. %)	Factor 4: Limestone addition (wt. %)	Factor 5: Induration Time (minutes)
1	1150	1	0	0	90
2	1010	0.5	0.5	1.5	60
3	870	0	1	3	90
4	1150	0	0	3	90
5	870	1	1	3	30
6	1150	0	1	3	30
7	870	0	0	3	30
8	870	1	0	3	90
9	1150	0	1	0	90
10	870	0	1	0	30
11	870	1	1	0	90
12	1150	1	1	3	90
13	1010	0.5	0.5	1.5	60
14	1010	0.5	0.5	1.5	60
15	1150	0	0	0	30
16	1150	1	1	0	30
17	870	0	0	0	90
18	1150	1	0	3	30
19	870	1	0	0	30

As seen in Table 2, a total of 19 runs were done for the first batch of paint sludge. A second sample was labeled as batch 2 of paint sludge and the half-factorial design is presented in Table 3. This presented with another set of 19 runs, totaling 38 between both samples of paint sludge. Runs 1 – 19 represent batch 1, while runs 20 – 38 represent batch 2.

Table 3. Half-Factorial Design Order for Batch 2 of Paint Sludge.

Run	Factor 1: Temperature (Celsius)	Factor 2: Paint Sludge addition (wt. %)	Factor 3: Bentonite addition (wt. %)	Factor 4: Limestone addition (wt. %)	Factor 5: Induration Time (minutes)
20	1150	1	0	0	90
21	1010	0.5	0.5	1.5	60
22	870	0	1	3	90
23	1150	0	0	3	90
24	870	1	1	3	30
25	1150	0	1	3	30
26	870	0	0	3	30
27	870	1	0	3	90
28	1150	0	1	0	90
29	870	0	1	0	30
30	870	1	1	0	90
31	1150	1	1	3	90
32	1010	0.5	0.5	1.5	60
33	1010	0.5	0.5	1.5	60
34	1150	0	0	0	30
35	1150	1	1	0	30
36	870	0	0	0	90
37	1150	1	0	3	30
38	870	1	0	0	30

The responses for this study are shown in Table 4 for all the runs done.

Table 4. Responses for half-factorial design order.

Runs 1 – 38	Response 1: Green Crushing Strength (Newtons)	Response 2: Cold Crushing Strength (CCS) (Newtons)	Response 3: Drop Test (Number of drops until fracture)	Response 4: Apparent Porosity (%)	Response 6: Percent Reduction (%)

Based on the information from the design of experiments, a variety of magnetite, paint sludge, bentonite and limestone combinations were given. The combinations include:

- 0 wt.% paint sludge, 0 wt.% bentonite, 0 wt.% limestone, and 100 wt.% magnetite ore.
- 0 wt.% paint sludge, 1 wt.% bentonite, 0 wt.% limestone, and 99 wt.% magnetite ore.
- 0 wt.% paint sludge, 0 wt.% bentonite, 3 wt.% limestone, and 97 wt.% magnetite ore.
- 0 wt.% paint sludge, 1 wt.% bentonite, 3 wt.% limestone, and 96 wt.% magnetite ore.
- 0.5 wt.% paint sludge, 0.5 wt.% bentonite, 1.5 wt.% limestone, and 97.5 wt.% magnetite ore.
- 1 wt.% paint sludge, 0 wt.% bentonite, 0 wt.% limestone, and 99 wt.% magnetite ore.
- 1 wt.% paint sludge, 1 wt.% bentonite, 0 wt.% limestone, and 98 wt.% magnetite ore.
- 1 wt.% paint sludge, 0 wt.% bentonite, 3 wt.% limestone, and 96 wt.% magnetite ore.
- 1 wt.% paint sludge, 1 wt.% bentonite, 3 wt.% limestone, and 95 wt.% magnetite ore.

Figure 1. Combination of materials: paint sludge (gray), magnetite ore (black) and limestone (white).

First, the materials were combined and mixed in a Tupperware™ container. A spray bottle is also used to moisten the materials. About 15 – 25 sprays per 100 grams of total material, which equals to about 1 – 1.5 mL of water for the specific spray bottle used in this project. This provided just enough water to wet the material but not enough to overly saturate it. A small amount of material was then taken and rolled into a sphere between the palms of the hand as shown in Figure 1. As described in the literature review, pellets used in the DRI and blast furnace ironmaking processes are between 9 and 16 mm in diameter and the same diameter range was used in this project as well. About 15 – 20 green pellets were made from 100 grams of material. This procedure was repeated for all the combinations of paint sludge, bentonite, limestone and magnetite ore provided above. After the green pellets were made, they were dried in a furnace for 12 hours at 100°C. After drying, the pellets are considered *dry pellets* and placed in a furnace for induration. Based on the design of experiments, specific combinations were fired at different temperatures and times. Pellets with the following combinations of materials were fired at 870°C for 30 minutes:

- 0 wt.% paint sludge, 0 wt.% bentonite, 3 wt.% limestone, and 97 wt.% magnetite ore.
- 0 wt.% paint sludge, 1 wt.% bentonite, 0 wt.% limestone, and 99 wt.% magnetite ore.
- 1 wt.% paint sludge, 1 wt.% bentonite, 3 wt.% limestone, and 95 wt.% magnetite ore.
- 1 wt.% paint sludge, 0 wt.% bentonite, 0 wt.% limestone, and 99 wt.% magnetite ore.

Pellets with the following combinations of materials were fired at 870°C for 90 minutes:

- 0 wt.% paint sludge, 1 wt.% bentonite, 3 wt.% limestone, and 96 wt.% magnetite ore.
- 0 wt.% paint sludge, 0 wt.% bentonite, 0 wt.% limestone, and 100 wt.% magnetite ore.
- 1 wt.% paint sludge, 0 wt.% bentonite, 3 wt.% limestone, and 96 wt.% magnetite ore.
- 1 wt.% paint sludge, 1 wt.% bentonite, 0 wt.% limestone, and 98 wt.% magnetite ore.

The next set of pellets were fired at 1010°C for 60 minutes for the following combination of materials:

- 0.5 wt.% paint sludge, 0.5 wt.% bentonite, 1.5 wt.% limestone, and 97.5 wt.% magnetite ore.

Pellets with the following combination of materials were fired at 1150°C for 30 minutes:

- 0 wt.% paint sludge, 1 wt.% bentonite, 3 wt.% limestone, and 96 wt.% magnetite ore.
- 0 wt.% paint sludge, 0 wt.% bentonite, 0 wt.% limestone, and 100 wt.% magnetite ore.
- 1 wt.% paint sludge, 1 wt.% bentonite, 0 wt.% limestone, and 98 wt.% magnetite ore.
- 1 wt.% paint sludge, 0 wt.% bentonite, 3 wt.% limestone, and 96 wt.% magnetite ore.

Finally, pellets with the following combination of materials were fired at 1150°C for 90 minutes:

- 1 wt.% paint sludge, 0 wt.% bentonite, 0 wt.% limestone, and 99 wt.% magnetite ore.
- 0 wt.% paint sludge, 0 wt.% bentonite, 3 wt.% limestone, and 97 wt.% magnetite ore.
- 0 wt.% paint sludge, 1 wt.% bentonite, 0 wt.% limestone, and 99 wt.% magnetite ore.
- 1 wt.% paint sludge, 1 wt.% bentonite, 3 wt.% limestone, and 96 wt.% magnetite ore.

TEST METHODS

When the green pellets were initially made, a drop test was conducted. Drop tests reveal how well the dry and fired pellets will handle transportation during the industrial pelletization process.

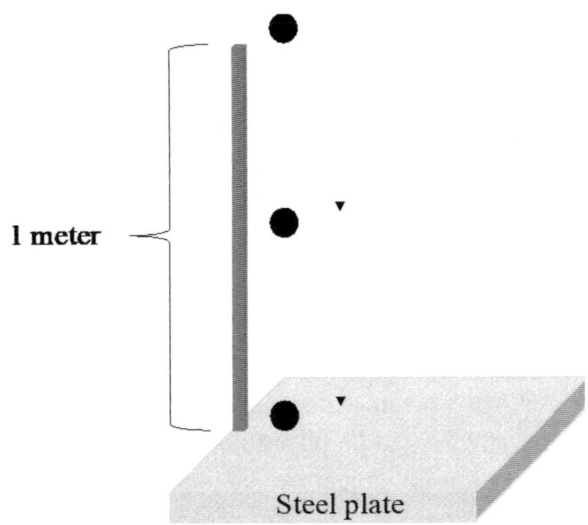

Figure 2. Schematic representation of drop test.

The pellets were dropped from one meter, measured using a meter stick, onto a steel plate until, counting the number of drops until they fracture. Figure 2 shows a schematic diagram of the drop test setup. From each combination set, 5 pellets were tested from batch 1 and batch 2 resulting in a total of 90 dry pellets. The average value of each set of 5 was recorded as the drop number for that specific material combination. 5 fired pellets from each of the material combinations for 870°C for 30 and 90 minutes, 1010°C for 60 minutes, and 1150°C for 30 and 90 minutes, were tested and the average drop number was recorded. This was done for batch 1 and batch 2 pellets, resulting in a total of 170 fired pellets tested.

The compressive strength tests were done in accordance with the ASTM E382-20 Standard Test Method for Determination of Crushing Strength of Iron Ore Pellets and Direct-Reduced Iron. This standard test method is similar to the ISO 4700 standard for cold crushing of iron ore pellets. The crushing strength of an iron ore pellet is determined by applying a load to a pellet at a specific speed until the pellet is fractured.

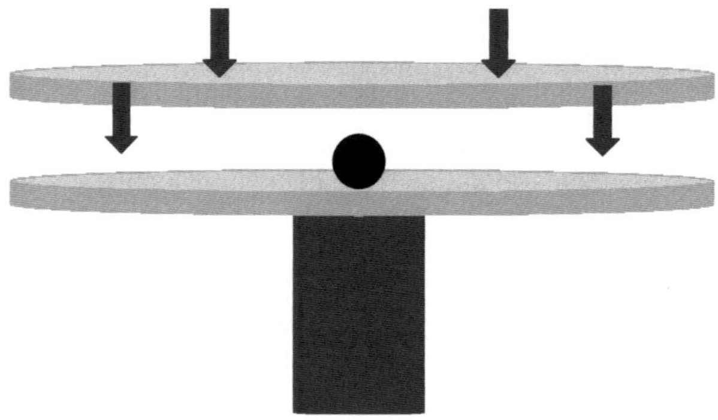

Figure 3. Schematic diagram of compressive plates and pellet.

This compression test was done for all the dry pellets made from each of the 9 material combinations. From each combination set, 5 pellets were tested from each resulting in a total of 90 dry pellets. The average value of each set of 5 was recorded as the crushing strength for that specific material combination. Since the fired pellets were indurated at different temperatures and times, 5 fired pellets from each of the material combinations for 870°C for 30 and 90 minutes, 1010°C for 60 minutes, and 1150°C for 30 and 90 minutes, were tested and the average was recorded. This was done for batch 1 and batch 2 pellets, resulting in a total of 170 fired pellets tested.

The procedure used to calculate the apparent porosity of fired pellets is the ASTM C20-00(2015) Standard Test Methods for Apparent Porosity, Water Absorption, Apparent Specific Gravity, and Bulk Density of Burned Refractory Brick and Shapes by Boiling Water [85]. Apparent porosity is the percentage ratio of the void space in a sample to the total bulk volume of the sample. Equation 3 describes the calculation of apparent porosity, W_{sat} is the weight of saturated sample, W_{dry} is the weight of the sample in air, and W_{sus} is the weight of sample suspended in water.

$$\textbf{Apparent Porosity}, \% = \frac{\mathbf{W_{sat} - W_{dry}}}{\mathbf{W_{sat} - W_{sus}}} \times \mathbf{100} \qquad \textit{Equation 1}$$

Determination of the dry weight is done by weighing the pellets with a scale in air, however, the pellets must have been dried in a furnace above 105°C. Since these pellets were fired, they were just weighed after induration. Four pellets were placed in the metal cage at a time. The metal cage was suspended from a watch glass. The cage was dropped into a beaker of boiling water and kept there for two hours. The pellets did not touch the bottom of the beaker and the watch glass did not allow for a lot of evaporation, so the metal cage was suspended in water for the duration of the two hours. A representation of the setup is shown in Figure 4.

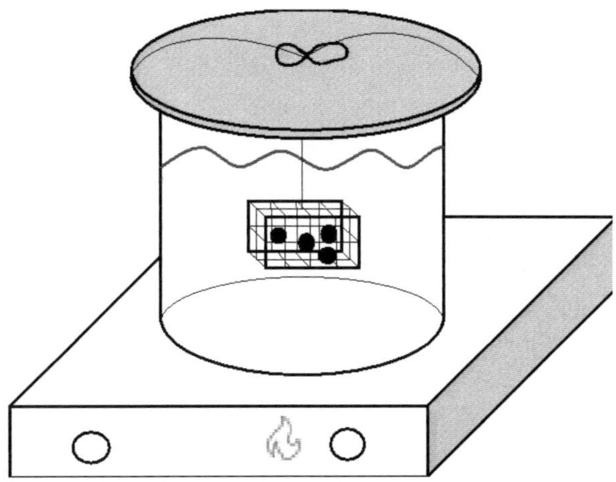

Figure 4. Schematic diagram on saturation process.

While the pellets are boiling, the air in the pores expand and are partially substituted by water. While the water and pellets are cooling, some of that water may stay within the pores, but the air that remained in the pores contracts, causing a negative pressure or vacuum. This vacuum is the driving force for the fluid to enter the pores. After the pellets were boiled, they were brought to room temperature while still suspended in the beaker, completely covered in water for about twelve hours. After twelve hours, they were weighed and recorded as the suspended weight. The saturation weight is determined after the suspended weight by blotting the pellets to remove any excess water on the surface of the pellets.

Reduction testing were conducted on the pellets. Figure 5 shows a representation of the tube furnace and sample setup.

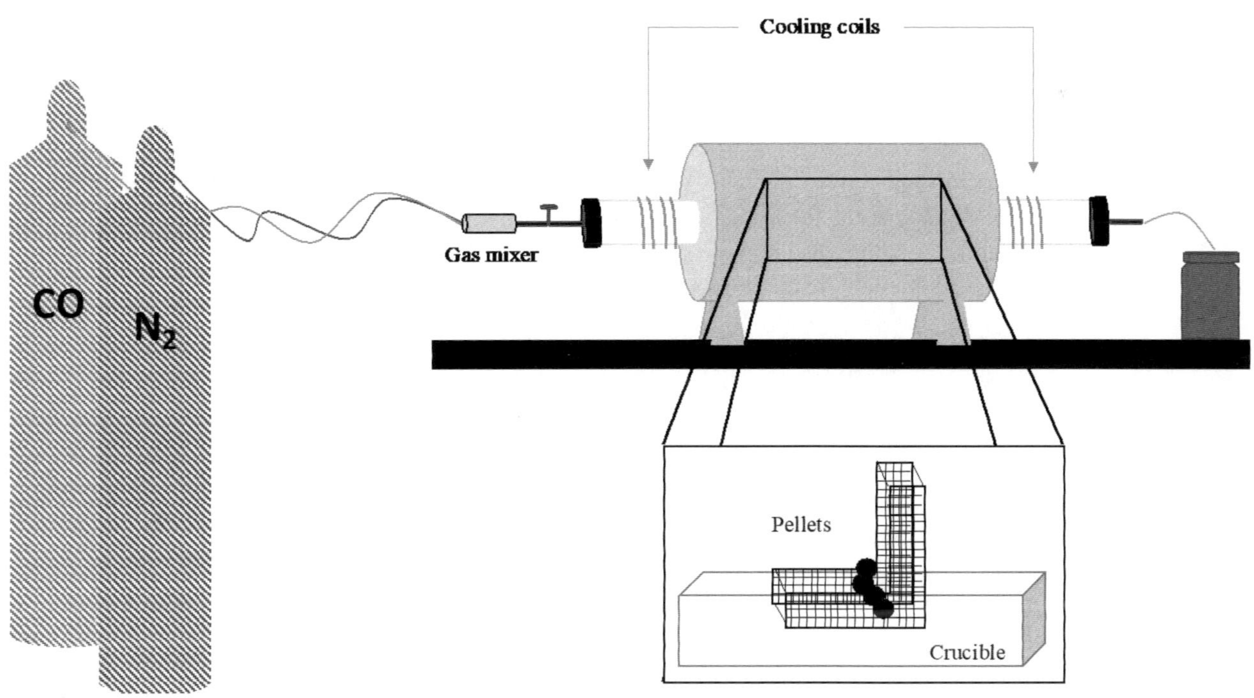

Figure 5. Tube furnace and sample setup for reduction tests.

The procedure involved reducing the pellets determined by the factorial design for batch 1 and batch 2 pellets. Four to five pellets at a time were placed on the metal mesh and then into the tube furnace. The furnace was heated to 950°C with 50 – 60 mL/min of nitrogen gas flowing. Once the furnace reached the desired temperature, the carbon monoxide gas was opened and increased to a flow rate of 150 mL/min. The nitrogen gas was also increased to 100 mL/min. Both gases were kept at this rate for one hour. The carbon monoxide was slowly shut off and the nitrogen gas flow was decreased to 50 mL/min while the furnace was cooled down. After the furnace was cooled, the pellets were taken out, weighed and their diameter's measured and recorded. A total of 38 pellets were reduced by this procedure.

RESULTS

Table 5 shows the crushing strength values in increasing order for dry and fired pellets made from the paint sludge sample from batch 1. As seen in the table, the biggest indicator of increased cold crushing strength is increased temperature. Most of the values of cold crushing strength above 250 kg/pellet were seen in pellets indurated at 1010°C and 1150°C. They were also left at that induration temperature for 60 minutes or longer. The type of pellets that pass the 250 kg/pellet threshold are the following:

- 1 wt.% paint sludge, 1 wt.% bentonite, and 0 wt.% limestone
- 1 wt.% paint sludge, 1 wt.% bentonite, and 3 wt.% limestone
- 0 wt.% paint sludge, 1 wt.% bentonite, and 3 wt.% limestone
- 0.5 wt.% paint sludge, 0.5 wt.% bentonite, and 1.5 wt.% limestone
- 1 wt.% paint sludge, 0 wt.% bentonite, and 3 wt.% limestone
- 0 wt.% paint sludge, 0 wt.% bentonite, and 0 wt.% limestone
- 1 wt.% paint sludge, 0 wt.% bentonite, and 0 wt.% limestone

Some of this material combinations can also be found in Table 5 to not pass the crushing strength threshold and that is due to low temperature of 870°C and short induration time.

The question driving this research was if waterborne automotive paint sludge could replace all or some of the bentonite additions made when producing iron ore pellets. Based on the data in Table 21, 0.5PS_0.5B_1.5LS, 1PS_0B_3LS, and 1PS_0B_0LS pellet types prove this to be possible with the paint sludge from batch 1. The pellet type 0PS_0B_0LS is interesting because at 1150°C for 30 minutes, it does not pass the crushing strength threshold, however, kept at that temperature for 90 minutes, the cold crushing strength increases from 249 to 254. This may be due to the small amounts the bentonite phase found in the AMICS analysis of the magnetite ore sample.

Table 6. Batch 1 pellet dry and cold crushing strength.

Pellet Type	Temperature (Celsius)	Time (minutes)	Dry Crushing Strength (kg/pellet)	Cold Crushing Strength (kg/pellet)
0PS-0B-0LS	870	90	12	197
0PS-0B-3LS	870	30	11	210
0PS-1B-0LS	870	30	12	219
1PS-0B-0LS	870	30	13	219
0PS-1B-3LS	870	90	10	240
1PS-0B-3LS	870	90	12	245
0PS-0B-0LS	1150	30	26	249
1PS-1B-0LS	870	30	11	253
1PS-1B-3LS	870	30	13	254
0PS-1B-3LS	1150	30	21	254
0PS-1B-0LS	1150	90	27	254
1PS-1B-0LS	1150	90	14	259
0.5PS-0.5B-1.5LS	1010	60	23	259
1PS-0B-3LS	1150	30	28	261
0.5PS-0.5B-1.5LS	1010	60	21	264
0PS-0B-3LS	1150	90	26	265
0.5PS-0.5B-1.5LS	1010	60	20	268
1PS-0B-0LS	1150	90	29	269
1PS-1B-3LS	115	90	23	284

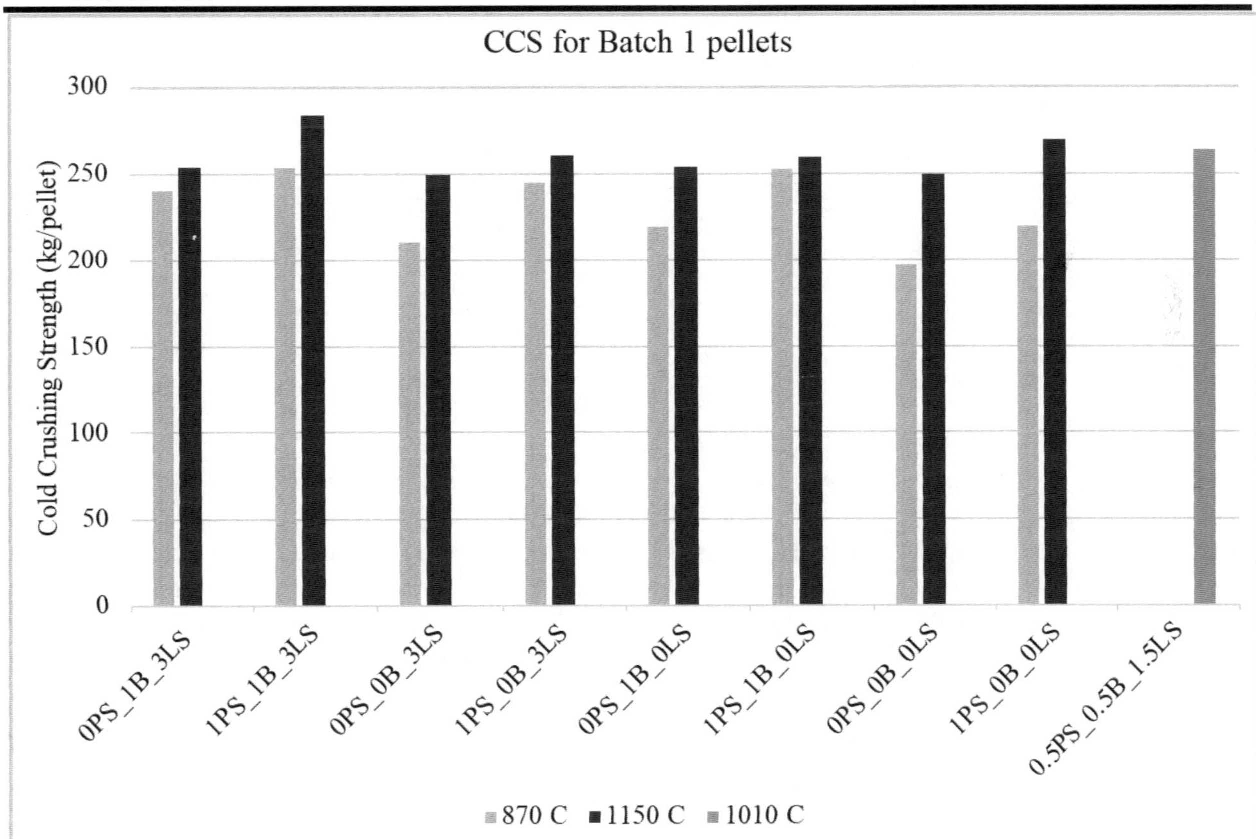

Figure 6. Cold Crushing Strength (CCS) for batch 1 pellets.

Figure 6 shows another representation of how different temperatures affect the cold crushing strength of pellets of the same material combinations. In all pellet type combinations, an increase in temperature increases the cold crushing strength. Pellet type 0.5PS_0.5B_1.5LS only shows one value of cold crushing strength because it was solely indurated at 1010°C, while the other pellet types were indurated at both 870°C and 1150°C.

A comparison between the crushing strength of dry and fired pellet types are shown in Figure 7 and Figure 8, for pellets fired at 870°C and 1150°C, respectively.

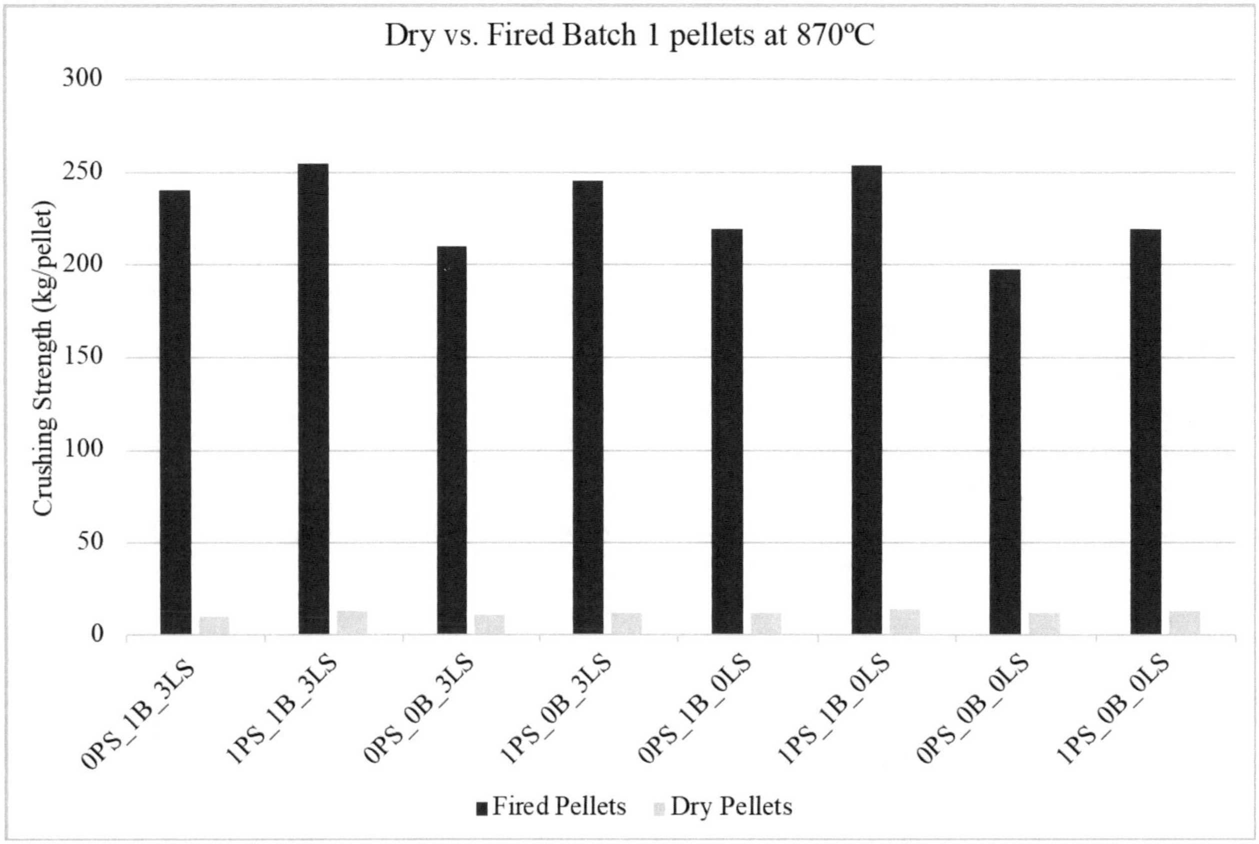

Figure 7. Crushing Strength of Dry vs. Fired Batch 1 Pellets at 870C.

These figures highlight the differences in chemical and physical strengthening mechanisms occurring while the pellet is exposed to different temperatures. A dry pellet is dried at 100°C and is considered more fragile than green pellets because the capillary forces that held the green pellets together are now gone due to water evaporation. The water evaporation leaves the dry pellets mechanically weakened, and it may be argued that the plasticity behavior once present in the green pellets is now gone. As shown in Figure 7 and Figure 8, the dry crushing strength values are significantly lower compared to those fired at 870°C and 1150°C. However, once the pellets have been indurated, they do become mechanically stronger but for different reasons at the two temperatures. Pellets indurated at 870°C become denser due to the phase change occurring during the oxidation from magnetite to hematite. On the other hand, pellets indurated at 1150°C are shown to have higher crushing strength values because of sintering effects. Sintering in iron ore pellets occurs above 1000°C and is a major contributor to the strength of iron ore pellets.

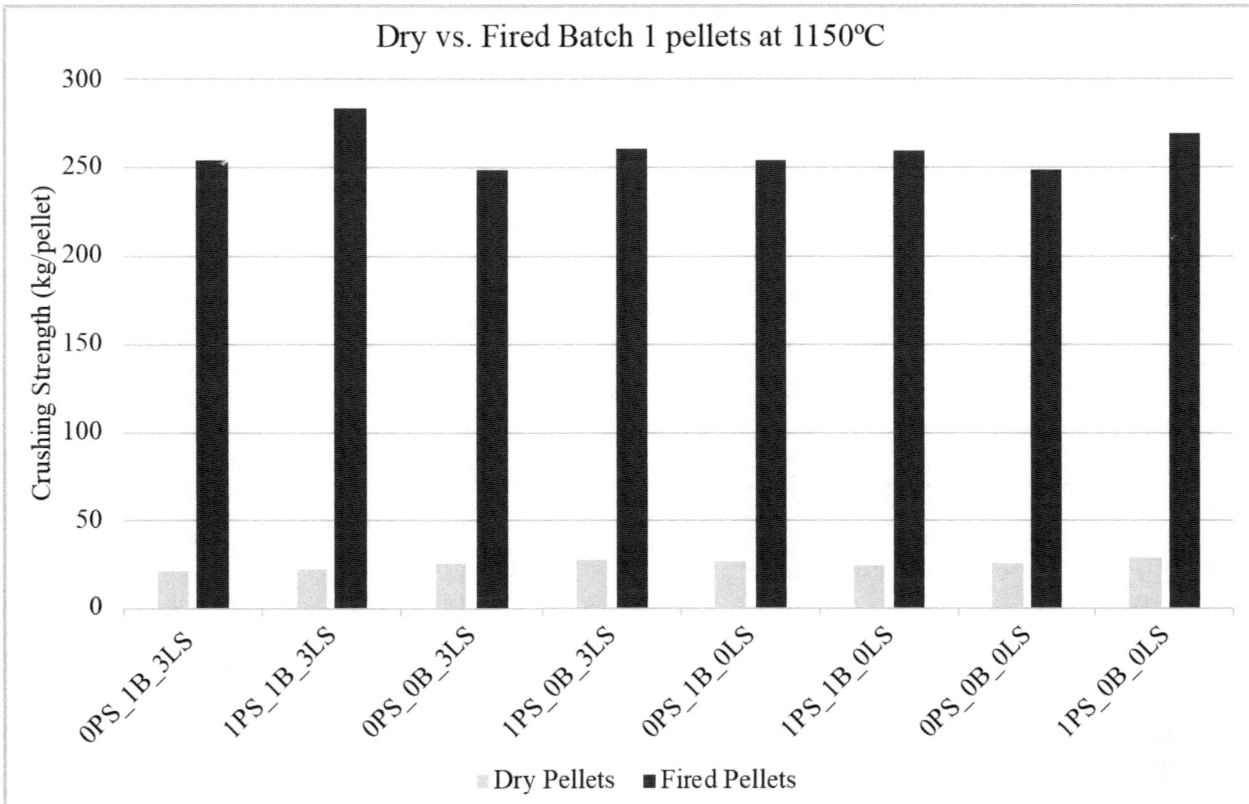

Figure 8. Crushing Strength of Dry vs. Fired Batch 1 Pellets at 1150C.

Crushing Strength Test Results for Batch 2 Pellets

Table 8 shows the dry and cold crushing strength values for both dry and fired pellets in increasing cold crushing strength values. As mentioned before, increased temperature is shown to be the biggest indicator of increased pellet cold crushing strength.

The same 250 kg/pellet crushing strength threshold was applied to Table 8 and it shows the following pellet type combinations as passing that value:

- 0.5 wt.% paint sludge, 0.5 wt.% bentonite, and 1.5 wt.% limestone
- 1 wt.% paint sludge, 1 wt.% bentonite, and 0 wt.% limestone
- 1 wt.% paint sludge, 0 wt.% bentonite, and 0 wt.% limestone
- 1 wt.% paint sludge, 0 wt.% bentonite, and 3 wt.% limestone
- 0 wt.% paint sludge, 1 wt.% bentonite, and 0 wt.% limestone
- 1 wt.% paint sludge, 1 wt.% bentonite, and 3 wt.% limestone

Some of these pellet type combinations are also seen in Table 8 to have crushing strength values below 250 kg/pellet, but those are due to their low induration temperature of 870°C. All the pellets that had crushing strength values over 250 kg/pellet were indurated at 1010°C or 1150°C for 60 minutes or 90 minutes. Figure 9 is another representation of this as it shows the cold crushing strength increase with increased temperature for pellets of the same material combination.

Table 8. Batch 2 pellets dry and cold crushing strength.

Pellet Type	Temperature (Celsius)	Time (minutes)	Dry Crushing Strength (kg/pellet)	Cold Crushing Strength (kg/pellet)
0PS-0B-0LS	870	90	12	190
1PS-1B-3LS	870	30	13	200
0PS-0B-3LS	870	30	11	213
1PS-0B-0LS	870	30	13	214
0PS-1B-0LS	870	30	12	221
1PS-1B-0LS	870	30	11	228
0PS-0B-0LS	1150	30	26	230
1PS-0B-3LS	870	90	12	245
0PS-1B-3LS	870	90	10	249
0PS-0B-3LS	1150	90	26	249
0.5PS-0.5B-1.5LS	1010	60	23	262
1PS-1B-0LS	1150	90	14	264
1PS-0B-0LS	1150	90	29	265
0.5PS-0.5B-1.5LS	1010	60	20	268
1PS-0B-3LS	1150	30	28	270
0.5PS-0.5B-1.5LS	1010	60	21	273
0PS-1B-0LS	1150	90	27	276
1PS-1B-3LS	1150	30	13	278
1PS-1B-3LS	1150	90	23	284

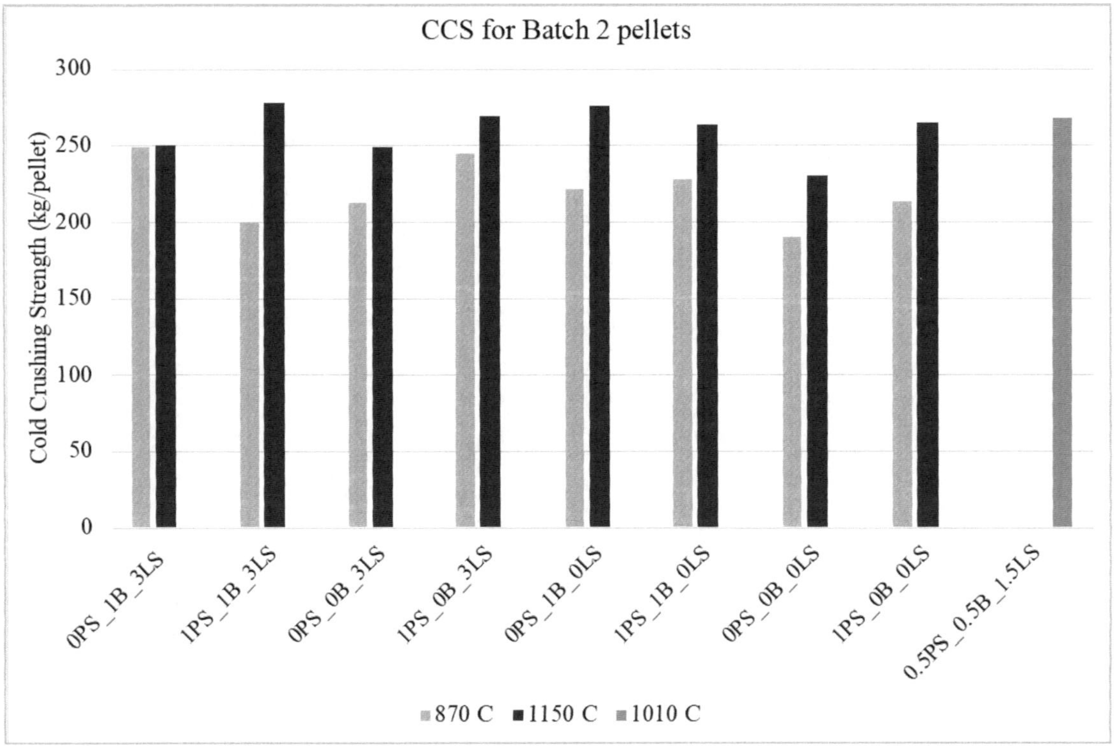

Figure 9. Cold Crushing Strength for Batch 2 pellets.

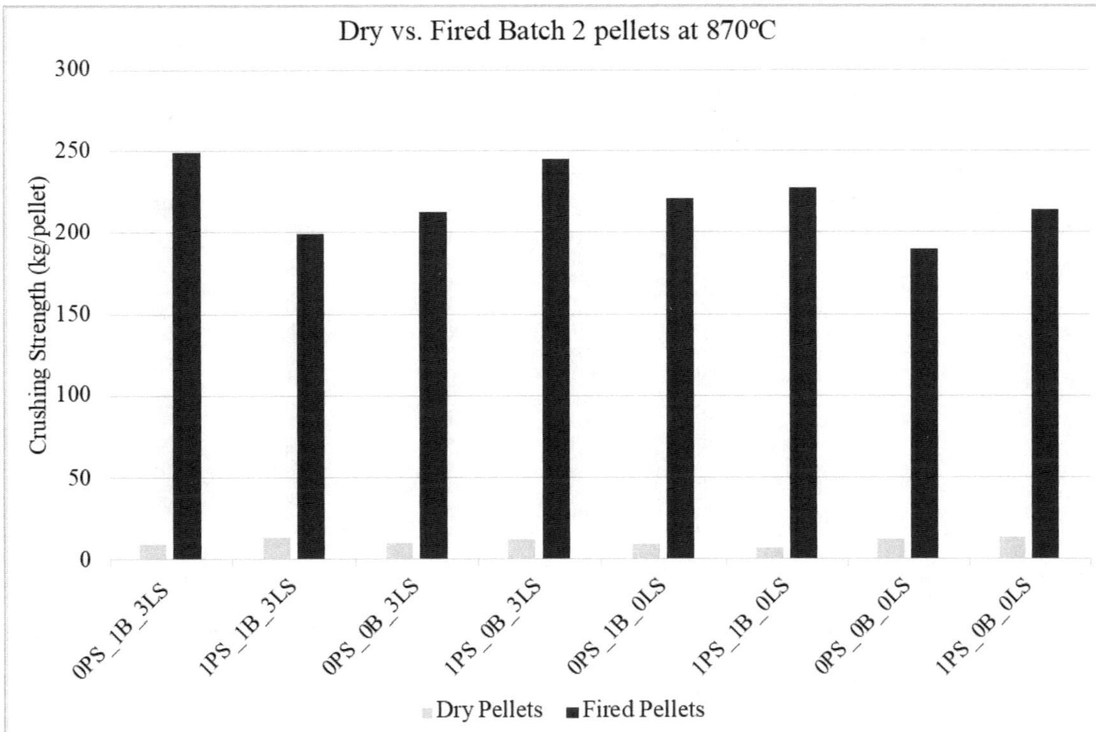

Figure 10. Crushing Strength for Dry vs. Fired Batch 2 Pellets at 870C.

Figure 10 and Figure 11show the crushing strength for dry and fired pellets indurated at 870°C and 1150°C, respectively. As mentioned in the previous section, differences in dry and cold crushing strength are most likely due to water evaporation in the dry pellets and the formation of denser hematite pellets at 870°C. Of course, as the temperature increased to 1150°C, sintering effects begin to substantially strengthen the pellets compared to what is seen at 870°C.

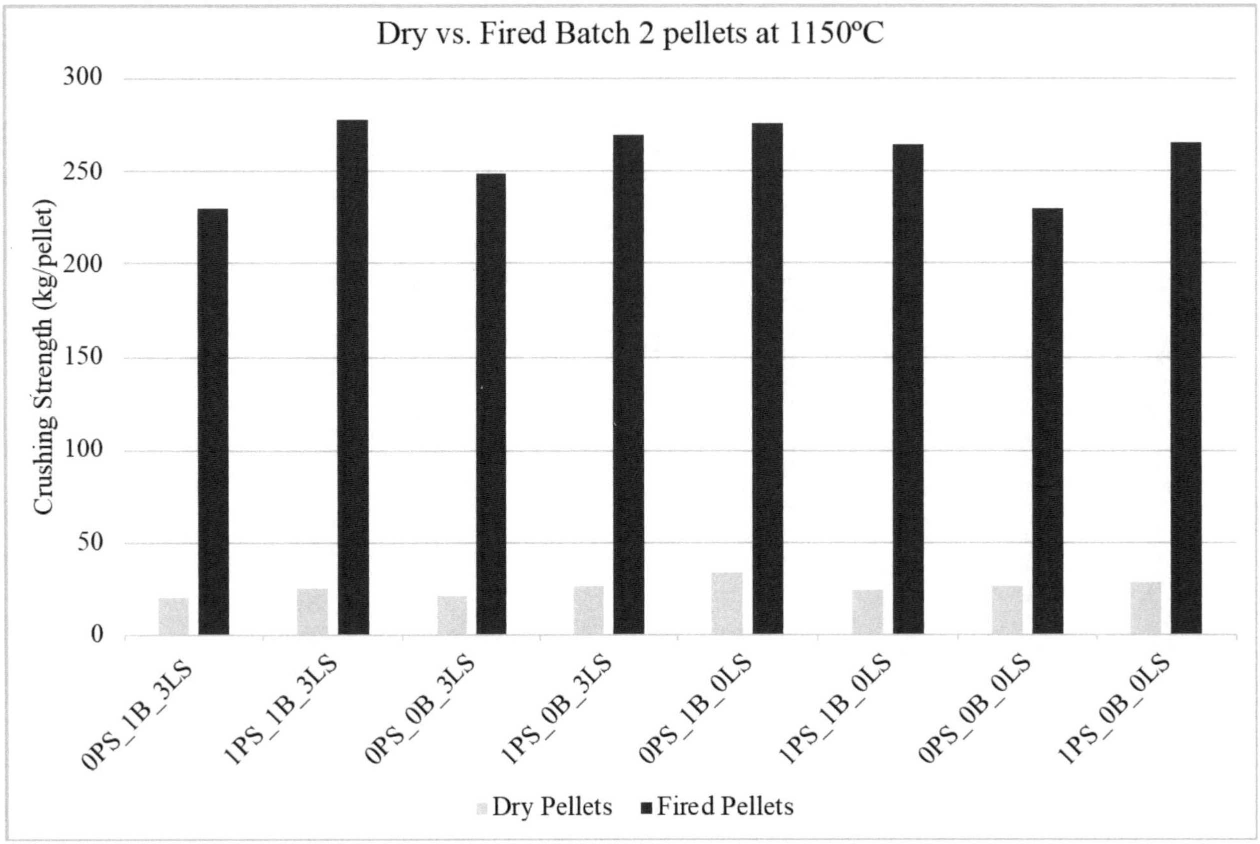

Figure 11. Crushing Strength for Dry vs. Fired Batch 2 Pellets at 1150C.

Drop Test Results for Batch 1 Pellets

A drop or impact test is conducted on the pellets as another measure in determining how well the pellets will withstand transportation and handling. Most literature data suggest drop number values over 8 as durable for fired pellets. The drop test differs from the compression test in that the pellet is free falling and only one part of the pellet is impacted.

Table 9 shows the drop test numbers for dry and fired pellets in increasing drop number for fired pellets. All the pellet types that passed the 8 drop number value were pellets indurated a high temperature: 1010°C and 1150°C. In Table 23 we see that some of the pellets that pass the drop number threshold were pellets with no additions of bentonite, and only consisted of paint sludge, magnetite, and/or limestone (e.g., 1PS_0B_3LS and 1PS_0B_0LS) or half of the bentonite addition was replaced with paint sludge (0.5PS_0.5B_1.5LS). It can be concluded then that magnetite ore pellets substituted completely or partially with automotive paint sludge still display impact values comparable to pellets with bentonite clay.

Table 9. Drop number for dry and fired batch 1 pellets.

Pellet Type	Temperature (Celsius)	Time (minutes)	Drop number for dry pellets	Drop number for fired pellets
0PS-0B-0LS	1150	30	1	1
0PS-1B-0LS	870	30	1	4
1PS-0B-0LS	870	30	2	4
1PS-1B-3LS	870	30	4	4
0PS-1B-3LS	870	90	2	5
0PS-0B-3LS	870	30	4	5
1PS-1B-0LS	870	30	1	7
0PS-0B-0LS	870	90	2	7
1PS-0B-3LS	870	90	3	7
0.5PS-0.5B-1.5LS	1010	60	6	9
1PS-0B-3LS	1150	30	6	9
0PS-1B-3LS	1150	30	7	9
0PS-0B-3LS	1150	90	5	10
0PS-1B-0LS	1150	90	6	10
0.5PS-0.5B-1.5LS	1010	60	7	10
1PS-1B-3LS	1150	90	4	11
1PS-1B-0LS	1150	90	6	11
1PS-0B-0LS	1150	90	5	12
0.5PS-0.5B-1.5LS	1010	60	5	12

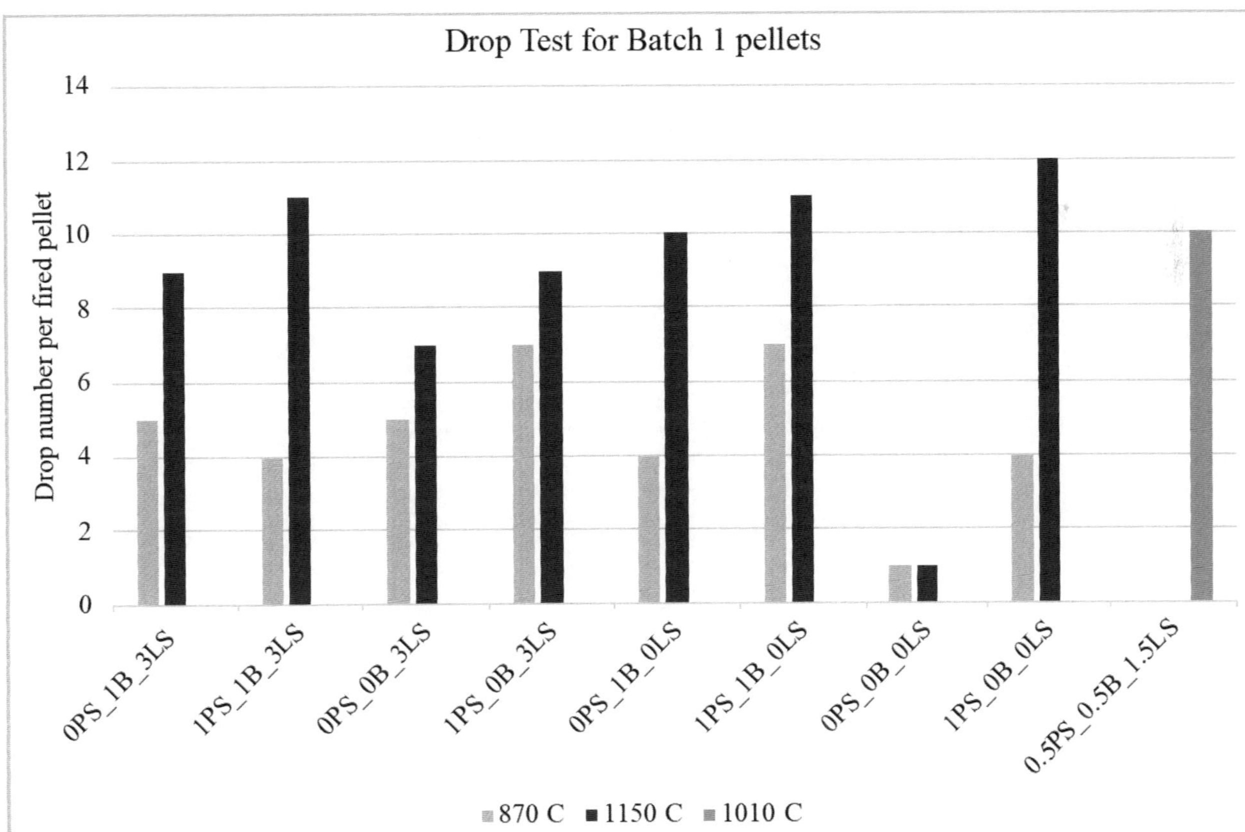

Figure 12. Drop Test Numbers for Fired Batch 1 Pellets

Figure 12 shows the drop test values for fired pellets made from batch 1 paint sludge material for induration temperatures 870°C, 1010°C, 1150°C. This graph shows the temperature dependence again, implying the importance of sintering in the strengthening of iron ore pellets. The pellet type 0PS_0B_0LS does not show any promising impact values, most likely due to the lack of bentonite and paint sludge materials.

Drop Test Results for Batch 2 Pellets

As discussed in the section before, the same drop number of 8 is considered the durable threshold for suitable iron ore pellets. Most of the pellets that pass this threshold value are pellets indurated at 1010°C and 1150°C where sintering effects significantly increase the strength and hardness of a pellet. Table 10 shows pellet type combinations that do not include the addition of bentonite or the partial addition of bentonite (e.g., 0.5PS_0.5B_1.5LS and 1PS_0B_0LS, and 1PS_0B_3LS), indicating the paint sludge material as a suitable complete or partial substitution.

Table 10. Drop number for dry and fired batch 2 pellets.

Pellet Type	Temperature (Celsius)	Time (minutes)	Drop Number for dry pellets	Drop Number for fired pellets
0PS-0B-0LS	870	90	2	2
0PS-0B-0LS	1150	30	2	3
0PS-0B-3LS	870	30	2	4
0PS-1B-0LS	870	30	2	4
1PS-1B-0LS	870	30	2	5
1PS-0B-3LS	870	90	3	5
1PS-1B-3LS	870	30	3	5
0PS-1B-3LS	870	90	2	6
0PS-1B-0LS	1150	90	7	9
0.5PS-0.5B-1.5LS	1010	60	5	10
0PS-0B-3LS	1150	90	6	10
1PS-1B-3LS	1150	90	7	10
0.5PS-0.5B-1.5LS	1010	60	8	10
1PS-0B-0LS	870	30	2	11
1PS-0B-3LS	1150	30	5	11
1PS-0B-0LS	1150	90	6	11
0.5PS-0.5B-1.5LS	1010	60	6	11
0PS-1B-3LS	1150	30	7	11
1PS-1B-0LS	1150	90	7	11

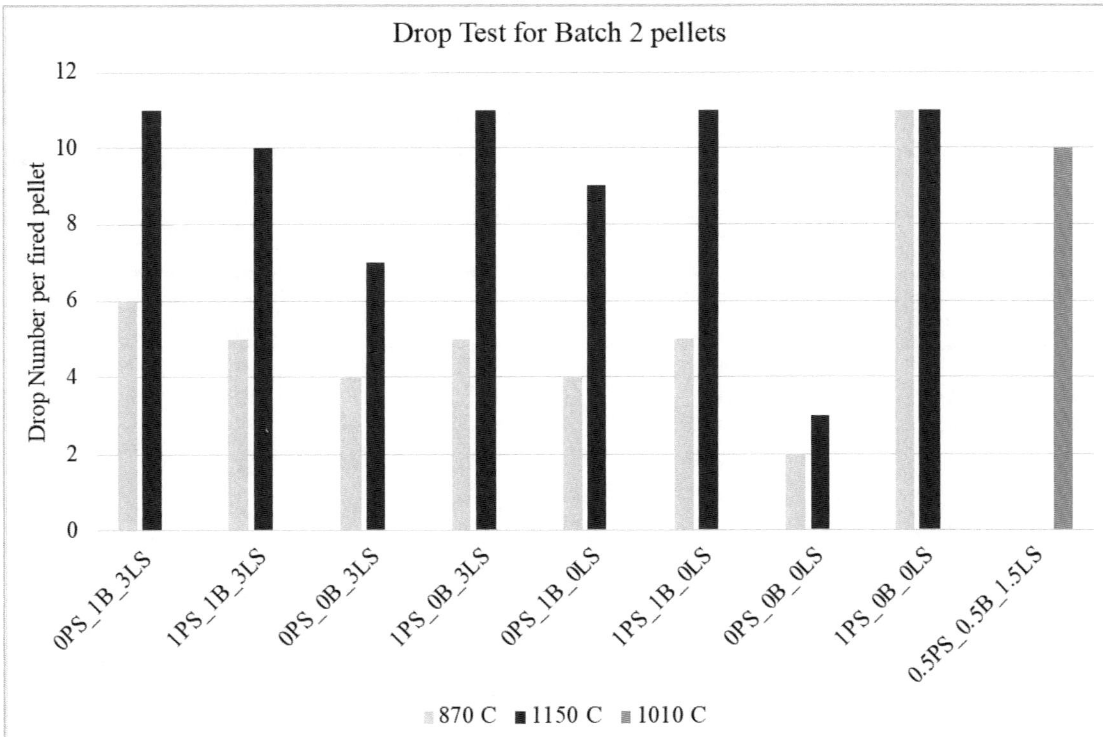

Figure 13. Drop Test Numbers for Fired Batch 2 Pellets.

Figure 13 displays the drop number values for fired pellets from batch 2 paint sludge material indurated at 870°C, 1010°C and 1150°C. While not all the fired pellets drop number, values pass the 8 drop threshold, it does show how the temperature dependence; the pellets withstand more drops as their induration temperature increases. The pellet type 0PS_0B_0LS cannot withstand numerous drops due to the lack of bentonite and paint sludge material to strengthen the pellets.

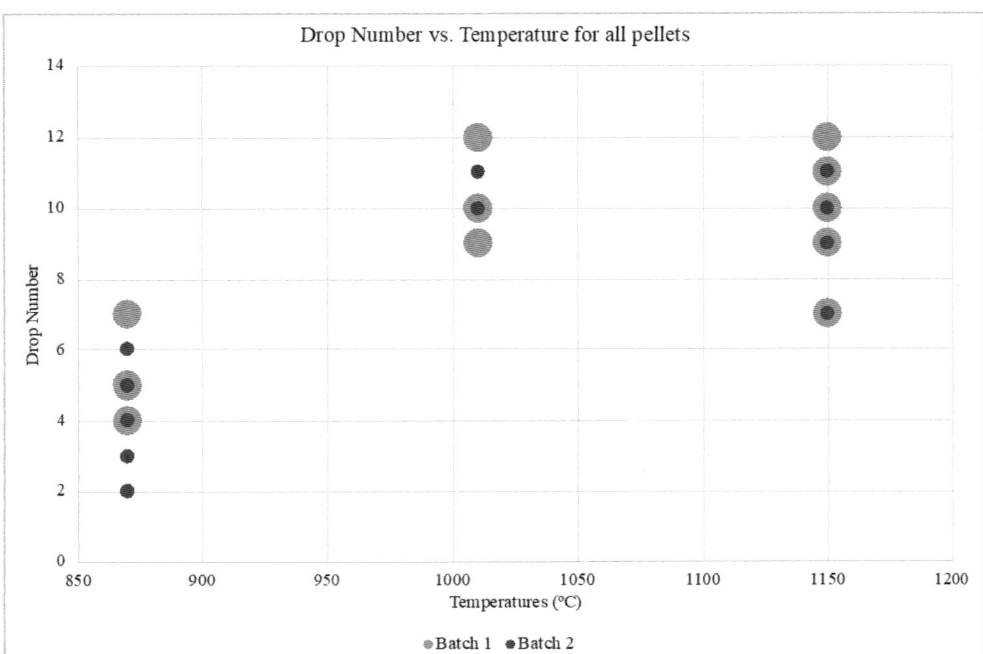

Figure 14. Drop number versus temperature of induration for pellets of batch 1 and 2.

Finally, Figure 14 shows a comparison between drop test values between batch 1 and batch 2 fired pellets. Pellets indurated above 1000°C are shown to withstand multiple drops and are considered durable enough for handling and transportation in a manner typical of an industrial pelletizing plant.

Table 11. Apparent porosity and Percent Reduction of batch 1 pellets.

Pellet Type	Temperature (Celsius)	Time (minutes)	Apparent Porosity (%)	Percent Reduction (%)
0PS-1B-3LS	870	90	43.33	47.2
0PS-1B-3LS	1150	30	44.68	75.2
1PS-1B-3LS	870	30	47.46	42.4
1PS-1B-3LS	1150	90	47.92	84.7
0PS-0B-3LS	870	30	15.00	34.6
0PS-0B-3LS	1150	90	45.45	76.2
1PS-0B-3LS	870	90	45.00	51.8
1PS-0B-3LS	1150	30	46.81	78.6
0PS-1B-0LS	870	30	36.84	57.4
0PS-1B-0LS	1150	90	39.71	75.9
1PS-1B-0LS	870	30	48.00	54.7
1PS-1B-0LS	1150	90	44.44	75.4
0PS-0B-0LS	870	90	44.44	49.6
0PS-0B-0LS	1150	30	47.78	75.1
1PS-0B-0LS	870	30	30.61	50.4
1PS-0B-0LS	1150	90	44.64	68.5
0.5PS-0.5B-1.5LS	1010	60	43.33	63.2
0.5PS-0.5B-1.5LS	1010	60	43.28	60.5
0.5PS-0.5B-1.5LS	1010	60	46.94	64.7

Table 12. Apparent porosity and Percent Reduction of batch 2 pellets.

Pellet Type	Temperature (Celsius)	Time (minutes)	Apparent Porosity (%)	Percent Reduction (%)
0PS-1B-3LS	870	90	43.3	45.4
0PS-1B-3LS	1150	30	63.3	72.3
1PS-1B-3LS	870	30	42.3	43.7
1PS-1B-3LS	1150	90	42.4	86.5
0PS-0B-3LS	870	30	28.6	36.8
0PS-0B-3LS	1150	90	47.6	73.4
1PS-0B-3LS	870	90	32.1	51.3
1PS-0B-3LS	1150	30	42.1	74.3
0PS-1B-0LS	870	30	20.0	56.3
0PS-1B-0LS	1150	90	48.8	75.4
1PS-1B-0LS	870	30	31.7	54.4
1PS-1B-0LS	1150	90	51.9	75.3
0PS-0B-0LS	870	90	15.2	45.3
0PS-0B-0LS	1150	30	42.2	74.2
1PS-0B-0LS	870	30	20.5	54.3
1PS-0B-0LS	1150	90	40.0	67.3
0.5PS-0.5B-1.5LS	1010	60	42.1	65.1
0.5PS-0.5B-1.5LS	1010	60	48.9	68.9
0.5PS-0.5B-1.5LS	1010	60	47.7	70.2

CONCLUSION

The goal of this research project was to investigate the effectiveness of using waterborne automotive paint sludge as a binder for making iron ore pellets. The typical binder used for iron ore pellets is bentonite clay, however, due to the high costs and low availability, alternatives to bentonite clay have been researched for years. Bentonite clay provides the iron ore pellets with an increase in silica and alumina, which are considered detrimental in the downstream ironmaking process. Too much silica and alumina increase the acidity of the slag while it is being processed in a blast furnace. Increased slag acidity increases the viscosity of the slag and the difficultly in tapping the slag. This is not a superficial issue that can be easily solved since the operations of a blast furnace cannot be turned on and off easily. In addition to the issues associated with the blast furnace, DRI pellets should also not contain high concentrations of silica or alumina because there is not a lot of room of impurities or to resolve the impurities within the DRI process.

Many of the alternatives investigated seek to eliminate or limit the silica and alumina. Organic materials, such as polymers, have been intensely studied as an alternative binder to bentonite clay because their long chains can hold together the pellets similar to bentonite. Because they are organic material, they may also add heat to the BF or DRI process, aiding in the energy costs. However, organic materials are very expensive, and, in many cases, the cost associated with creating an organic binder for the amount of pellets used cannot be justified. This is precisely why automotive paint sludge should be considered in a technical and economical alternative binder. It not only contains a substantial amount of organic material, including polymers, and low amount of silica and alumina, but is also economically favorable for automotive companies.

Recycling of automotive paint sludge is an important topic of late because many automotive companies are trying to reduce their waste in landfills. The paint sludge consists of organic and inorganic material, in this case, mostly titanium dioxide with significantly lower percentages of silica and alumina compared to bentonite. To test how well the paint sludge could substitute as a binder compared to bentonite, iron ore pellets were made of typical industrial standard with and without bentonite. These pellets were subject to a crushing strength test, a drop test, determination of apparent porosity and percent reduction. All these properties are considered important for the durability and efficiency of the iron ore pellets. It was determined that iron ore pellets where the bentonite was completely and partially replaced with paint sludge materials from two different paint shops, had comparable cold crushing strength values above 250 kg/pellet as per industry standards. In addition to the cold crushing strength values, the pellets also withstood multiple drops above 8 drop which is also typical of industry standards. Apparent porosity and percent reduction were also determined to have suitable values showing that the paint sludge can replace bentonite as a binder.

REFERENCES

[1] G. Salihoglu and N. K. Salihoglu, "A review on paint sludge from automotive industries: Generation, charateristics and management," Journal of Environmental Management, vol. 169, pp. 223-235, 2016.

[2] S. Friess, "Carmakers Try to keep Waste Out of the Ground as Well as the Air," The New York Times, 21 December 2017. [Online]. Available: https://www.nytimes.com/2017/12/21/business/car-companies-recylcing.html. [Accessed 2 2021].

[3] United States Environmental Protection Agency, "How Communities Have Defined Zero Waste," December 2018. [Online]. Available: https://www.epa.gov/transforming-waste-tool/how-communities-have-defined-zero-waste. [Accessed 2 2021].

[4] Simscale, "What is FEA (Finite Element Analysis)?," 20 January 2021. [Online]. Available: https://www.simscale.com/docs/simwiki/fea-finite-element-analysis/what-is-fea-finite-element-analysis/. [Accessed 2021].

[5] ArcelorMittal, "Steel making process," 2016. [Online]. Available: https://annualreview2016.arcelormittal.com/fact-book/additional-information/steel-making-process. [Accessed 2021].

Institute for Briquetting and Agglomeration

2022 IBA CONFERENCE PAPERS

Paper Title:
Advantages of Cold Bonded Iron Ore Pellets as a Feedstock

Presenter:
Richard Joyce

Company:
Binding Solutions

Advantages of Cold Bonded Iron Ore Pellets as a Feedstock

Richard Joyce, Head of Research and Development, Binding Solutions Ltd, Materials Processing Institute, Teesside, United Kingdom.

Matthew Bennett Ph.D, Research and Development Scientist, Binding Solutions Ltd, Materials Processing Institute, Teesside, United Kingdom.

Introduction

The steel industry contributes between 7 and 9% of the global anthropogenic CO_2 emissions released.[1] Socio-economic factors have led to a huge drive for reducing these emissions.

Binding Solutions' Ltd (BSL) have developed technology to have a significant impact on lowering these CO_2 emissions.

The established technology for exploiting iron ore resources for maximum efficiency is to upgrade the Iron Oxide content in the Iron Ore, by separation from the non-contributory minerals. Pellets are then made by a process known as induration which involve forming ceramic bonds in gas/oil or solid fuel kilns at temperatures >1200°C

BSL Technology omits the induration process and forms the bonds by a chemical process, so the carbon intensity of the production is far lower.

The carbon intensity (Mt CO_2 per Mt pellet) of the BSL cold bonded pellet to be 0.04 compared to 0.13 for Indurated product *which is a significant percentile difference for the volumes involved.

**Commissioned by independent 3rd party assessment*

Environmental and Financial Benefits

The Iron and Steel Industry have set targets for reduction of CO_2 with the main areas for development of:

- Hydrogen Gas Reduction
- Sustainable Carbon Sources and Carbon Capture
- Electro-winning Technology

Whilst these methods are very important, there will be a significant transition time to develop and adopt them.

A BSL cold-bonded pellet can be introduced in a relatively short timescale to give an immediate impact on carbon emissions at a site.

Climate change emissions are categorised as Scope 1, 2 and 3.

Table 1. Potential impact of BSL CB pellets on each category in relation to mine operators and Iron making.

	Scope 1 – generated from production source	Scope 2 -generated from generation of energy supply	Scope 3 – generated from materials supply chain
Miners -Pellet Producers	Yes	Yes	No
Iron Making	If Pelletising at works	If pelletising at works	Yes

In terms of the financial benefits of adopting cold bonded technology, this can include:

- Taxes and penalties in respect of carbon emissions
- Lower Capex for plant construction

Technical Advantages of the Cold Bonded Pellet

These can be categorised in terms of Physical Properties and Metallurgical Properties.

A key consideration when operating an ironmaking furnace is having a good quality burden. Parameters including resilience during handling and resilience to high temperatures may be quantified by ISO tests (or by variant methods in certain jurisdictions).

The test results that are achieved for BSL pellets are shown below in Table 2.

Table 2. List of tests carried out for BSL pellets including, ISO standards, units measured and current results.

Indicator	Standard	Units	Current Results
Cold Compressive Strength	ISO 4700:2015	daN	200-300
Porosity	IN HOUSE	%	c.40%
Tumble Strength	ISO 3271:2015	% + 6.3mm	85-95%
Swelling	ISO 4698:2007	Free Swelling	<15%
Dynamic Low Temperature Disintegration	ISO13930:2015	% + 6.3mm	95-97%
Dynamic Low Temperature Disintegration	ISO13930:2015	% - 0.5mm	3-5%
Relative Reducibility R180	ISO7215: 2015	%	65-75%

The ISO test standards were designed for testing the quality of iron ore pellets, lump and sinter. As such there may be different characteristics displayed by CB pellets by the same test method. In time, new standards will be developed around the technology and as part of that process, different characteristics may be studied

A series of experiments were carried out to compare the properties and behaviour of the BSL CBRPPs (Roller-Pressed Pellet) and indurated pellets. The source material was identical: Magnetite Iron Ore Concentrate with 4.5% SiO_2 and pellets were of the acid type, with a basicity of 0.2%.

The tests were performed in the context of a blast furnace feedstock although there will be some commonalities to other operations such a Direct Reduction by gas.

Images of both pellet types on a 10mm square aperture grid as a visual reference are shown in Figure 1.

All test work was carried out at the BSL Technical Centre unless stated otherwise

BSL RPP

Market Indurated Pellet

Figure 1. Images of BSL RPPs (left) and indurated pellets on a 10mm square aperture grid. The dimensional aspects of the BSL RPP was developed to give the optimum balance of properties, be demonstrably similar in appearance to a standard pellet and be viable for large scale production.

Experimental Data

Pellet Size Distribution vs Burden Stability

The size distribution of each type of pellet tested has been measured by sieve analysis and shown in Figure 2.

Indurated pellets have been shown to have a broader size distribution due to the nature of the production method from diameters 6.3 to 16 mm.

The BSL RPPs are formed under confined conditions, resulting in a narrow and specific size distribution. This gives the potential of a more consistent burden porosity, which is beneficial to operators as well control over the entire pellet size distribution.

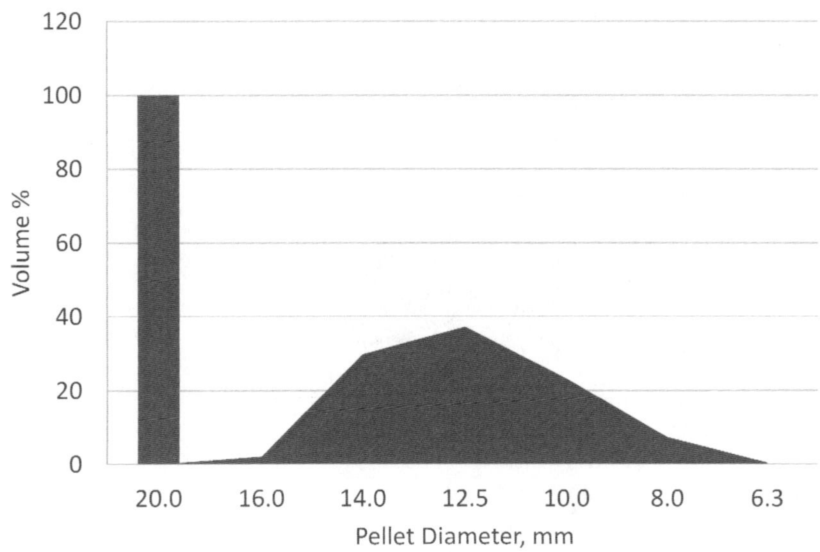

Figure 2. BSL RPPs (green) and indurated pellets (red) size distributions

Angle of Repose vs Burden Stability

A representative sample of each pellet type was placed in a cylindrical tube of 20 litre volume, height equal to diameter.

The tube was lifted away to allow the samples to flow naturally. From this the angle of repose was calculated by measuring the static height of the cone and calculating the angle relative to circumference of the base with a graphical representation of this calculation in Figure 3. The data from this study on both pellet types is presented in Figure 4.

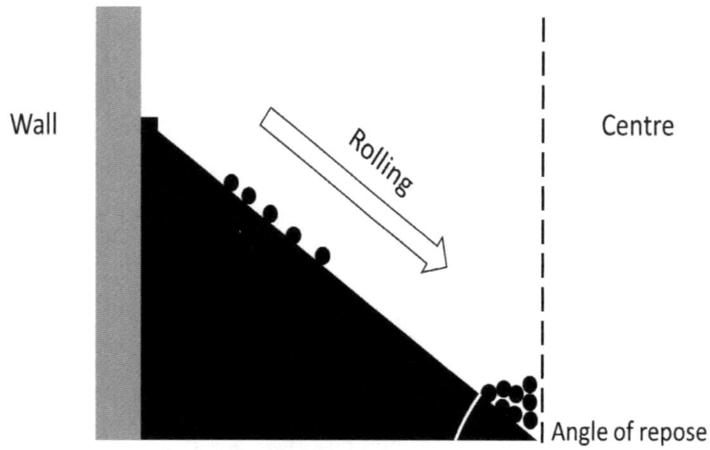

Figure 3. Graphical representation of angle of repose for pellet pile.

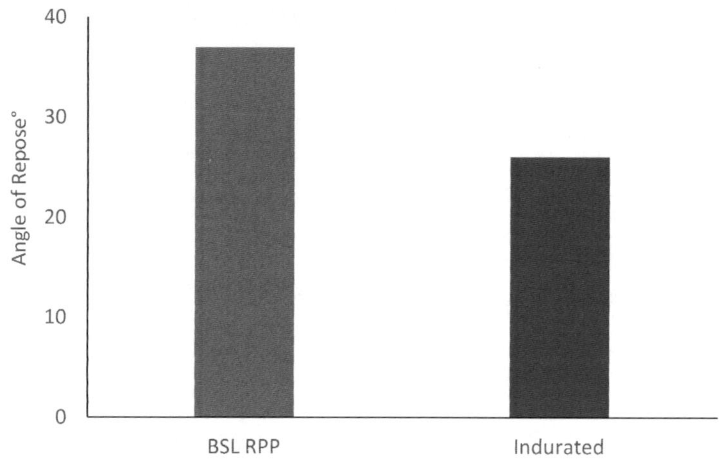

Figure 4. Angle of repose for BSL RPP 37° and indurated pellets 26° calculated.

The BSL Pellets show a higher angle of repose than that of the Indurated Pellets. The value recorded for the indurated pellets is representative of typical values which are quoted.(2)

A lower angle of repose indicates a higher tendency to redistribute within a vessel. This can lead to segregation of different pellet sizes within the overall pellet lead.

A value of 37° for BSL RPPs indicates compatibility with other burden constituents such as sinter and lump hence less likelihood of segregation between different size pellets and even distribution.

We can speculate that there may well be a benefit of greater stability during bulk shipping, with less fines generated in transit, adding quality and value to a cargo.

Bulk Density and Voids relative to Burden

The uncompacted bulk density was calculated for both pellet types, using the test method prescribed in BS EN 1097-3.

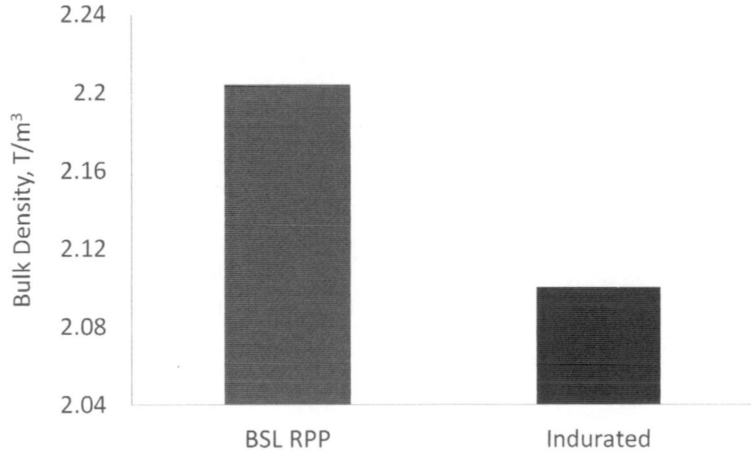

Figure 5. Bulk Density Values showing a higher density value for BSL CBRPP (2.204 T/m^3) compared to that of indurated pellets (2.1 T/m^3).

The air void contents of each pellet were measured by a volumetric method and the results are shown in Figure 6.

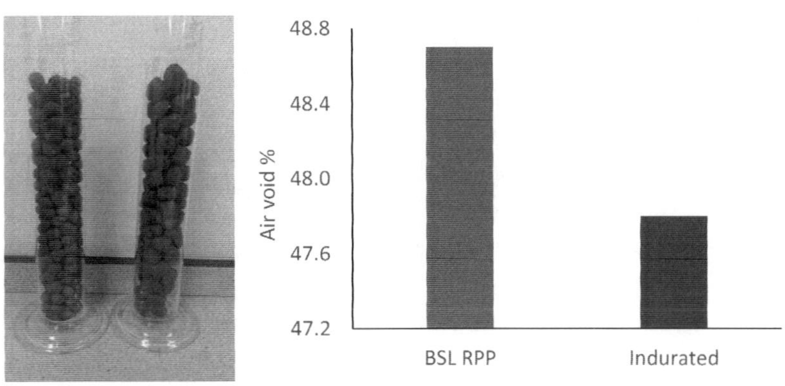

Figure 6. Volumetric method -BSL RPP (48.7%), indurated pellet (47.8%)

The results show that a higher furnace charge by weight can be facilitated by the BSL RPP, whilst also displaying a slightly higher void content in a confined situation. More iron units per volume and improved gas permeability give an efficiency advantage to a blast furnace operator.

Strength Variance by Pellet Type

The pellets were tested in accordance with ISO 4700 : Determination of crushing strength. A Mecmesin Omni-test 10 apparatus was used to apply the load and record the force required.

This involves testing a representative sample and testing 60 pellets to determine the force required to break the pellet. The average value is reported and there is commonly an allowable percentage that falls below the client-specified value. This is to allow for variance in the induration production process.

An additional pellet type was included for this test – a fluxed type from a hematite source concentrate and the pellets had been kept in the same storage conditions, outside stockpiles, for a period of 6 months.

The boxplot illustration in Figure 7 shows that the BSL RPP has a low standard deviation than the conventional pellet types. A consistent standard of burden component for a blast furnace is one less variable to consider when the aim is to run at the highest efficiency

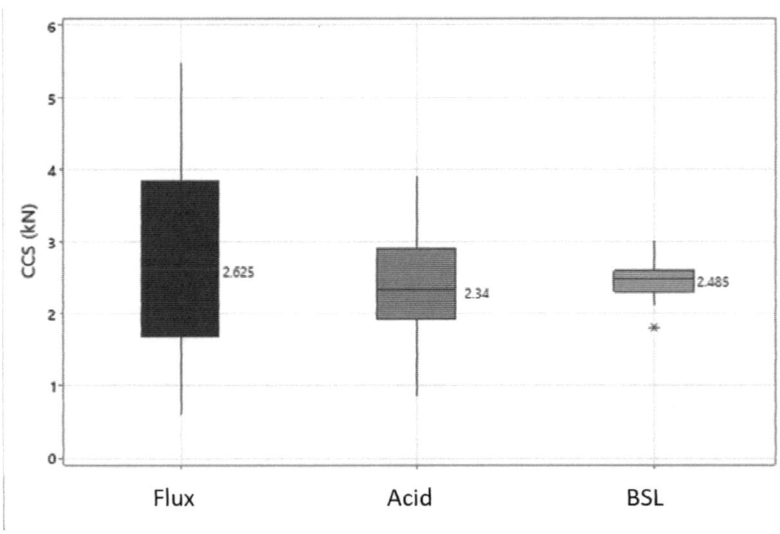

Figure 7. Comparative strength variance within a pellet batch.

Metallurgical Behaviour

Some key requirements to consider are:

- Available Iron in the pellet – as reflected with pellet pricing
- Favourable Rate of Reduction – for throughput efficiency
- Porosity to enable gas particle contact and enable a favourable rate of reduction

Experimental Data

Table 3 shows the Chemical Analysis for the BSL CB pellet in comparison to an indurated pellet. The Indurated pellet data is shown in two states- before and after the heating stages.

It may be seen that in the post- induration phase, the total iron content is lower than for the cold-bonded product. This is due to the source material in this case occurring in the Fe_3O_4 phase. The induration process has an oxidative condition, which converts the pellet to a predominant hematite phase. The net gain in oxygen to Fe_2O_3 gives a resultant lower mass percentage of elemental Iron.

For the cold-bonded process, the Iron Oxide remains in its original state so there is no downgrading in terms of iron units. This results in a higher value in use, both for the pellet producer and the ironmaker.

Table 3. XRF results of elements present in pellets from different process measured using a Rigaku ZSX Primus IV.

	Cold Bonded Material	Hot Process	
	BSL	Green State	Indurated
Fe	63.61%	63.30%	61.72%
CaO	0.98%	0.96%	0.95%
SiO_2	4.91%	5.12%	5.10%
Mn_3O_4	0.14%	0.13%	0.14%
Mn	0.05%	0.05%	0.05%
Al_2O_3	0.80%	0.90%	0.92%
MgO	0.82%	0.79%	0.80%
P_2O_5	0.05%	0.05%	0.05%
P	0.02%	0.02%	0.02%
K_2O	0.06%	0.06%	0.06%
TiO_2	1.39%	1.36%	1.35%
Na_2O	0.19%	0.18%	0.18%

The use of magnetite iron ore within the ironmaking industry raises several concerns.[3] These relate to two subjects:

An energy penalty via an endothermic phase reaction and potential for progressive lowering of porosity during reduction through the Magnetite-Wustite phase change.

There are known cases of successful direct charge of magnetite lump ore to Blast Furnaces, even though the lump may be highly impermeable. By the nature of indurated iron ore pellet production, it is not possible to produce an indurated pellet as a magnetite phase. This means the only data would be in respect of a cold-bonded pellet.

Thermal characteristics of blast furnace burden constituent materials may be assessed in accordance with relevant ISO test standards, which typically use a static temperature/reducing gas combination.

In order to give a fuller picture and especially when introducing a new technology, bespoke test methods have been developed within the industry.[4] These tests have a varying temperature and gas profile in order to simulate the journey through a blast furnace.

The HOSIM test was selected to give additional verification of the performance of the BSL Magnetite cold-bonded pellet. This is an operating line assessment where the gas composition is adjusted relative to the O/Fe ration, measured by weight loss. A representative sample of 500g is placed in a retort which has onboard loss in weight measurement. Initial chemistry testing is used to determine the content of Iron and Oxygen. The temperature ramp rate is fixed and the loss in weight determines the adjustment to gas composition ratio.

The reportable findings are:

- The time taken to reach a set reduction point
- The level of attrition after reduction and tumbling

A sample of BSL CB pellet was tested and an indurated pellet as a control (hematite phase). The curves showing the mass loss rate i.e the reducibility rate over time and temperature is shown in Figure 8. The reducibility rate %/min of these pellet was calculated from this data and is shown in Table 4.

Tests were carried out at The Steel and Metals Institute, Swansea, UK.

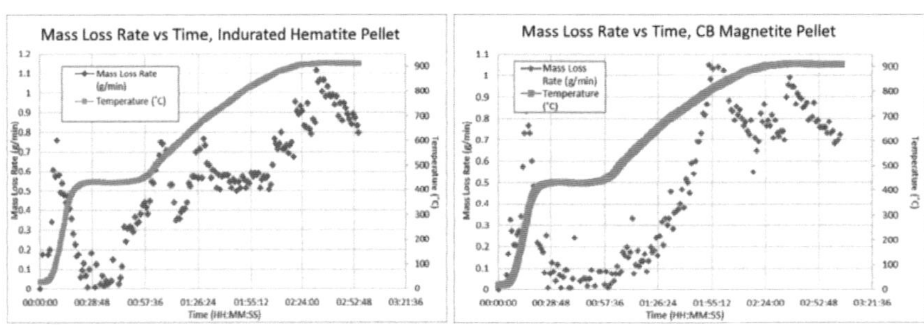

Figure 8. HOSIM graphs of an indurated hematite pellet and CB magnetite pellet. Curves show the rate of mass loss (g/min) over time and temperature.

Table 4. The O/Fe ratio content, reduction time and reducibility rate for both types of pellets.

Type	O/Fe Start	O/Fe End	Reduction time (min)	% < 3.15
BSL CB	1.332	0.520	140	11.8
Indurated Pellet	1.489	0.520	132	0.30

The data from the HOSIM tests shows that the BSL Magnetite Pellet is reduced in a similar time pattern to the control hematite pellet. The reduction time is slightly longer for the BSL magnetite pellet by 8minutes.

The attrition is higher for the BSL Magnetite at 11.8% compared to 0.3% for the indurated pellet. It is noted that 0.3% is an exceptionally low value and 11.8% gives an assurance of suitable strength for a blast furnace. Typical acceptance values are 0 to 25% for pellets and 25-40% for sinter.

Porosity

BSL RPPs are produced by a compressive, confined force whereas indurated pellets are produced by low pressure. In addition, the induration process creates a phase change with associated swelling, which creates a high level of porosity. Porosity is important to enable a high level of gas-solid interaction for reducing the iron oxide. It could be reasonably expected that the BSL RPP would have a far lower level of porosity though by giving due consideration to particle characteristics and engineering parameters, a good level of micro and macro porosity is achievable.

To demonstrate this, sections of pellets were mounted and polished before examination with an Olympus DSX1000 Microscope. Images of BSL RPP pellet and indurated pellet cross-sections and shown in Figure 9. Is the difference in porosity from the different process.

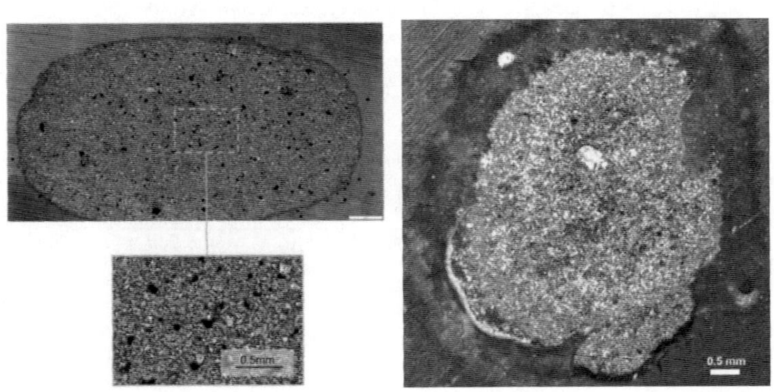

BSL RPP   Indurated Pellet

Figure 9. Microscope images at x100 magnification showing cross-section of BSL RPP pellets and indurated pellets.

Porosity can be observed as the dark areas in the sectional microscopy.

Pellet Additives

Inclusion of carbon within a pellet will improve the rate of reducibility, due to the particle/particle contact. This property may be used to reduce the volume of coke addition to a blast furnace by a rate of 0.36kg/Tonne of Hot Metal per every 1kg/Tonne of Hot Metal of Carbon in a composite pellet.[5]

Carbon may be added to the induration process to reduce fuelling demand and there may be a small residual amount, but this will largely be burnt out of the pellet during induration. The use of carbon in indurated pellets can also counteract some porosity generation from its effect on the sintering of the grains within the pellet.

For a CB pellet, the embedded carbon remains in its original state until it is in the furnace reduction zone. There is also scope to use a renewable carbon source to better effect, in particular where the properties show unsuitability for direct charge or injection.

A simplification of the Chemistry is shown below in Equations 1-3.

Indurated pellet production process

1. $Fe_2O_3 + C\,(s) \rightarrow Fe_3O_4 + FeO + CO/CO_2\,(g)$ reduction >1000 °C (1)
2. $Fe_3O_4 + FeO + O_2\,(g) \rightarrow Fe_2O_3 + Fe_3O_4$ re-oxidation >1000 °C (2)

CB pellet production process

3. $Fe_2O_3 + C\,(s) \rightarrow Fe_2O_3 + C\,(s)$ reduction <100 °C (3)

Table 5. Fe content and Reducibility Index (ISO 7215) for CB pellets with different carbon %. Note: this dataset relates to a different magnetite source material, where a project specific requirement is to reduce the coke rate.

	CB pellet			
	0% Carbon	5% Carbon	10% Carbon	15% Carbon
Fe	66.1%	62.7%	59.3%	55.9%
RI	60	82	84	N/A

The data shows that carbon addition increases the reducibility. The 15% addition was deemed commercially unviable. The viability was determined by value in use calculations for coke rate reduction vs T/hm productivity vs iron units.

Conclusion

The research at BSL has been towards the development of a cold-bonded technique to produce iron ore-based pellets. The standard approach of indurated pellets requires temperatures above 1200°C that is not only of high energy and cost, but also contributes to high amounts of environmentally harmful emissions. BSL's cold-bond pelletising approach offers a fast impact on reducing carbon emissions.

A comparison of pellets found that BSL's cold-bonded approach results in greater control and reproducibility over in pellet size and dimensions, making them stack in a more stable and homogenous manner. This also provides better void space for gas penetration during stacking for reducibility whilst still having high individual pellet density.

In respect of the metallurgical properties of a magnetite cold- bonded pellet, appropriate simulation of the blast furnace conditions has shown a demonstrably similar performance to the standard indurated pellet.

In conclusion, BSL has shown that not only are cold-bonded pellets a more cost effective and greener alternative. They also have the potential to provide various technical advantage to the existing technology.

References

(1) World Steel Association: Climate change and the Production of Iron and Steel- an industry view 19.5.2021

(2) US4129437A, Iron ore pellet having a specific shape and a method of making the same, Taguchi et al., 1976

(3) Heikkilä, A., Iljana, M., Bartusch, H. and Fabritius, T. (2020), Reduction of Iron Ore Pellets, Sinter, and Lump Ore under Simulated Blast Furnace Conditions. steel research int., 91: 2000047. https://doi.org/10.1002/srin.202000047

(4) Chaigneau, R., Bakker, T., Steeghs, A. and Bergstrand R., Quality Assessment Of Ferrous Burdens: Utopian Dream?, PR-016-58 - 2001 Ironmaking Proceedings.

(5) NIPPON STEEL TECHNICAL REPORT No. 123 March 2020

Institute for Briquetting and Agglomeration

2022 IBA CONFERENCE PAPERS

Paper Title:
Optimization of Oral Dosage Forms for Flow

Presenters:
Greg Mehos and Devang Patel

Company:
Greg Mehos & Associates LLC and Natoli Scientific, a Division of Natoli Engineering Co. Inc.

Optimization of Oral Dosage Forms for Flow

Greg Mehos, Greg Mehos & Associates LLC
Devang Patel, Natoli Scientific, a Division of Natoli Engineering Co. Inc.

Introduction. Solid dosage forms are capsules, tablets, or other similar drug products intended for oral use. The product is comprised of an active pharmaceutical ingredient (API), binders, disintegrants, glidants, and lubricants. Glidants are added to improve the flowability of the formulation so that it will reliably fill a capsule or enter the die of a tablet press.

A formulation is prepared by mixing the API and other ingredients in a blender and then transferring the formulation to a storage hopper or feed hopper. In some cases, a powder is then fed directly into a tablet press, *i.e.*, tablets are manufactured by direct compression, or fed directly to a capsule filling machine. Alternatively, the powder is first fed into a granulator, such as a roller compactor, to improve its flowability by increasing its particle size.

Figure 1 is a schematic of roller compaction equipment. The roller compactor has three parts: (1) a feeding system, which conveys the powder to the compaction area, (2) a compaction unit, where powder is compacted between two counter rotating rolls to a ribbon by applying a force, and (3) a size reduction unit, for milling the ribbons to the desired particle size. The feeding system can have an integrated hopper or be flood fed by an upstream hopper that is directly connected to the compacting machine. It is critical that the powder can flow without obstructions to the feeder.

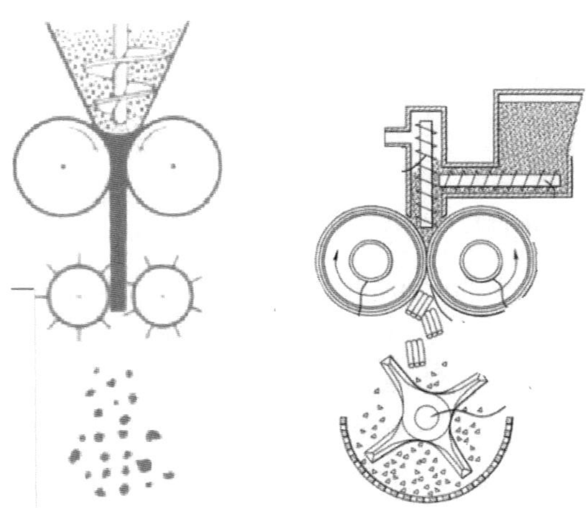

Figure 1. Roller compactor schematic.

Feed hoppers are frequently an afterthought. They are often conical with walls sloped 30° from vertical or pyramidal with the straight walls sloped at 30°. The valleys formed between adjacent walls, however, are shallower, and for a 30° pyramidal hopper, valley angles are *ca.* 39°.

As such, flowability of a solid dosage form blend is most critical in two parts of the process: the feed hopper to the feeding system and the feeding system itself.

Formulators have a choice of tests to quantify the flowability of powders. Methods include the angle of repose, Carr and Hausner ratios, and various flowability indices. Unfortunately, these methods are not predictive, as they do not simulate actual powder handling conditions. At best, they can be used to rank the flowability of similar powders, but the test results cannot be used to predict its flow behavior in a hopper or bin. The flowability coefficient *FFC*, the ratio of the pressure to the powder's cohesive strength is frequently used.

A better test method is one that measures a powder's fundamental properties under consolidation stresses that simulate those anticipated when a powder is handled and measures its fundamental properties. The fundamental solids flow properties are cohesive strength, internal friction, compressibility, wall friction, and permeability.

Test methods for measuring fundamental flow properties. Shear cell testers measure the cohesive strength, internal friction, compressibility, and wall friction of a powder. A sample is placed in a cell and then pre-sheared, *i.e.,* consolidated by exerting a normal stress σ and then shearing it until the measured shear stress τ is steady. Next, the shear step is performed, in which the normal and shear stresses are removed and the vertical load is replaced with a reduced load. The sample is then again sheared until failures. These pre-shear and shear steps are repeated at the same consolidation level for a number of reduced normal stresses, and the yield locus is then determined by plotting the failure shear stress against normal stress.

The flow properties of the powder are determined from the yield locus as shown in Figure 2. The semicircles used in the analysis may be mysterious to some formulators. Very quickly, a Mohr's circle allows the determination of normal and shear stresses for conveniently chosen frames of reference.

The major consolidation stress is determined from a Mohr's circle that intersects the point of steady state flow (σ_{SS}, τ_{SS}) and is tangent to the yield locus. The larger point of intersection of the Mohr's circle with the horizontal axis is the major consolidating stress σ_1. The effective angle of friction δ is determined from the angle formed when a line passing through the origin is tangent to the Mohr's circle. The unconfined yield strength f_C is determined by a Mohr's circle that is tangent to the yield locus and passes through the origin. Because the sample volume is recorded and the sample mass is known, the powder's bulk density is also measured during a test. Figure 3 gives example yield locus for a blend containing 67 percent acetaminophen (APAP), 29 percent microcrystalline cellulose (MCC), and 4 percent hydroxypropyl cellulose (HPC).

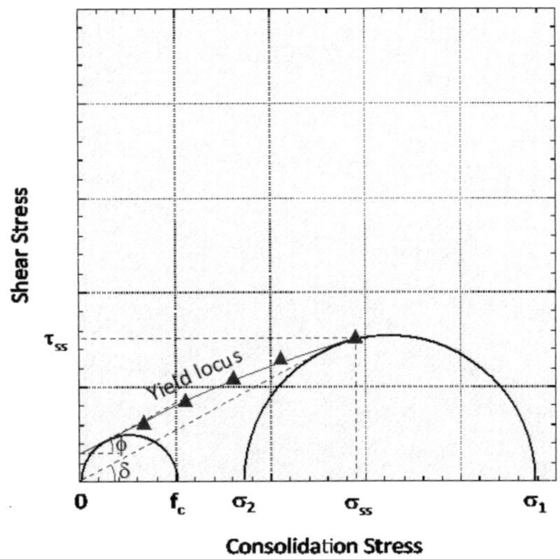

Figure 2. Construction of a yield locus and determination of the effective angle of friction δ, kinematic angle of internal friction ϕ, major consolidation stress σ_1, minor consolidation stress σ_2, and unconfined yield strength f_C.

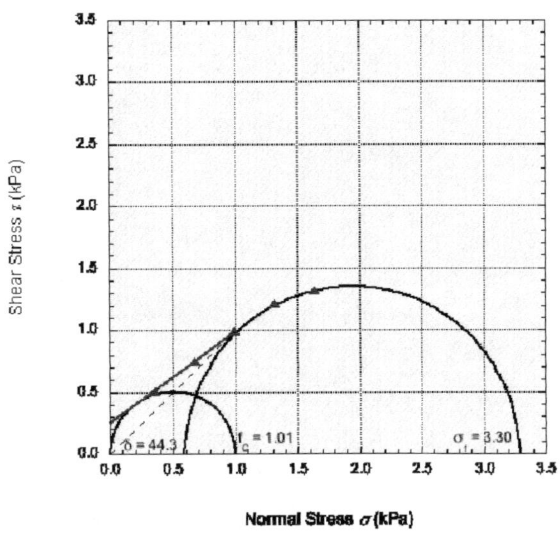

Figure 3. Yield locus of acetaminophen/microcrystalline cellulose/hydroxypropyl cellulose blend, σ_{SS} = 1.63 kPa.

By conducting the test over a range of consolidation states, the relationship between major consolidation stress and the cohesive strength of the powder can be established. This relationship is commonly called the material's flow function. The powder's compressibility, the relationship between a powder's bulk density and the major consolidation stress, is also determined. The flow function, effective angle of friction, and compressibility of the APAP/MCS/HPC blend are shown in Figures 4 - 6.

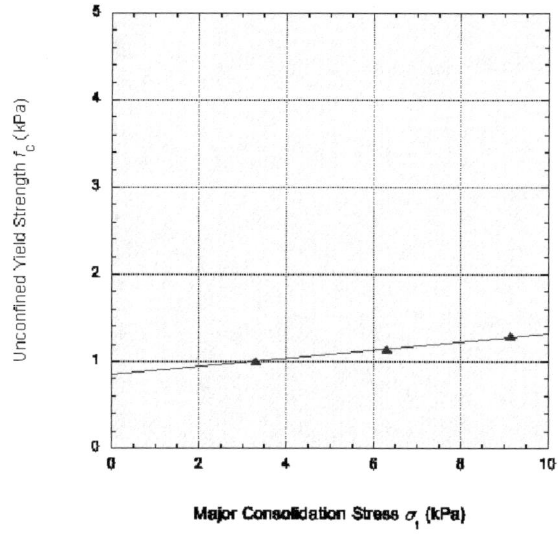

Figure 4. Flow function of acetaminophen/microcrystalline cellulose/hydroxypropyl cellulose blend.

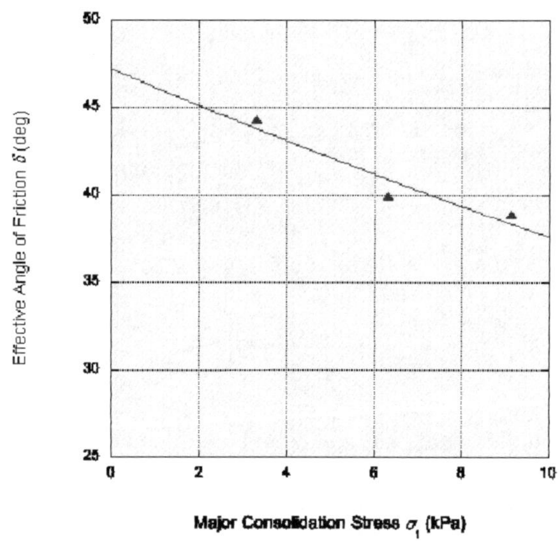

Figure 5. Effective angle of friction of APAP/MCC/HPMC blend.

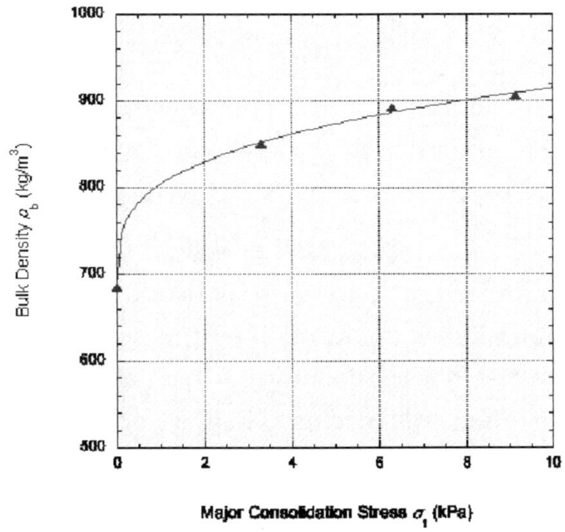

Figure 6. Effective bulk density of APAP/MCC/HPMC blend.

To conduct a wall friction test, the shear stress required to allow a sample of powder to slide along a coupon of wall material is measured for a range of normal loads. A plot of the shear stress against normal stress gives the wall yield locus. The angle of wall friction ϕ' is the angle that is formed when a line is drawn from the origin to a point on the wall yield locus. Figure 7 presents the wall yield locus determined from wall friction tests of the APAP/MCS/HPC blend on a coupon of 314 stainless steel with a #2B finish.

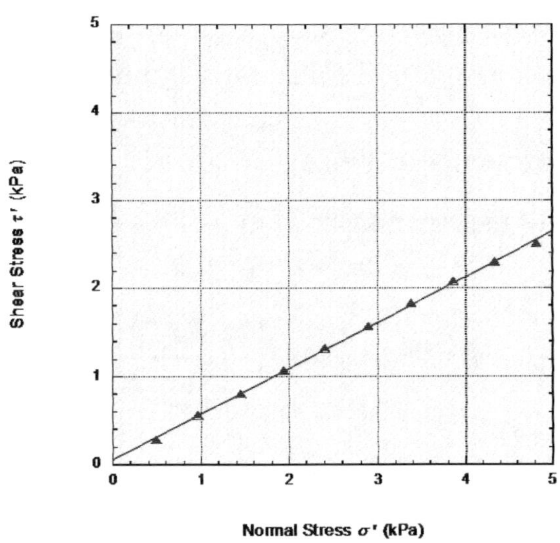

Figure 7. Wall friction of APAP/MCC/HPMC blend on 304 #2B stainless steel.

Permeability is determined by measuring the pressure drop that results when a gas is fed into a bed of powder at a low velocity. The superficial gas velocity is related to the gas pressure gradient by

$$u_s = -\frac{K}{\rho_b g}\frac{dP}{dz} \qquad (1)$$

where u_s is the gas superficial velocity, K is the powder's permeability, ρ_b is its bulk density, g is equal to acceleration due to gravity, and dP/dz is the gas pressure gradient. Permeability test results are useful for estimated solids discharge rates.

Mass flow hopper angle. Two flow patterns can occur in a hopper: mass flow and funnel flow. In mass flow, the entire bed of solids is in motion when material is discharged from the outlet. This behavior eliminates the formation of ratholes in the vessel and provides a more uniform velocity profile during operation. A uniform velocity profile mitigates sifting segregation, which frequently occurs when a hopper is filled with free-flowing material.

In funnel flow, an active flow channel forms above the outlet, with stagnant material (*i.e.*, ratholes) remaining at the periphery of the hopper. Hoppers in which funnel flow occurs may require a very large outlet to ensure that the ratholes collapse and the hopper empties. Because funnel flow can cause erratic flow and exacerbate segregation, mass flow hoppers are often preferable for handling pharmaceutical formulations.

The hopper angle required to allow mass flow depends on the effective angle of friction and the wall friction angle. Figure 8 provides mass flow boundaries for conical hoppers based on analyses developed by Jenike [1]. Values of the allowable hopper angle θ' are on the horizontal axis, and values of angle of wall friction ϕ' are on the vertical axis. The theoretical boundaries between mass flow and funnel flow depend on the effective angle of friction δ. Any combination of θ' and ϕ' that falls within the limiting mass flow region of the chart will provide mass flow. A 2-3° safety factor with respect to the theoretical mass flow hopper angle is recommended in the design of a conical mass flow hopper.

An analytical expression for the recommended mass flow boundary is given by Equation 2 [2].

$$\theta' = 90° - \frac{1}{2}\cos^{-1}\left(\frac{1-\sin\delta}{2\sin\delta}\right) - \beta \qquad (2)$$

where

$$\beta = \frac{1}{2}\left(\phi' + \sin^{-1}\left(\frac{\sin\phi'}{\sin\delta}\right)\right) \qquad (3)$$

A 2-3° safety factor should be subtracted from the result of Equation 2.

The wall friction angle ϕ' depends on the effective angle of friction δ and the major consolidation stress σ_1. It is determined from the intersection of the Mohr's circle associated with σ_1 and δ and the wall yield locus (see Figure 9). The Mohr's circle is given by

$$(\sigma-\sigma_{avg})^2+\tau^2=R^2 \tag{4}$$

where

$$R=\frac{\sigma_1-\sigma_2}{2} \tag{5}$$

and

$$\sigma_{avg}=\frac{\sigma_1+\sigma_2}{2} \tag{6}$$

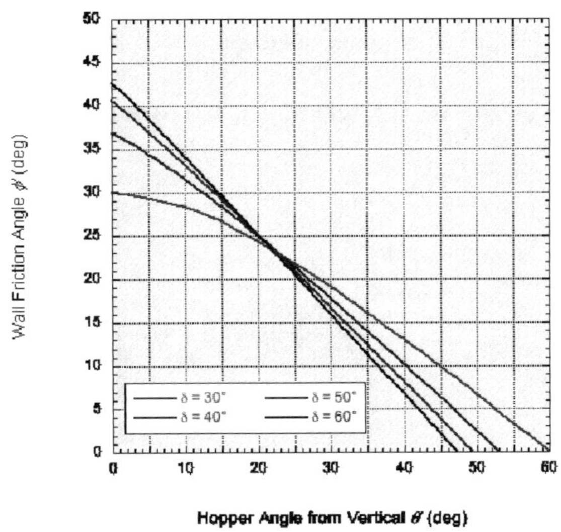

Figure 8. ***Theoretical*** **mass flow boundaries. A safety factor of 3° is recommended.**

The minor principal stress σ_2 is related to the effective angle of friction δ by

$$\frac{\sigma_2}{\sigma_1}=\frac{1-\sin(\delta)}{1+\sin(\delta)} \tag{7}$$

If the wall yield locus is linear, which is often true at low stresses, it can be described by

$$\tau'=a\sigma'+b \tag{8}$$

where τ' and σ' are the shear and normal stresses at the wall surface, respectively and a and b are empirical constants determined from regression. The normal stress can then be calculated from

$$\sigma'=\frac{-\beta+\sqrt{\beta^2-4\alpha\gamma}}{2\alpha} \tag{9}$$

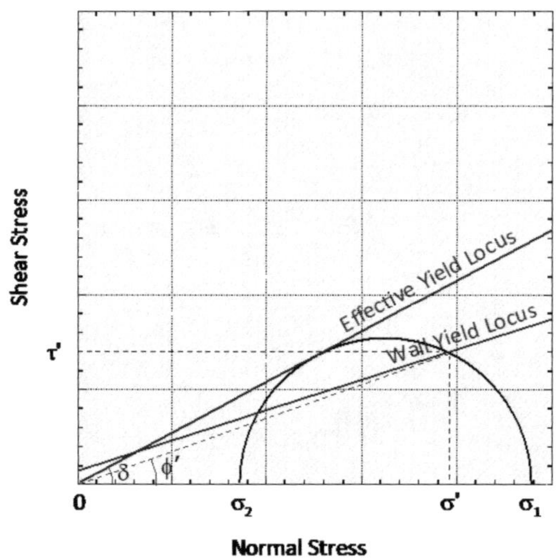

Figure 9. Determination of the wall friction angle from the major consolidation stress and effective angle of friction.

where

$$\alpha = a^2 + 1 \tag{10}$$

$$\beta = 2(ab - \sigma_{avg}) \tag{11}$$

and

$$\gamma = b^2 + \sigma_{avg}^2 - R^2 \tag{12}$$

The wall friction angle is then calculated from

$$\phi' = \tan^{-1}\left(\frac{\tau'}{\sigma'}\right) \tag{13}$$

where the shear stress at the wall τ' is calculated from Equation 8.

Minimum outlet dimension. To prevent the formation of a stable cohesive arch at the outlet of a hopper, the external stress must be greater than the powder's unconfined yield strength. Jenike [1] defined the flow factor *ff* as the ratio of the major consolidation stress σ_1 to the stress on the abutment of the arch that naturally forms at the outlet $\bar{\sigma}$:

$$ff = \frac{\sigma_1}{\bar{\sigma}} \tag{14}$$

The flow factor depends on the powder's effective angle of friction δ, the wall friction angle ϕ', and the hopper angle θ'. Charts that provide flow factors are provided by Jenike [1], and an example of a chart is given in Figure 10, which gives the flow factor for powders having an effective angle of friction equal to 50° that are handled in conical hoppers.

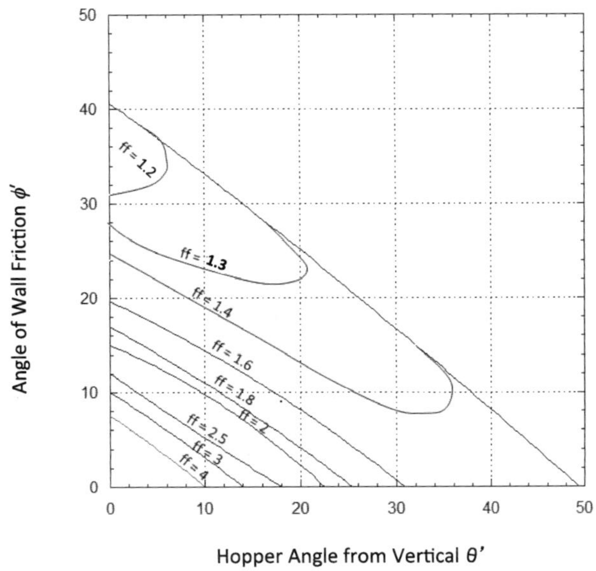

Figure 10. Flow factors for conical hoppers, δ = 50°

Analytical expressions of the flow factor are provide by Arnold and McLean [4,5]. For conical hoppers, the flow factor can be determined from

$$ff = \frac{Y(1+\sin\delta)H(\theta')}{2(X-1)(\sin\theta')} \quad (15)$$

where

$$X = \frac{2\sin\delta}{1-\sin\delta}\left[\frac{\sin(2\beta+\theta')}{\sin\alpha}+1\right] \quad (16)$$

$$Y = \frac{[2(1-\cos(\beta+\theta'))]\sin\theta' + \sin\beta\sin^2(\beta+\theta')}{(1-\sin\delta)\sin^3(\beta+\theta')} \quad (17)$$

and

$$H(\theta') = \left(\frac{130° + \theta'}{65}\right) \quad (18)$$

These equations may be serpentine, but they can readily be input into spreadsheets and other computer software. Flow factors typically range between 1.2 and 1.6 but can be much greater if wall friction is exceptionally low and hopper walls are very steep.

Jerry Johanson defined a critical flow factor for which the hopper angle was near the theoretical mass flow boundary. His critical flow factor is approximately the same value that would be calculated for wall friction angles greater than about 12° and hopper angles in the neighborhood of the mass flow boundary. The critical flow factor for conical hoppers is plotted against effective angle of friction in Figure 11.

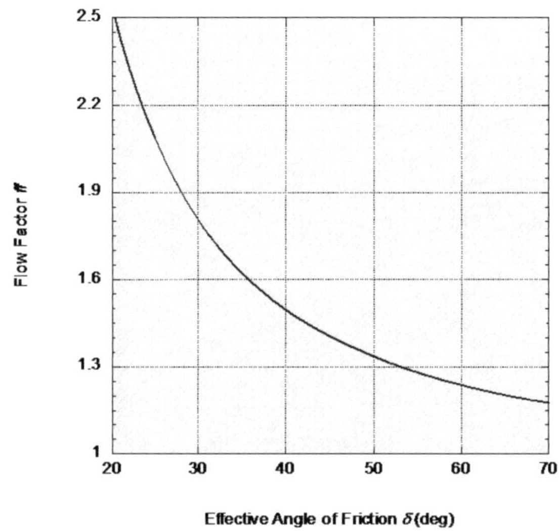

Figure 12. Critical flow factor chart for axisymmetric hoppers.

An analytical expression for the critical flow factor is:

$$ff = 1.118 + \frac{0.285}{(\tan\delta)^2} \tag{19}$$

The cohesive strength and arch stress can be compared by superimposing the flow factor and flow function on the same graph. The flow factor is constructed by drawing a line having a slope equal to $1/ff$ through the origin. As shown in Figure 13, three possibilities exist:

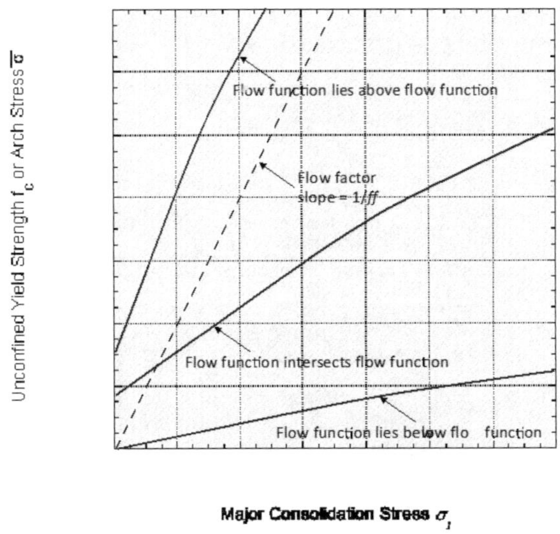

Figure 13. Plot showing both flow function and flow factor.

1. The flow function lies below the flow factor, and the two do not intersect. When this is the case, the stress imparted on the abutment of the arch is always greater than the material's cohesive strength, and there is no minimum outlet dimension requirement to prevent cohesive arching. Instead, the outlet dimension B is determined by other considerations such as required discharge rate. The hopper angle required for mass flow requires the major consolidation stress σ_1 at the outlet to be known. This stress is calculated from

$$\sigma_1 = ff \frac{\rho_b g B}{H(\theta')} \tag{20}$$

2. The flow function lies above the flow factor and the curves do not intersect. The powder will not flow due to gravity alone. Consideration should be given to changing the flow properties of the material, such as increasing its particle size or using a flow aid.
3. The flow function and flow factor intersect. At the intersection of the two lines, the arch stress and the cohesive strength of the bulk solid are the same and equal to the critical stress σ_{crit}. The hopper outlet diameter that must be exceeded to prevent arching, B_{min}, can be calculated from

$$B_{\min} = \frac{H(\theta')\sigma_{crit}}{\rho_b g} \tag{21}$$

The bulk density ρ_b, the effective angle of friction δ, and the angle of wall friction ϕ' depend on stress, and therefore calculating critical hopper angles and arching dimensions is an iterative procedure. Figure 14 gives a flowchart for calculating the minimum hopper outlet diameter and recommended mass flow hopper angle for the case where the flow function and flow factor intersect. A flowchart for determining the recommended mass flow hopper angle for selected outlet diameters is given in Figure 15.

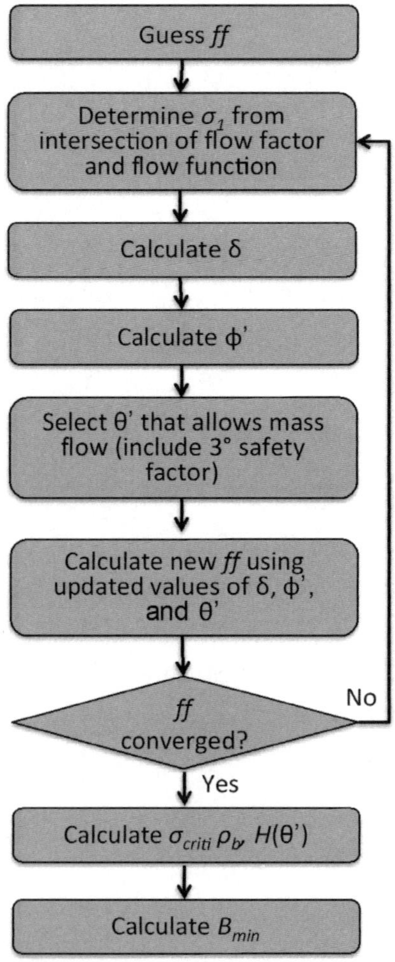

Figure 14. Flowchart for determining critical hopper outlet size and mass flow hopper angle.

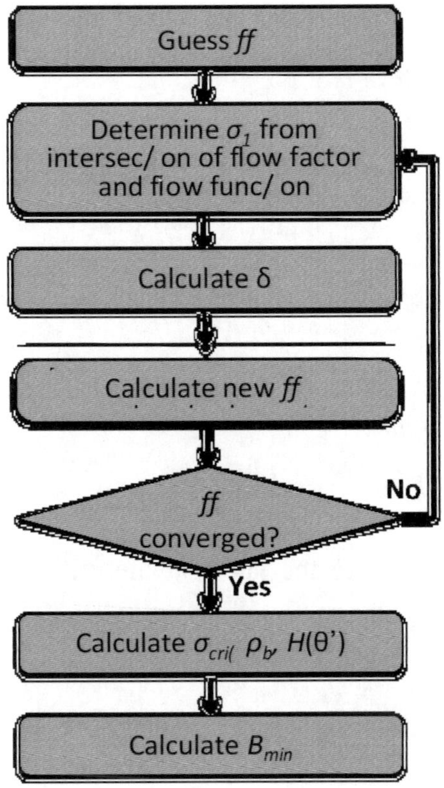

Figure 15. Flowchart for determining recommended mass flow hopper angle for a specified outlet diameter.

For funnel flow hoppers, the outlet must be large enough to prevent both a cohesive arch and stable rathole from developing. From Jenike [1], the critical rathole diameter D_F can therefore be calculated from:

$$D_F = \frac{G(\phi_t) f_c}{\rho_b g} \tag{22}$$

where $G(\phi_t)$ is a function defined by Jenike [1] and ϕ_t is the kinematic angle of internal friction. The unconfined strength f_C is assumed to equal that at the solids stress at the hopper-cylinder junction. The function $G(\phi_t)$ can be calculated from [6]

$$G(\phi_t) = 4.3 \tan \phi_t \tag{23}$$

The outlet must be large enough to provide the desired discharge rate. For coarse powders, the solids discharge rate $\dot{m}_s$ is given by

$$\dot{m}_s = \rho_{bo} \frac{\pi B^2}{4} \sqrt{\frac{Bg}{4\tan(\theta')}} \tag{22}$$

The maximum discharge rate of a fine powder can be orders of magnitude less than that of a coarse powder due to an adverse (negative) gradient that naturally develops near the outlet as the powder dilates:

$$\dot{m}_s = \rho_{bo} \frac{\pi B^2}{4} \sqrt{\frac{Bg}{4\tan\theta'}\left(1 + \frac{1}{\rho_b g} \frac{dP}{dz}\bigg|_o\right)} \tag{23}$$

For fine powders, the following equation provides a conservative estimate of the maximum discharge rate [7]:

$$\dot{m}_s = \rho_{bo} \frac{\pi B^2 K_o}{4\left(1 - \frac{\rho_{bo}}{\rho_{b\max}}\right)} \tag{24}$$

where the subscripts *o* and *max* denote the value at the outlet and the maximum value, respectively. The maximum bulk density ρ_{bmax} is its bulk density at the major consolidation stress at the hopper cylinder junction, which is calculated from the Janssen equation:

$$\sigma_1 = \frac{\rho_b g D}{4k\tan(\phi')}\left[1 - \exp\left(-\frac{4k\tan(\phi')h}{4}\right)\right] \tag{25}$$

where D is the cylinder diameter, h is the depth of powder in the cylinder section, and k is the Janssen parameter. Average values of the bulk density and wall friction angle are used. The Janssen parameter can be assumed equal to 0.4.

Optimization example. A powder containing 67 percent acetaminophen (AAP), 29 percent microcrystalline cellulose (MCS), and 4 percent hydroxypropyl cellulose (HPC) was prepared using a V-blender. Additional blends were then prepared by adding fumed silica (CAB-O-SIL® M-5P) and magnesium stearate from Mallinckrodt at various levels.

Jenike's analyses were performed to determine critical arching and ratholing dimensions and recommended mass flow hopper angles for axisymmetric (conical and pyramidal) hoppers. Results of the calculations are summarized in Table 1. The critical rathole diameter assumed a small hopper with a cylinder height of 1 m and a hydraulic radius of 0.25 m completely filled with powder. Wall friction angle often depends on solids stress and therefore hopper outlet diameter; however, for the blends tested, the wall friction angle was essentially constant, and therefore the recommended hopper angle for mass flow was independent of outlet diameter.

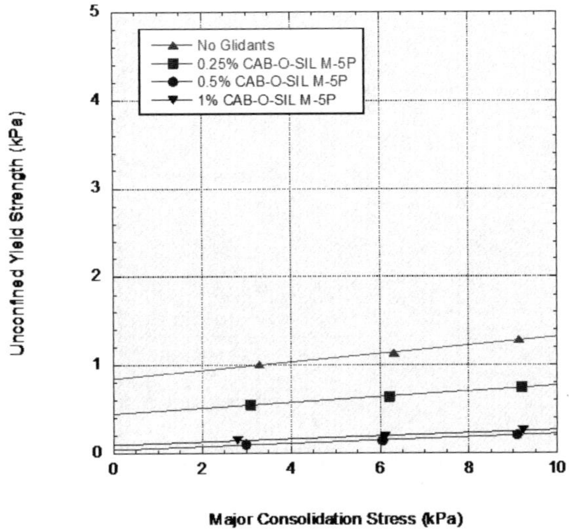

Figure 16. Flow functions of APAP/MCC/HPMC blend with varying levels of CAB-O-SIL M-5P.

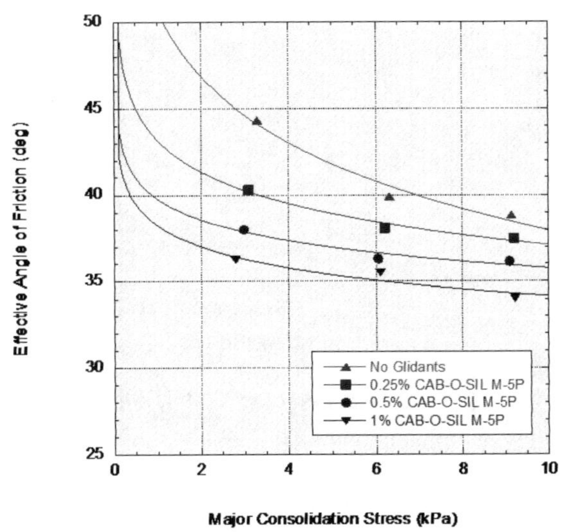

Figure 17. Effective angle of friction of acetaminophen/microcrystalline cellulose/ hydroxypropyl cellulose blend with varying levels of CAB-O-SIL M-5P.

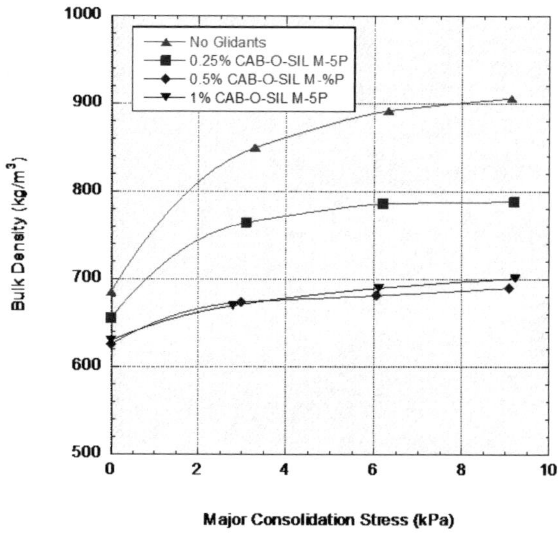

Figure 18. Bulk density of APAP/MCC/HPMC blend with varying levels of CAB-O-SIL M-5P.

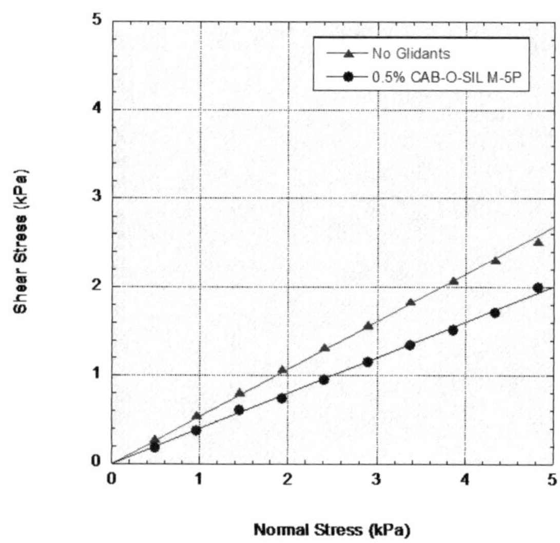

Figure 19. Wall friction of APAP/MCC/HPMC with varying levels of CAB-O-SIL M-5P on 304 #2B stainless steel.

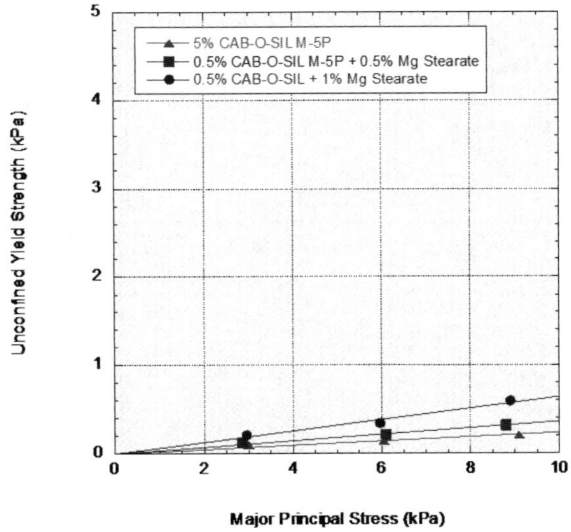

Figure 20. Flow functions of APAP/MCC/HPMC blend with 0.5% CAB-O-SIL M-5P and varying levels of magnesium stearate.

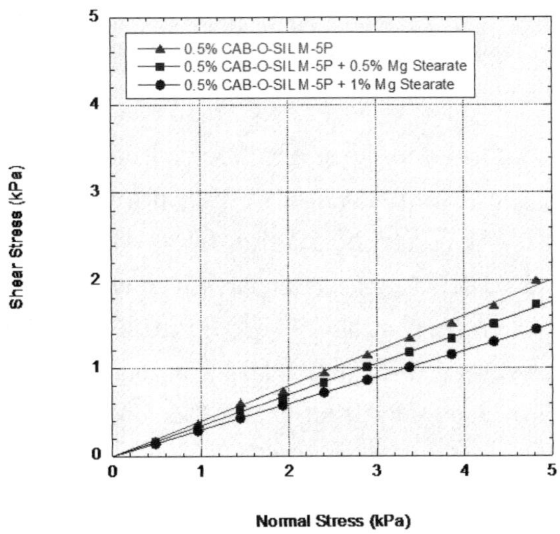

Figure 20. Wall yield locus of APAP/MCC/HPMC blend with 0.5% CAB-O-SIL M-5P and varying levels of magnesium stearate on 304 #2B stainless steel.

Table 1
Analysis of Flow Property Test Results

SiO_2 Content	Mg Stearate Content	Critical Arching Diameter	Recommended Mass Flow Hopper Angle	Critical Ratholing Diameter
0%	0%	12"	12°	28"
0.25%	0%	7"	-	15"
0.5%	0%	1"	22°	2"
1.0%	0%	2"	-	4"
0.5%	0.5%	2"	25°	2"
0.5%	1.0%	2"	30°	4"

A typical hopper or bin is fabricated from 304 #2B stainless steel and is pyramidal or conical in shape. Hopper walls generally range between 30° from vertical and 45°. Outlet diameters of hoppers affixed to roller compaction equipment are often 2 in. Those of portable bins are larger and around 4 in. Formulators should ensure that no obstructions to flow develop in these vessels.

Without glidants, the formulations require a hopper with a large outlet to prevent arching and a significantly larger outlet to prevent a stable rathole from developing. As seen in Figure 17, the addition of CAB-O-SIL M-5P significantly reduces the cohesive strength of APAP/MCC/HPMC. Fumed silica acts as a parting agent, which increases the distance between powder particles thereby reducing the magnitude of the cohesive forces. At high levels, however, its effectiveness diminishes and can lead to increases in strength due to the abundance of small particles that attract each other.

A fumed silica level of 0.5 percent appears to be optimal. However, the required hopper angle or mass flow is 22° from vertical, significantly steeper than is found in typical portable bins or feed hoppers.

Magnesium stearate was added to the blend that was previously mixed with 0.5 percent SiO_2. Magnesium stearate acts as a lubricant for reducing wall friction in tablet presses as well as in hoppers. The analyses showed that by adding 1 percent magnesium stearate, mass flow is possible in 30° hoppers, and arching will not occur provided that the hopper outlet is 2 in. or greater.

Unfortunately, a level of 1 percent magnesium is detrimental to tablet press performance. A blend containing 0.5 percent CAB-O-SIL M-5P and only 0.5 percent magnesium stearate will not discharge in a mass flow pattern. However, its critical ratholing diameter is 1 in., and funnel flow will not result in the development of a *stable* rathole. As such, even a crude 45° pyramidal hopper can reliably handle this blend.

Note that the outlet should be sized to allow the desired solids discharge rate. Based on a permeability of 0.022 m/s, the maximum steady solids discharge rate from a mass flow hopper with a 4-in. diameter outlet was estimated to be *ca.* 4500 kg/hr. The discharge rate from a funnel flow hopper can be expected to be somewhat greater due to the steep flow channel that develops.

Closing remarks. By adding glidants, in particular fumed silica to reduce a blend's cohesive strength and magnesium stearate to lower its wall friction, formulations for solids dosage forms can be optimized. The formulator must be familiar with the powder handling equipment associated with the agglomeration process. By measuring the formulation's fundamental properties, *i.e.*, its cohesive strength, internal friction, compressibility, wall friction, and permeability, Jenike's methods can be used to predict powder flow behavior in the storage bin and feed hopper and if necessary, specify and replace the equipment with one appropriate for the material.

References

1. Jenike, A.W., Storage and Flow of Solids, Bulletin 123, University of Utah Engineering Station, 1964 (revised, 1976).
2. Jenike, A.W., Gravity Flow of Solids, Bulletin 108, University of Utah Engineering Station, 1961.
3. Kulwiec, Materials Handling Handbook, John Wiley and Sons, Hoboken, NJ, 1985.
4. Arnold, P.C. and A.G. McLean, "An Analytical Solution for the Stress Function at the Wall of a Converging Channel", *Powder Techn.*, **13**, 255 (1976).
5. Arnold, P.C. and A.G. McLean, "Improved Analytical Flow Factors for Mass-Flow Hoppers", *Powder Techn.*, **15**, 276 (1976).
6. McGlinchey, Bulk Solids Characterization, Blackwell Publishing Co., Carlton, Victoria Australia, 2005.
7. Johanson, K., "Successfully Dealing with Erratic Flow Rates", *Powder Pointers,* **3**, A (2009).

Institute for
Briquetting and
Agglomeration

2022 IBA CONFERENCE PAPERS

Paper Title:
Improvement in Powder Flowability by Spheronizing

Presenters:
Greg Mehos, Scott Miller, and
Alva Godfrey,

Company:
Greg Mehos & Associates LLC,
Solids Handling Technologies, Inc.
LCI Corporation

Improvement in Powder Flowability by Spheronizing

Greg Mehos, Greg Mehos & Associates LLC
Scott Miller, Solids Handling Technologies, Inc.
Alva Godfrey, LCI Corporation

Agglomeration is often desirable because the product that has a higher bulk density and improved flowability. This is especially the case in the processing of solid dosage forms in pharmaceutical equipment. Figure 1 shows samples of a blend of fine acetaminophen (APAP), microcrystalline cellulose (MCC), and hydroxypropylmethylcellulose (HPMC) powders before and after agglomeration.

Figure 1. APAP/MCC/HPMC blend – fine (left) and spheronized (right).

Fine powders often exhibit flow problems in a hopper or bin, such as flow stoppages, erratic flow, and sluggish discharge rates. Flow stoppages can occur if a cohesive arch develops at the vessel outlet. In some cases, a stable rathole can develop and the bin will not completely empty.

The likelihood of a solids flow problem often depends on the flow pattern present inside a bin. There are two primary flow patterns that can occur: mass flow and funnel flow (see Figure 2).

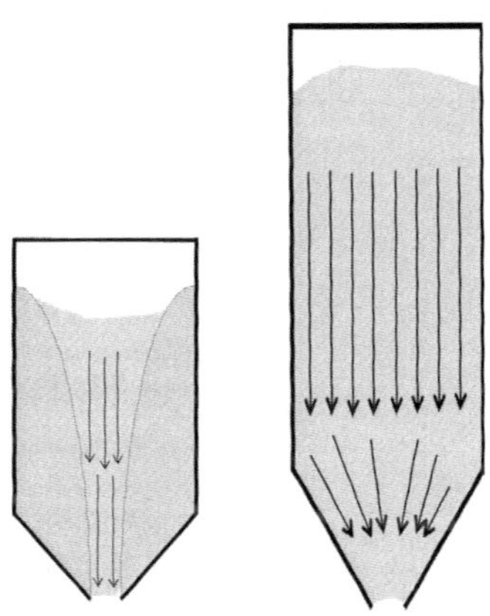

Figure 2. Flow patterns – funnel flow (left) and mass flow (right).

In funnel flow, an active flow channel forms above the outlet, with stagnant material remaining at the periphery (*i.e.*, ratholes). This occurs when the walls of the hopper section of the storage vessel are not steep enough or have low enough friction to allow flow along them. The size of the resultant flow channel is approximately the largest dimension of the outlet, and for a conical funnel flow hopper, the fraction of its volume that is active can be dramatically small. If the bulk material is cohesive, the ratholes may be stable and the effective capacity of the bin will be just a small fraction of its intended capacity.

In mass flow, the entire bed of solids is in motion when material is discharged from the outlet, including material along the walls. Mass flow hoppers typically have steep and/or low-friction walls. Provided that the outlet is large enough to prevent arching, all material will be discharged from the bin, as ratholes will not form. Eliminating flow problems can often be accomplished by ensuring that a mass flow pattern exists in the vessel.

The flow pattern inside a bin or hopper – funnel flow or mass flow – can be predicted by measuring the friction between the powder and the hopper wall material. Wall friction is measured by applying various normal loads to a sample of powder and forcing it to slide along a coupon of wall material. The resulting shear force is measured as a function of the applied normal force, and a wall yield locus is constructed by plotting shear force against normal force. The angle of wall friction at a particular pressure (ϕ') is the angle that is formed when a line is drawn from the origin to a point on the wall yield locus. A wall yield locus determined using a Jenike direct shear cell test on a sample of the fine APAP/MCC/HPMC powder on 304 # 2B finish stainless steel is shown in Figure 3.

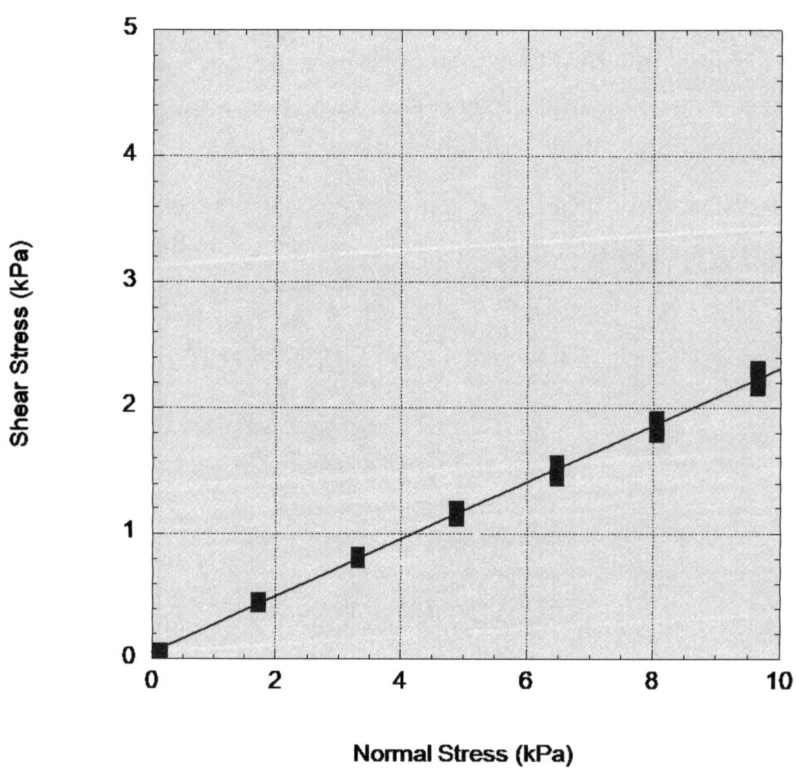

Figure 3. Wall friction between APAP/MCC/HPMC powder and 304 #2B stainless steel.

Jenike [1] developed design charts that provide allowable hopper angles for mass flow given values of the wall friction angle and the effective angle of friction δ, which is determined by shear cell testing. Jenike's design charts for axisymmetric (*e.g.*, conical, pyramidal) and planar (*e.g.*, wedge, transition, chisel) are shown in Figure 4.

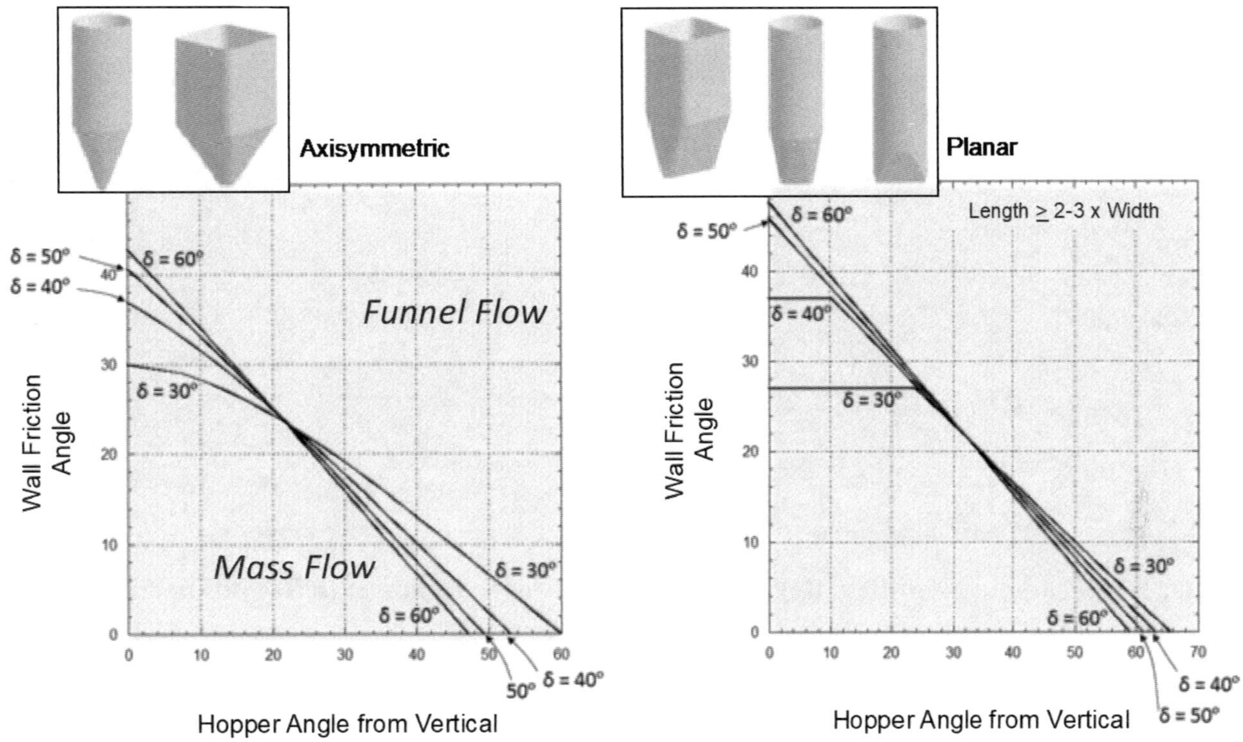

Figure 4. Jenike's recommended mass flow hopper angles – axisymmetric (left) and planar (right); a safety factor of 3-4 degrees should be used for axisymmetric hoppers.

Values of the allowable hopper angle are on the horizontal axis, and values of the wall friction angle (ϕ') are on the vertical axis. Any combinations of ϕ' and the hopper angle (from vertical) θ that lie within the mass flow region of the chart will provide mass flow. Designing right to the limit of the mass flow region is not recommended for conical bins. If the combination of wall friction angle and hopper angle lies too close to the funnel-flow line, a switch to funnel flow can occur. Hence, a 3-4-degree margin of safety is employed with respect to the mass flow boundary. For planar hoppers, mass flow can take place in hoppers shallower than Jenike's recommendations.

Because the wall friction angle depends on the wall stress, which decreases with decreasing outlet size, the recommended mass flow hopper angle depends on the size of the hopper outlet. Figure 5 presents recommended mass flow hopper angles for conical and planar hoppers that store and handle the APAP/MCC/HPMC powder having wall friction described by Figure 3.

Flow stoppages will be prevented if the stresses imparted on an obstruction to flow (such as a cohesive arch or stable rathole) are greater than the cohesive strength that the material gains due to its consolidation in a bin or hopper. The cohesive strength of a bulk solid can be determined using a shear cell tester to measure the failure strength of a material under varying consolidation pressures. The relationship between strength and pressure is called the flow function. The flow function for the sample of fine powder, measured using a Schulze RST-01.pc ring shear tester, is shown in Figure 6.

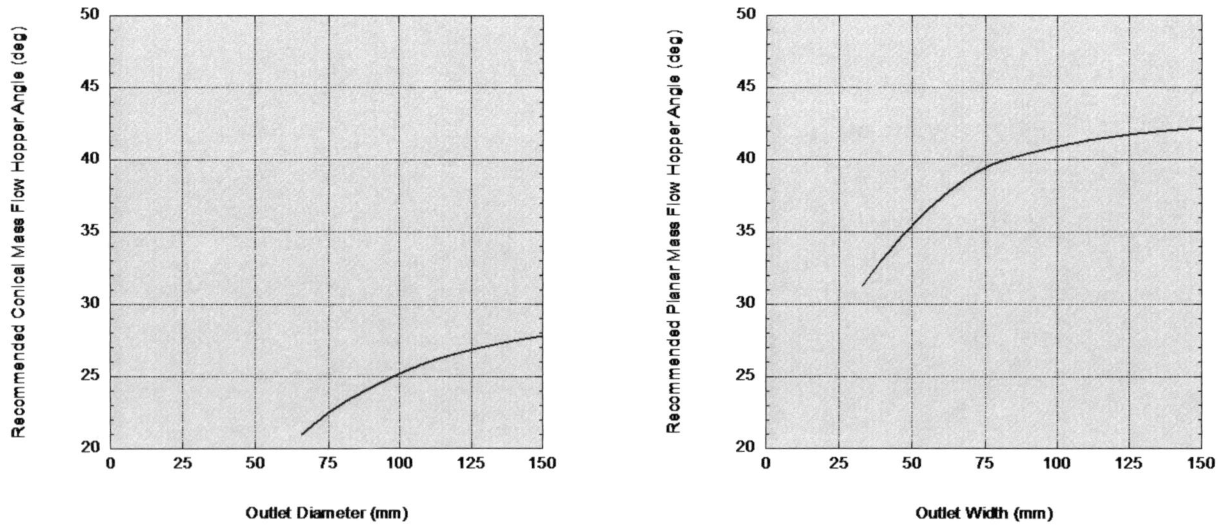

Figure 5. Recommended mass flow hopper angles – axisymmetric (left) and planar (right).

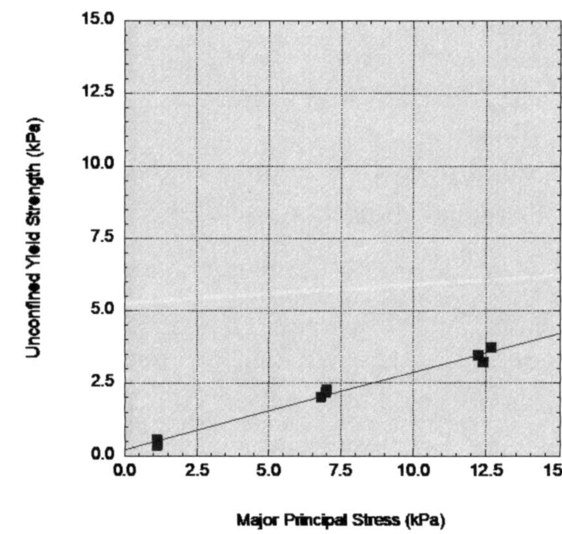

Figure 6. Flow function of fine APAP/MCC/HPMC powder.

The stress imparted on an arch of powder that forms at the vessel outlet is proportional to the material's bulk density. Provided that this stress is greater than the powder's cohesive strength, arching will not occur. Once a material's flow function has been determined and its bulk density has been measured, the minimum outlet diameter that will prevent a cohesive arch from developing can be calculated following an analysis developed by Jenike [1]. The critical arching outlet dimension can be calculated from

$$B_{min} = H(\theta')\frac{\sigma_{crit}}{\rho_b g}$$

where B_{min} is the minimum outlet diameter or width to prevent arching, $H(\theta')$ is a function defined by Jenike [1] (approximately equal to 2 for round outlets, 1 for slotted outlets), σ_{crit} is the critical stress, ρ_b is the bulk density, and g is acceleration due to gravity. The critical stress is that where the stress on the abutments of an arch is equal to the bulk material's cohesive strength, which is described by the material's flow function. Jenike's method to determine the minimum outlet required to prevent arching in a mass flow hopper is described by Mehos [2].

The analysis shows that a conical mass flow hopper requires a 65-mm diameter outlet to prevent arching when handling fine APAP/MCC/HPMC powder. For a planar hopper with a slotted outlet, the width of the outlet should exceed 30 mm. (Recall that $H(\theta')$ is approximately equal to 2 for round outlets and 1 for elongated outlets.)

In general, flowability improves with increasing particle size. Cohesive strength usually increases with decreasing particle size due to greater specific surface-area and a greater number of contacts between particles. To improve the flowability of the APAP/MCC/HPMC powder, the blend was agglomerated using an LCI Corporation blender, extruder and spheronizer (see Figure 7).

Figure 7. LCI Corporation MG-55 extruder and QJ-230T Marumerizer spheronizer.

The cohesive strength, internal friction, wall friction and bulk densities of the fine and spheronized blend are compared in Figure 8. Note that spheronizing dramatically reduces the cohesive strength of the material and its wall friction and increases its bulk density.

While a 65-mm diameter outlet is recommended to prevent the fine powder from arching in a conical hopper, the shear cell tests and subsequent analysis reveal that cohesive arching will not occur in a hopper or bin that handles the spheronized product. Instead, the outlet size of a vessel that handles the agglomerates should be selected by consideration of particle interlocking or desired discharge rates. For 1-mm diameter particles, a 6-mm diameter outlet is sufficiently large to prevent arching due to mechanical interlocking.

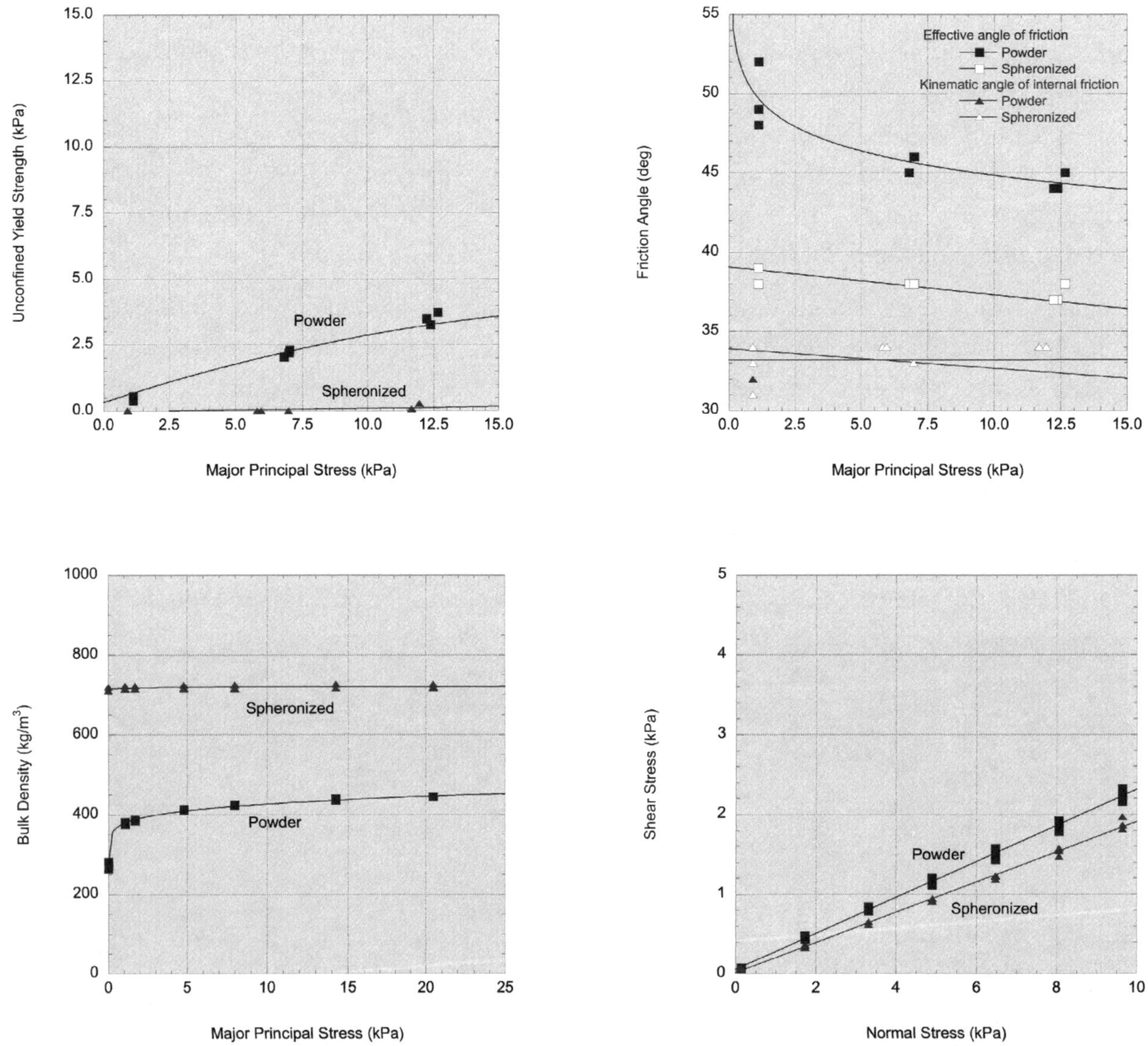

Figure 8. Flow properties of powdered and spheronized APAP/MMC/HPMC – cohesive strength (upper left), internal friction (upper right), bulk density (lower left), and wall friction (lower right).

In addition, wall friction test results reveal that the spheronized material requires hopper walls that are significantly less steep to allow mass flow. Recommended mass flow hopper angles for axisymmetric and planar hoppers handling fine and spheronized powder are given in Figure 9. If a conical hopper, bin, or silo with a 65-mm diameter outlet (*i.e.*, the minimum arching diameter) is fabricated or lined with 304 #2B finish stainless steel, walls sloped 22 degrees from vertical are recommended to ensure mass flow. A hopper fabricated using the same wall material sloped 44 degrees from vertical and a 5-mm diameter outlet will discharge spheronized material in mass flow.

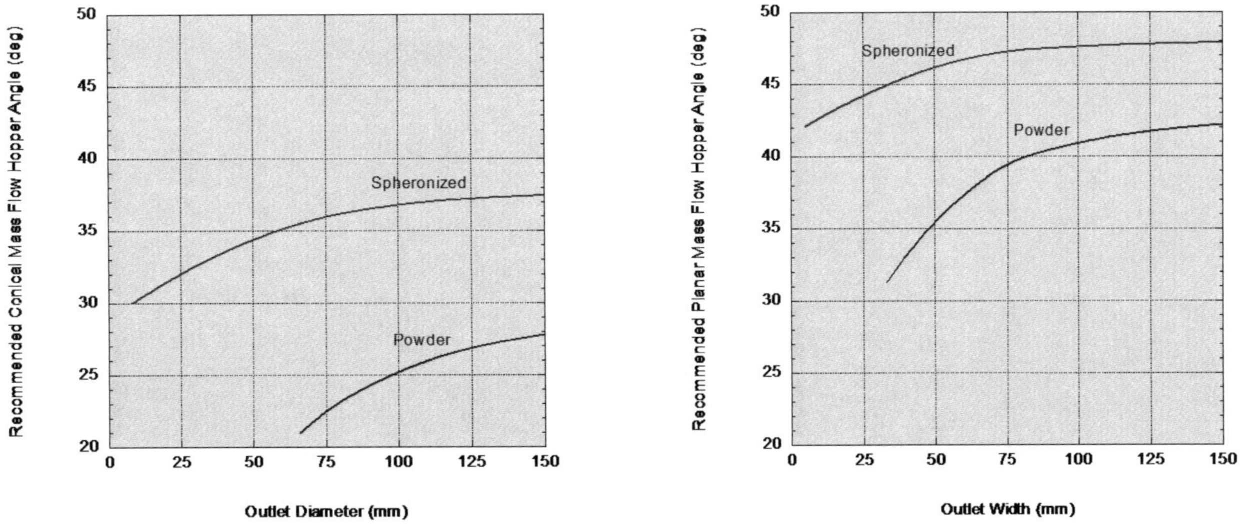

Figure 9. Comparison of recommended mass flow hopper angles – axisymmetric (left) and planar (right) – for bins handling fine and spheronized APAP/MCC/HPMC.

A funnel flow hopper or bin can be used provided its outlet is large enough to prevent a stable rathole from forming. From Jenike [1], D_F, the minimum outlet diameter of a funnel flow conical hopper or diagonal of a planar funnel flow hopper with a slotted outlet, can be calculated from

$$D_f = \frac{G(\phi)f_{Cmax}}{\rho_b g}$$

where $G(\phi)$ is a function defined by Jenike [1], ϕ is the kinematic angle of internal friction (determined from shear cell testing), and f_{Cmax} is the cohesive strength at the maximum solids stress level in a funnel flow hopper. The maximum solids stress is assumed equal to that at the junction of the straight-walled and converging sections of the bin or hopper and can be calculated from the Janssen equation:

$$\sigma_v = \frac{\rho_b g R_H}{k \tan \phi'}\left[1 - \exp\frac{(-k \tan \phi')}{R_H} z\right]$$

where σ_v is the solids stress, R_H is the hydraulic radius, k is the Janssen coefficient, assumed to equal 0.4, and z is the solids depth in the cylinder. The critical outlet diameter of a funnel flow bin will therefore depend on the maximum solids stress inside the hopper, which depends on the properties of the powder, the diameter of the cylinder section, and the powder depth.

Critical rathole outlet diameters of funnel flow bins handling fine and spheronized APAP/MCC/HPMC are summarized in Figure 10. Funnel flow bins used to store the fine powder require large outlets to ensure that the ratholes that develop will collapse. For example, a funnel flow bin with a 1-m diameter, 0.5-m tall cylinder completely filled with fine powder requires a 380-mm to prevent a stable rathole.

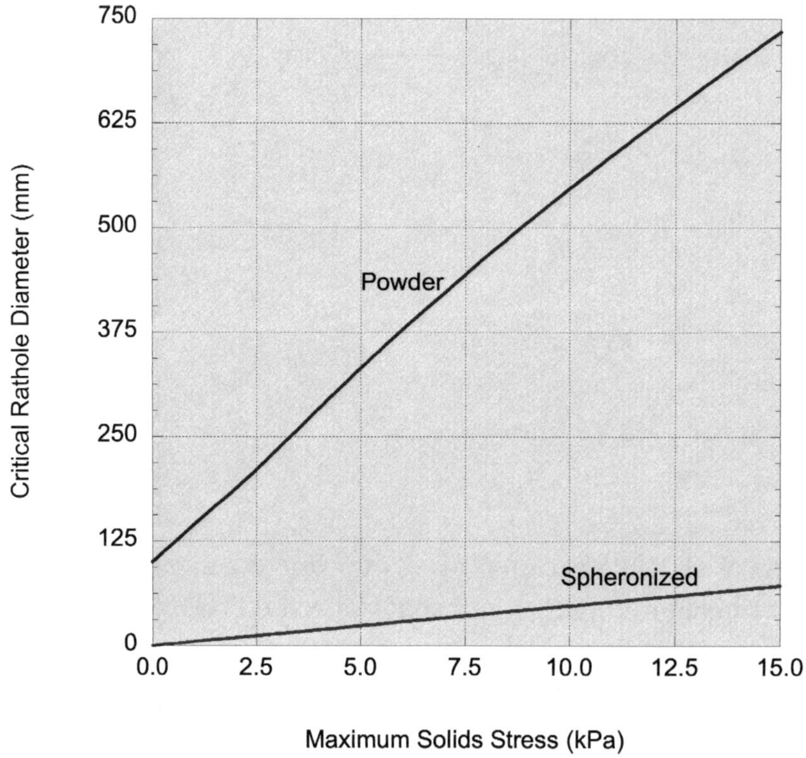

Figure 10. Critical rathole diameters.

The outlet of a planar funnel flow must be wide enough to prevent arching. The minimum width of a slotted outlet of a planar funnel flow hopper is 30 mm when the fine powder is handled. A cohesive arch will not develop if spheronized material is stored.

Concluding remarks

Fine powders are often challenging to handle due to their high cohesive strength, low bulk density, and high wall friction on most surfaces. Spheronization improves the flowability of a powder by dramatically reducing its cohesive strength, increasing its bulk density, and reducing its wall friction. When storing and handling spheronized powders, hoppers with shallow walls can often be used since mass flow is readily achieved and if not, ratholes are likely to be unstable.

References

1. Jenike, A.W., Storage and Flow of Solids, Bulletin 123, University of Utah Engineering Station, 1964 (revised, 1976).
2. Mehos, G., "Using Solids Flow Properties to Design Mass- and Funnel-Flow Hoppers", Powder Bulk Engr., 34, 2 (February 2020).

Institute for
Briquetting and
Agglomeration

2022 IBA CONFERENCE PAPERS

Paper Title:
Pelleting of Poorly Flowable Battery Raw Materials

Presenters:
Lauren (Wood) Petraglia and Alva Godfrey

Company:
LCI Corporation

Pelleting of Poorly Flowable Battery Raw Materials

Part of the Nederman Group

Agenda

- What is driving the need to pelletize?
- What is driving the need for this type of pelletizing?
- Case study 1
- Case study 2
- Questions?

What's driving the need to pelletize in the battery industry?

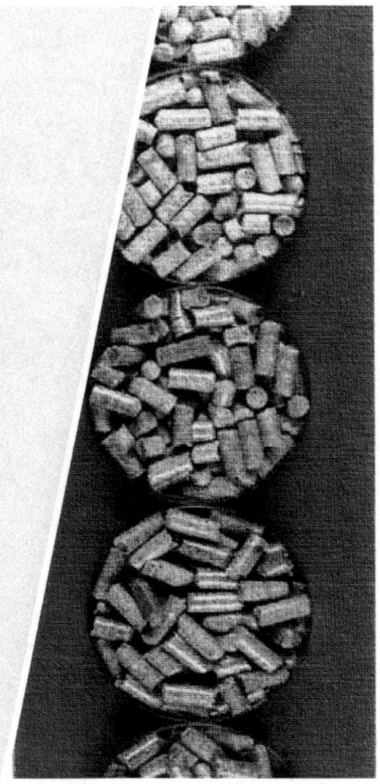

Part of the Nederman Group

End Product Characteristics Wanted

- Dust-free (safety)
- Improved Flow Properties (handling)
- Improved Density (performance and transport)
- High Yield (high value materials)
- Surface area (end use)
- Packing characteristics (end use)

What is driving the need for this type of pelletizing?

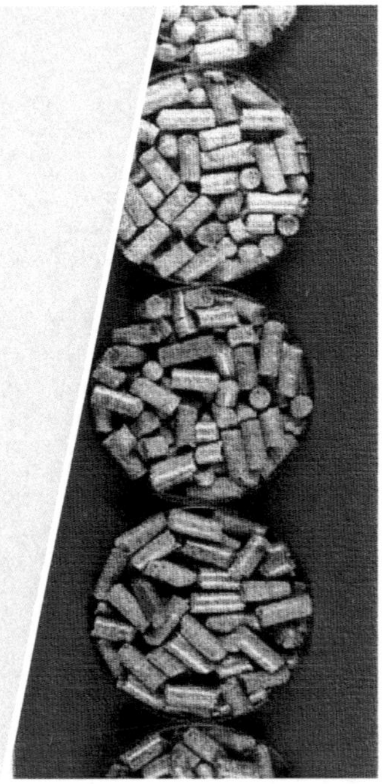

Background on Typical Battery Project Development

LCI
Part of the Nederman Group

- Plenty of other good pelleting technologies out there
- Customers are often starting with more well known or common technologies first
- Where we often come in is where those technologies are not able to achieve the required specifications of the project

What is driving the need for this specialty pellet mill?

Part of the Nederman Group

- Higher bulk density pellets wanted
- Higher throughput needed / larger units available
- Variety of sizes and densities needed
- Need for more options for better in process control
- More consistent product required
- Higher yield / less fines

Note: These are based on specific battery applications where other pelleting technology was not successful – not true for all applications

Case Study 1

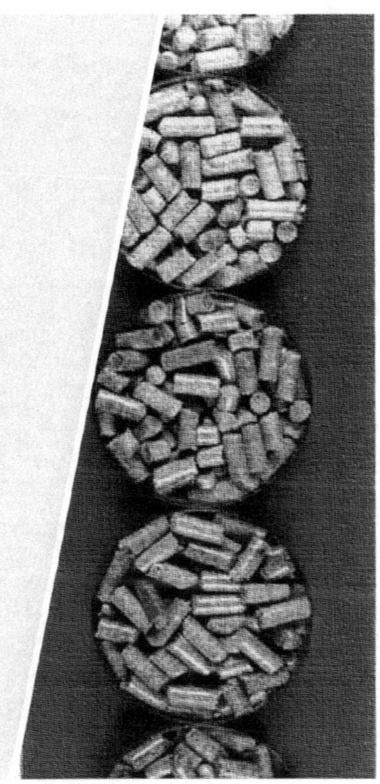

Battery Application Example

- Higher bulk density pellets wanted
- Higher throughput needed
- Robust pellets that can withstand downstream processing

Features of the Mill that benefited the Battery Application

- Larger Rollers
- Maximum pellet chamber volume
- Gravity fed device
- Adjustable pressure on rollers
- Adjustable pellet length
- 3-20 mm diameter pellets

This is not meant to be a sales presentation – but it's important context as to what were the drivers in this particular application that necessitated this particular technology

Large Roller Benefits

- Longer bearing life due to fewer revolutions
- Larger shafts for additional strength
- Shallow Nip angle for less slipping

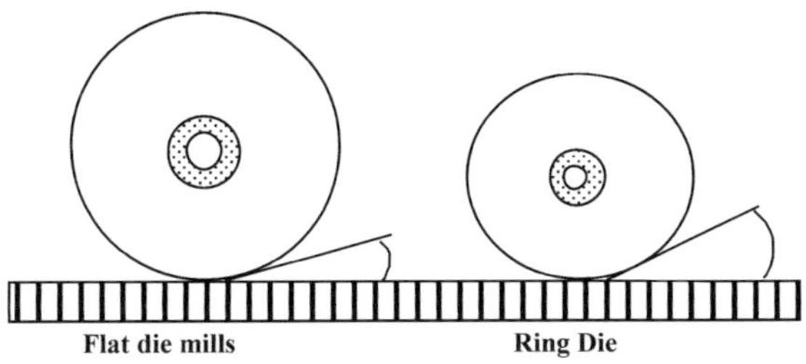

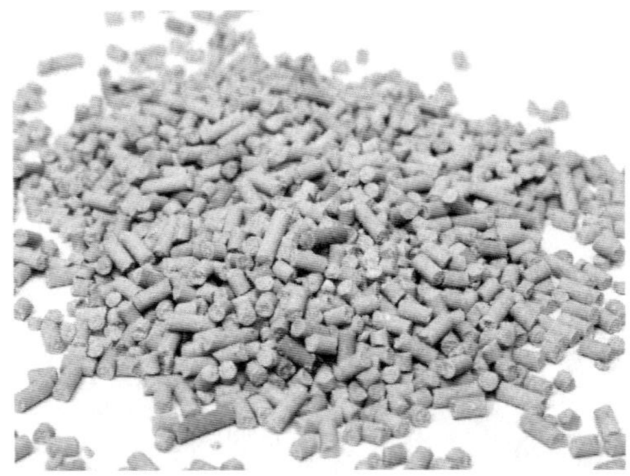

Maximum Pellet Chamber Volume

Vs

Adjustable Pressure with Hydraulic Nut

Part of the Nederman Group

Spacers limit metal-to-metal contact

Case Study 2

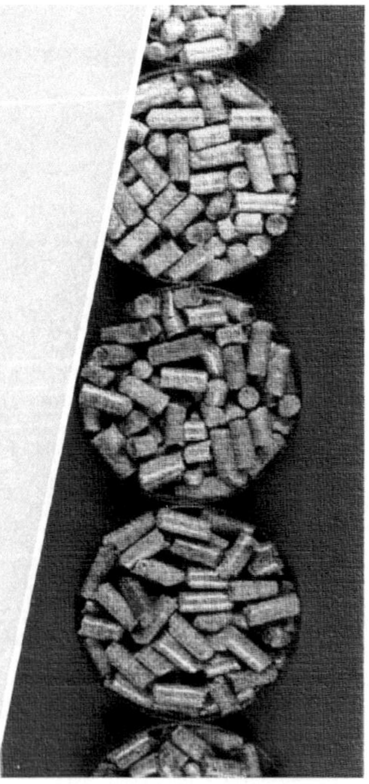

Battery Application Example – Low Pressure Extrusion

Part of the Nederman Group

- Higher bulk density pellets wanted to lower transportation costs
- Decreased inhalation hazard and better worker safety in handling and transporting

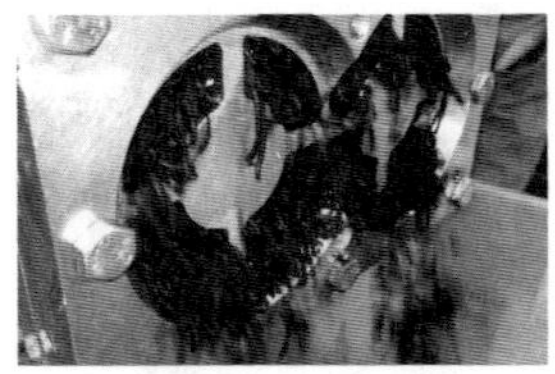

Battery Application Example – Low Pressure Extrusion

Part of the Nederman Group

- Able to produce smaller pellet sizes
- Low pressure low temperature
- High yield and process repeatability

Part of the Nederman Group

Questions

Part of the Nederman Group

LCI GRANULATION TEAM

CONTACT INFORMATION

Lauren (Wood) Petraglia
Sales Manager, Granulation
LCI Corporation
Phone: 704 398 7890
Mobile: 704 241 1590
Lpetraglia@lcicorp.com

Alva Godfrey
Sales Engineer, Granulation
LCI Corporation
Phone: 704 398 7825
Mobile: 704 770 7060
alva.godfrey@lcicorp.com

www.lcicorp.com

www.youtube.com/lcicorp

Institute for Briquetting and Agglomeration

2022 IBA CONFERENCE PAPERS

Paper Title:

Industrial trial of Recycled iron Briquettes produced with iron ore fines and sludge from sedimentation piles in a Direct Reduced Iron Reactor

Presenters:

Erick Bubniak, Joel Morales, and Andrés Villa

Company:

Diproinduca

Industrial trial of Recycled iron Briquettes produced with iron ore fines and sludge from sedimentation piles in a Direct Reduced Iron Reactor

Authors: Erick Bubniak, Joel Morales, Andrés Villa

Abstract

To demonstrate the technical and operational feasibility of processing briquettes made from iron fines in a Direct Reduction (DR) HYL Module. An industrial trial was conducted by loading the DRP reactor with a mixture of Iron Ore Pellets and Recycled iron Briquettes (RiB) made of iron ore pellets fines and sludge from the settling ponds.

The physical properties of the RiB before the reduction process allow for conventional handling with industrial equipment to be fed to the reactor. The quality of the reduced RiB in Metallization and Carbon content is superior to the quality of the DRI pellets. Reduced RiB shows a compressive strength similar to or superior to the DRI pellets processed with the current Iron Ore Pellets.

The results of the Industrial Trial carried out at a DR HYL Module, have sufficient physical and metallurgical properties to demonstrate the technical feasibility of the RiB technology. This allows the recycling of the iron ore pellet fines and sludge from the settling ponds in the direct reduction plants by producing RiB and mixing them with the iron ore pellets.

Key Words: RiB, Module, Direct Reduction, HYL, Recycling, DRI, Iron Ore Pellet Fines, Sludge from the settling ponds, Iron Ore Pellets, Circular Economy.

Introduction

World crude steel production increased from 189.8 million tons in 1950 to more than 715 million 35 years later (IISI, 1990) and by 2020's +1900 million tons in 2021. (*2022 World Steel in Figures*, 2022) In the course of this growth, two main routes have been maintained in the production of steel from iron ore. One is the BF/BOF route, which refers to Basic oxygen furnaces that use pig iron and small amounts of scrap as their primary material inputs and typically melt the furnace charge with coke oven, blast furnace, and natural gas. (Ruth, 2004)

The alternative route is a relatively new method that combines the production of direct reduction iron (DRI) with the making of steel in electric arc furnaces (EAF). It is known as the DR/EAF route. (De Buzin et al., 2017)

Direct reduction (DR) is defined as any process in which metallic iron is produced by the reduction of iron ore, or any iron oxide, below its melting temperature. The product of direct reduction is known as Direct Reduced Iron (DRI). (Lu et al., 2015)

Already in the XIX century, the steel industry was interested in the possibility of producing iron directly from the ore in the solid state, since this process would avoid the high temperatures necessary to reach the liquid state, with the consequent energy savings.

In addition to this immediate advantage, direct reduction would allow the use of a greater number of reducing agents, such as gases, and avoid the problems associated with the use of refractory materials to contain molten materials.

Some of the qualities of the DRI and its obtaining process are:

- The absence in the final product of elements such as copper, zinc, chromium, molybdenum, tungsten, among others, which are usually present in scrap metal.
- Low sulfur content.
- Allows the use of low-grade fuels.
- DRI is suitable for some special metallurgical processes, such as the production of metal objects by compaction of powders, (Stephenson, 1980).

By 2021 the production of iron by Direct Reduction reached 113.85 million tons, compared to less than 1 million tons in the early '70s and less than 50 million tons in the early '00s. (World Direct Reduction Statistics 2021 Contents, 2022). It is expected that DRI production will continue to grow due to its role in the decarbonization of the iron and steel industry as a technology that generates less CO2 emissions than the BF/BOF route. For every ton of steel produced by the BF/BOF route, 1.6 tons of CO2 are generated, versus 0.6 tons of CO2 by the DRI/EAF route. (de Beer et al., 2003) This could be further reduced by switching to green hydrogen as a reductant when the economics of this path is ready.

Even though the environmental advantage of using the DRI technology as an iron-making route of production, higher quantities of by-products are still being generated and will only increase when more DRI modules come into operation. Recycling methods for the by-products of the Direct Reduction process must be devised and applied, focusing on reducing the environmental impact and closing the recycling loop in this process.

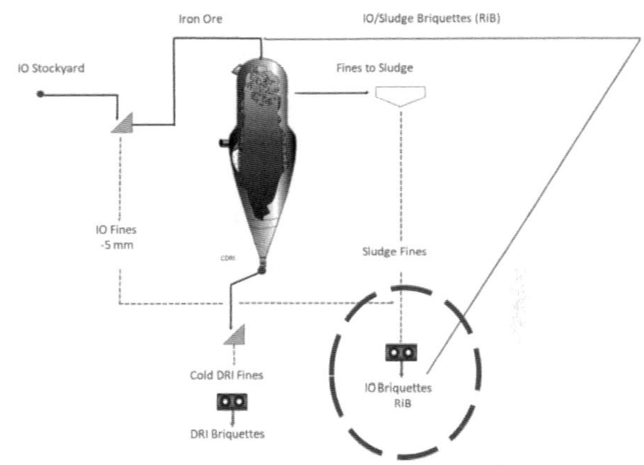

Figure 1: DRI Process with generated by-products

In a DRP, the recycling of the iron ore pellets fines from the screens and the sludge from the settling ponds of the process water system (shown in **Figure 1),** is an opportunity area to improve the yield in the conversion of the iron ore pellets into DRI. This alternative can be applied in the reactors of the interested DRP's.

Due to the lack of proven industrial options to use the iron ore pellet fines and sludge in the DRI process, the most common practice in the industry is to store and sell these by-products occupying land in the steel mill and selling them at a low price to other industries, losing valuable iron units that otherwise could be taken advantage of in the DRI process.

Diproinduca and Tenova HYL have presented to the interested DR HYL Module the characteristics of the RiB (Recycled iron Briquettes) technology, a solution that recycles the iron ore pellet fines and sludge in DRI Plants. RiB technology is based on producing cold briquettes using these iron oxide materials; subsequently, these briquettes are fed in the DR HYL Module mixed with iron ore pellets.

As an initial step to demonstrate the possible use of the Recyled iron Briquettes, several bag tests were carried out in the last years in the interested DRP Reactor using briquettes made of of iron ore pellet fines and sludge from the settling ponds with different proportions. The results of the bag tests indicated that the RiB; after the reduction process, achieved a level of metallization, carbon and compression strength similar to the DRI made with the iron ore pellets from the DRP own mining operations.

Materials and Methods

The Industrial trial was carried out adding RiB as a part of the regular Iron Ore load to the reactor. These briquettes were made of a mixture of 25% of iron ore pellets fines and 75% of sludge from the settling ponds as per DRP's requirements.

The DR HYL Module provided Diproinduca with the required quantities of iron ore pellets fines from the screening stations and sludge from the settling ponds to produce 40 tons of RiB, as shown in **Figure 2** and **Figure 3**.

Figure 2: Green Recycled iron Briquettes

Figure 3: Recycled iron Briquettes stored in super bags

To prepare the RiB, the Iron ore pellets fines and the sludge from the settling ponds underwent different processes: separation of impurities and foreign objects, moisture conditioning, screening, and grinding for the oversized material.

The RiB preparation process starts with a mixture of 25/75 of iron ore pellet fines /sludge from sedimentation piles. These materials are fed into the mixer to be homogenized. Binders are added to the mixer. The mixture is then fed to the briquetting machine for its agglomeration.

The obtained briquettes, also known as green or fresh briquettes, are screened to separate fines and chips from the RiB. The green briquettes are stored in 1 ton capacity Super Sacks for their curing process at room temperature.

The RiB were transported to the DRP's storage yards in trucks using super sacks to prevent dust emissions on the way. The unloading of the Super sacks was performed with a crane, and the Briquettes were piled up in the iron ore pellets yards' warehouse as **Figure 4** shows.

Figure 4: Recycled iron Briquettes in DRP's Yard

The RiB were mixed with iron ore pellets using reclaiming hopper to feed the RiB to the belt conveyor with iron ore pellets. The RiB were fed with payloader to the reclaiming hopper of the conveyor belts.

The 40 tons of RiB mixed with the iron ore pellets were loaded into the DR HYL Module, these represented 5.21% of the standard total Iron Ore pellets load of the reactor. This mix then went through the screening station and the coating system, until it reached the atmospheric charging bin. The mixture then passed through the DR HYL Module which was operating under the normal conditions established to process Iron Ore Pellets. The mix of Iron Ore Pellets / RiB were fed to the reactor for 7 hours during the night shift.

Results and discussion

The chemical quality of the RiB after passing through the Reactor were determined showing a good reduction degree and presence of carbon, with higher silica and lower total iron.

The physical quality was determined using the RiB collected from the belt conveyor at the discharge of the DR HYL Module.

Figure 5, shows an image of the RiB before and after their processing during the Industrial Trial on the DR HYL Module. Based on the photos and observations from **Figure 5** and **Figure 6**, the oxide briquettes made it through the reactor without much physical degradation.

Figure 5: RiB Briquettes before and after processing in the DRP Reactor

Figure 6: RiB Briquettes after processing in the DRP Reactor

The 40 tons of RiB were loaded into the DR HYL Module, representing a 5.21% of its composition RiB/Total Load. Its discharging from the reactor can be observed in **Figure 7**.

Figure 7: Prescence of RiB at the discharge of the DRP Reactor on the Industrial Trial

With 5-6% of RiB in the mixture of Iron Ore Pellets, there are no significant changes in the granulometry of the DRI or changes in fines generation.

The results of the Industrial Trial reproduced the results of the bag tests with RiB carried out in advance at the DR HYL Module.

The chemical analysis of the material can be observed in **Table 1**, which shows satisfactory results for Metallization, Carbon, Al_2O_3, CaO and MgO.

Table 1: Chemical analysis of RiB Briquettes post processing on the DRP Reactor

Chemical Analysis	Post Reactor Reduced RiB	DRI Pellet
Fe Tot	74.6 %	85%
Metallization	95.3 %	94%
Carbon	4.8 %	4%
SiO_2	7.3 %	5%
Al_2O_3	2.4 %	
CaO	2.3 %	
MgO	1.1 %	1.1%

The Total Fe content of the RiB is lower than the value of the DRI Pellets and the SiO_2 is higher, this is expected due to the use of by products with less Fe content and the use of binders to produce the briquettes.

The results of the metallization and carbon content of the RiB can be observed in **Figure 8** and **Figure 9**, respectively. The DRI Pellets had an average of 94% Metallization and a carbon level between 3.5 and 4.0%

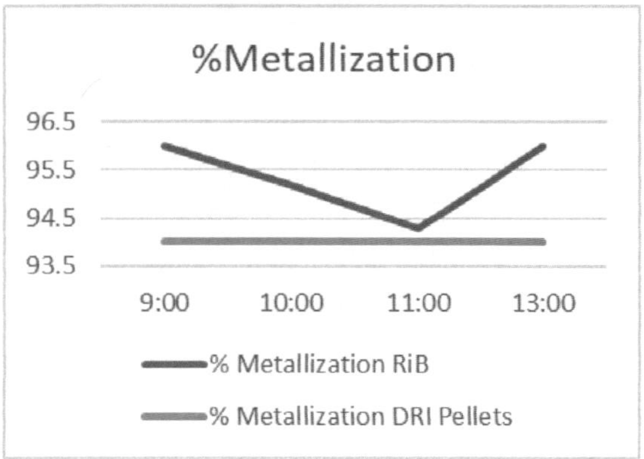

Figure 8: Metallization of RiB

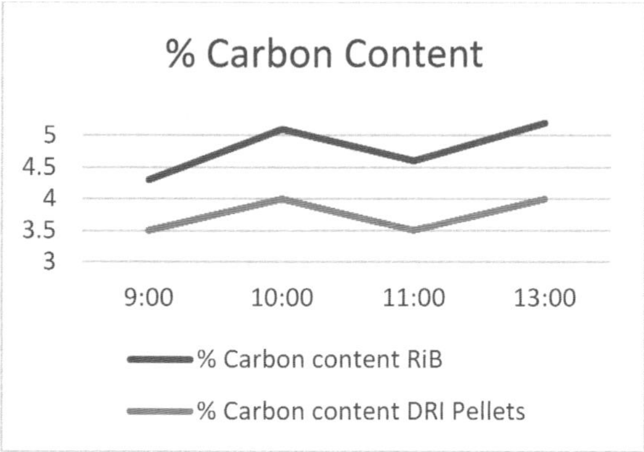

Figure 9: Carbon Content of RiB

The quality of the reduced RiB in Metallization and Carbon content is superior to the quality of the DRI pellets.

In **Figure 10**, the Total Fe of the RiB can be observed.

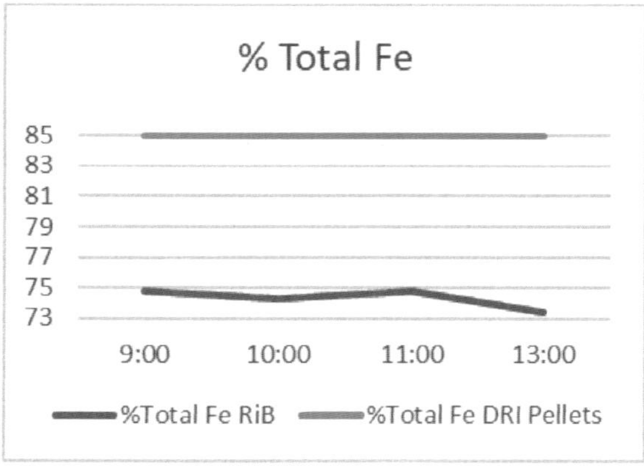

Figure 10: Fe Total content of RiB

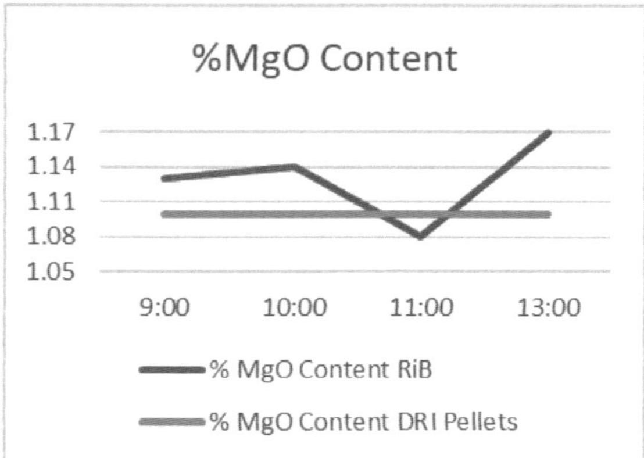

Figure 11: MgO content of RiB

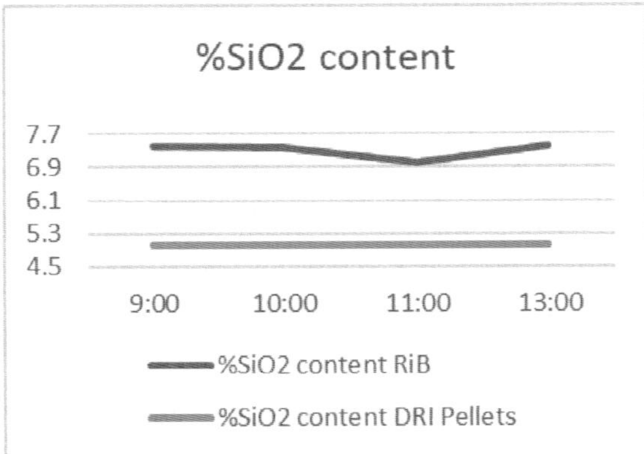

Figure 12: SiO_2 content of RiB

The reduced RiB have a higher level of MgO and SiO_2 than these chemical compounds' levels in the DRI pellets. The level of MgO is higher due to the presence of the Sludge, as it includes part of the magnesium hydroxide used in the coating system of the iron ore pellets. The higher SiO_2 is part of the binders used to produce the briquettes.

The results for the compressive strength are shown on **Table 2**: Compressive strength of the Reduced RiB.

Table 2: Compressive strength of the Reduced RiB

Reduced RiB **Direct Reduction DRP Reactor** Compressive Strength	
Average CSAR, kgf	**Standard deviation**
136.6	42.8

Conclusions

The physical properties of the Briquettes before the reduction process allow their handling with industrial equipment to be fed to the reactor using the belt conveyors system and the charging system.

The RiB have physical and metallurgical properties that allow adequate processing in the reactor and undergo the reduction process, while mixed with Iron Ore Pellets, using the normal process conditions of the DR HYL Module.

A level of Metallization higher than DRI Pellets. Carbon content of RiB is superior to the DRI Pellets. The Fe Total content in the reduced Briquettes is lower than the Total Fe content in the DRI pellets. Still, it can be increased by including other by-products in the composition of the mixture. Compressive strength after reduction was similar or superior to the DRI pellets.

The results of the Industrial Trial demonstrate the technical feasibility of the RiB technology to recycle the iron ore pellet fines and sludge from the settling ponds in the direct reduction plants by producing RiB and mixing them with Iron Ore Pellets.

It is programmed to execute further industrial tests using other iron oxides by-products from the steelmaking plant to confirm the technical feasibility of the RiB technology using additional by-products.

Acknowledgements

Diproinduca would like to thank Tenova HYL for the continuous support in coordinating and managing the bag tests performed and to the DR HYL Module, for its collaboration with by-products supply and testing facilities.

Bibliography

2022 World Steel in Figures. (2022). https://worldsteel.org/wp-content/uploads/2022-World-Steel-in-Figures.pdf

Ahmed, H. M., Persson, A., Sundqvist, L., & Bjorkman, B. (2014). Utilization of Steelmaking Industry Waste Materials in Producing Direct Reduced Iron. *European Steel Environment & Energy Congress*. https://www.researchgate.net/publicatio

n/280090746_Utilization_of_Steelmaking_Industry_Waste_Materials_in_Producing_Direct_Reduced_Iron

Bustamante-Rúa, M. O., Bustamante-Baena, P., Osorio-Botero, J. D., Daza-Álvarez, C. A., Bustamante-Rúa, M. O., Bustamante-Baena, P., Osorio-Botero, J. D., & Daza-Álvarez, C. A. (2019). Diseño geométrico de espesador-sedimentador y espesador en contra-corriente (CCD) en minería de oro para disposición de relaves. *Boletín de Ciencias de La Tierra*, *46*(46), 19–26. https://doi.org/10.15446/RBCT.N46.77553

de Beer, J., Harnisch, J., & Kerssemeeckers, M. (2003). GREENHOUSE GAS EMISSIONS FROM MAJOR INDUSTRIAL SOURCES-III IRON AND STEEL PRODUCTION . *IEA Greenhouse Gas R&D Programme*. https://ieaghg.org/docs/General_Docs/Reports/PH3-30 iron-steel.pdf

De Buzin, P. J. W. K., Heck, N. C., & Vilela, A. C. F. (2017). EAF dust: An overview on the influences of physical, chemical and mineral features in its recycling and waste incorporation routes. *Journal of Materials Research and Technology*, *6*(2), 194–202. https://doi.org/10.1016/J.JMRT.2016.10.002

Garcia, J. (n.d.). *LIXIVIACION DE MINERALES MEDIANTE PILAS Y BATEAS*.

Lu, L., Pan, J., & Zhu, D. (2015). Quality requirements of iron ore for iron production. *Iron Ore: Mineralogy, Processing and Environmental Sustainability*, 476–504. https://doi.org/10.1016/B978-1-78242-156-6.00016-2

Moraes, S. L. de, Lima, J. R. B. de, & Ribeiro, T. R. (2018). Iron Ore Pelletizing Process: An Overview. *Iron Ores and Iron Oxide Materials*. https://doi.org/10.5772/INTECHOPEN.73164

Ruth, M. (2004). Steel Production and Energy. *Encyclopedia of Energy*, 695–706. https://doi.org/10.1016/B0-12-176480-X/00371-5

Steel Statistical Yearbook 1990, Iron and Steel Institute, Brussels 1990

Stephenson, E. T. (1980). The effect of tin on the toughness of some common steels. *Metallurgical Transactions A*, *11*(3), 517–524. https://doi.org/10.1007/BF02654575

WORLD DIRECT REDUCTION STATISTICS 2021 CONTENTS. (2022).

Institute for Briquetting and Agglomeration

2022 IBA CONFERENCE PAPERS

Paper Title:

SNF Organic Binder
Polyacrylamide based binders

Presenters:

Gilles Zakosek

Company:

SNF

SNF Organic Binder

Polyacrylamide based binders

March 2022 – Gilles Zakosek

SNF
WATER SCIENCE

CONTENT

SNF

1 SNF Group Company Overview

SNF
WATER SCIENCE

SNF BUSINESS OVERVIEW

As of Dec. 31, 2021

- WE ARE A SPECIALTY CHEMICAL COMPANY,
- WORLD LEADER IN POLYACRYLAMIDE PRODUCTION

- **2021 sales c. €3.6 billion**
  - Sales multiplied by 2x in 10 years
  - More than 400,000 end-users
- **Privately held company, founded in 1978**
- **Treatment of water for more than:**
  - 850 million people
  - 10,000 industrial sites
- **6,900 employees worldwide and a market share of 48%**
- **Key success factors**
  - Manufacturing excellence
  - Combined chemical and engineering expertise
  - Product and process innovation
  - Everyday commitment to sustainability

- OUR PRODUCTS ARE USED IN APPLICATIONS
- USING WATER, EITHER TO TREAT OR TO PRESERVE IT

- **Flocculation (Solid / Liquid separation)**
  - Water Treatment
  - Mining
  - Paper
- **Viscosity Modification**
  - Enhanced oil recovery
  - Personal care
- **Drag Reduction (Reduced energy consumption for pumping)**
  - Fracking
  - Water transportation

SNF is an expert in water chemistry.

Our markets are driven by the increasing scarcity of key natural resources.

SNF
WATER SCIENCE

DIVERSIFIED BUSINESS MODEL ACROSS GEOGRAPHIES AND INDUSTRIES

SALES BY GEOGRAPHIES

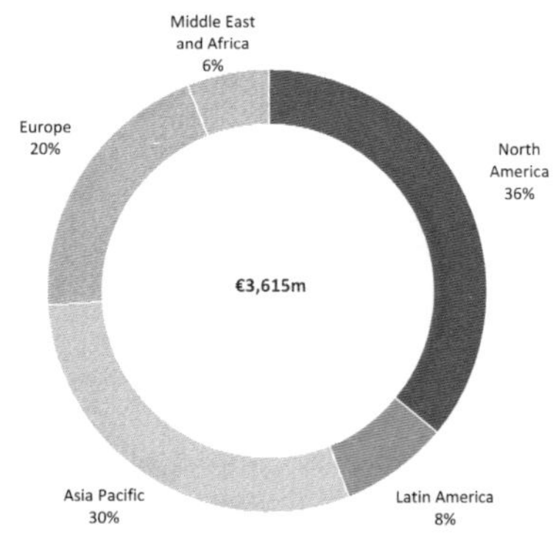

SALES BY MARKETS

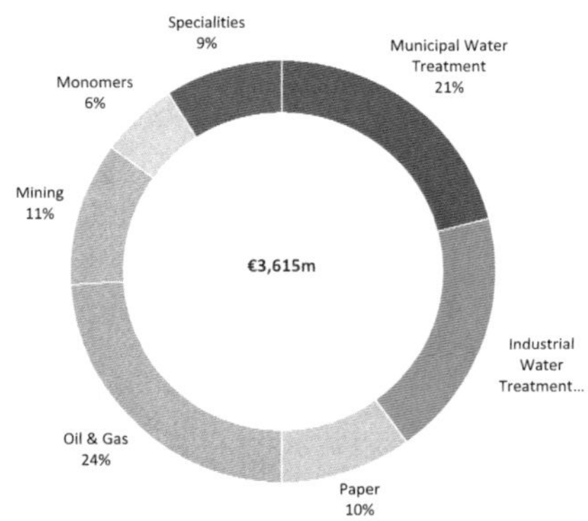

12M21

- **North America is our largest area of sales at 36%, followed by AP at 30%.**
- **O&G share has increased to 24% (was 20% in 2020 and 27% in 2019).**

SNF WATER SCIENCE

MODERN AND GEOGRAPHICALLY DIVERSE PRODUCTION CAPACITY

As of Dec. 31, 2021

- *PAM CAPACITY: 1,325 kT*

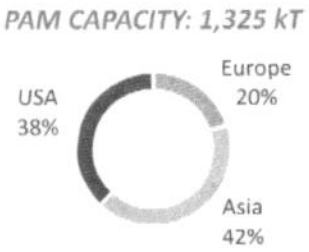

- **Worldwide capacity : 2,770 kT**

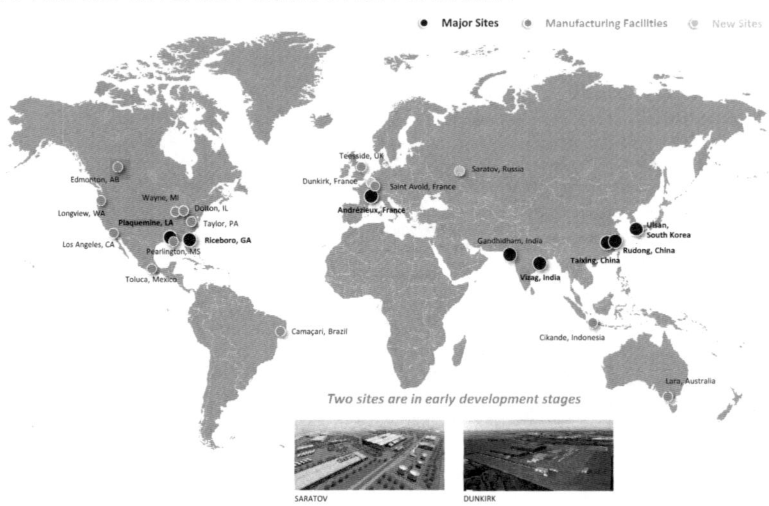

- **We have 8 major sites and a total of 21 manufacturing facilities to match our revenue to our cost base and therefore be "naturally" hedged.**

SNF WATER SCIENCE

SNF CHEMISTRY

2

SNF
WATER SCIENCE

Monomers and Polymers

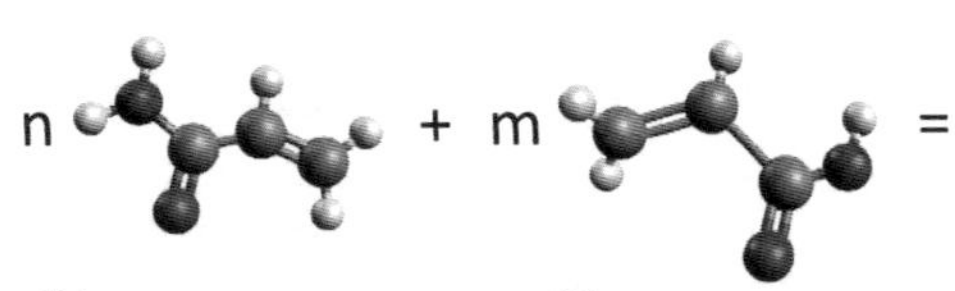

Monomer #1 Monomer #2

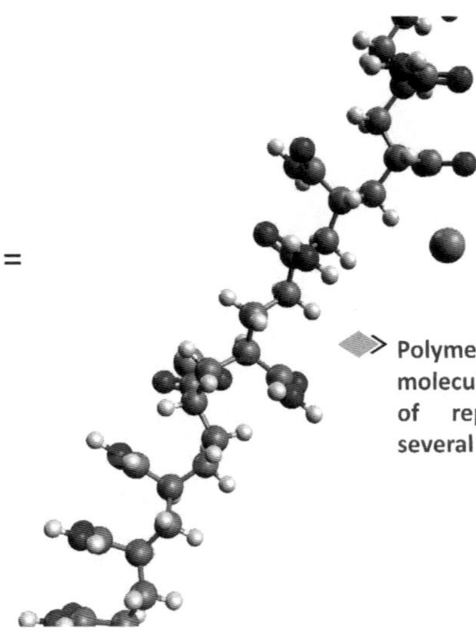

Polymers are large molecules composed of repetitions of several monomers

SNF
WATER SCIENCE

What is a polyacrylamide ?

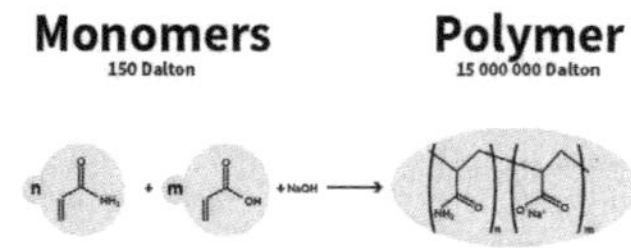

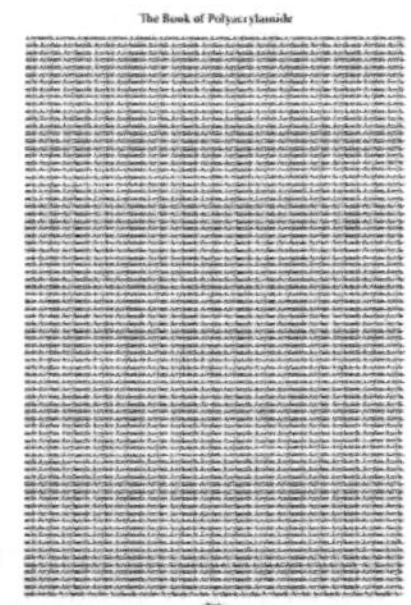

- In the case of polyacrylamides this repetition is gigantic.
- Some of the products we make can reach 15 and even 20 million Daltons
  - You can see here the size of a book where the words Acrylamide-Acrylate are repeated as often as in our polyacrylamides
- Polyelectrolyte is the generic name

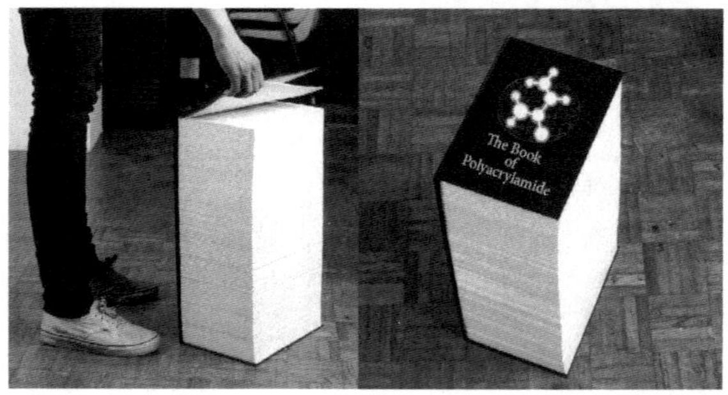

SNF WATER SCIENCE

Radical Polymerization

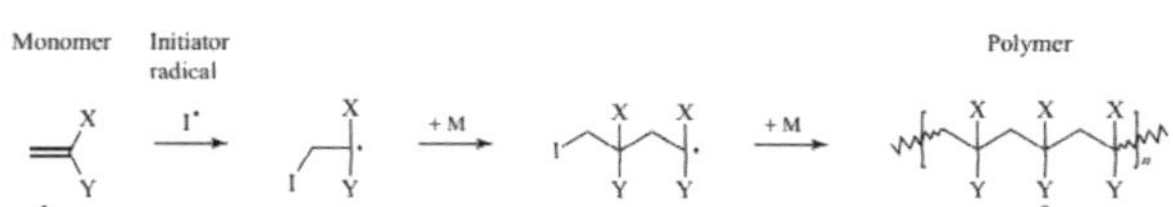

Scheme 1 Radical polymerization of a C=C monomer.

Initiation	Initiator cleavage	$I_2 \xrightarrow{k_d} 2\ I^\bullet$	Primary radicals
	Chain initiation	$I^\bullet + M \xrightarrow{k_i} I\text{-}M^\bullet$	Initiating radicals
	Propagation	$P_n^\bullet + M \xrightarrow{k_p} P_{n+1}^\bullet$	
Chain transfer	Transfer	$P_n^\bullet + T \xrightarrow{k_{tr}} P_n + T^\bullet$	
	Reinitiation	$T^\bullet + M \xrightarrow{k_{ri}} T\text{-}M^\bullet$	
	Termination	$P_n^\bullet + P_m^\bullet \xrightarrow{k_{tC}} P_{n+m}$; $\xrightarrow{k_{tD}} P_n^= + P_m^H$	

I_2 is initiator, M is monomer, $P_n^\bullet$ is a radical of chain length n, T is a chain transfer species, P_n is a polymer

- Radical Polymerization in Industry, Peter Nesvadba

SNF WATER SCIENCE

Raw Materials

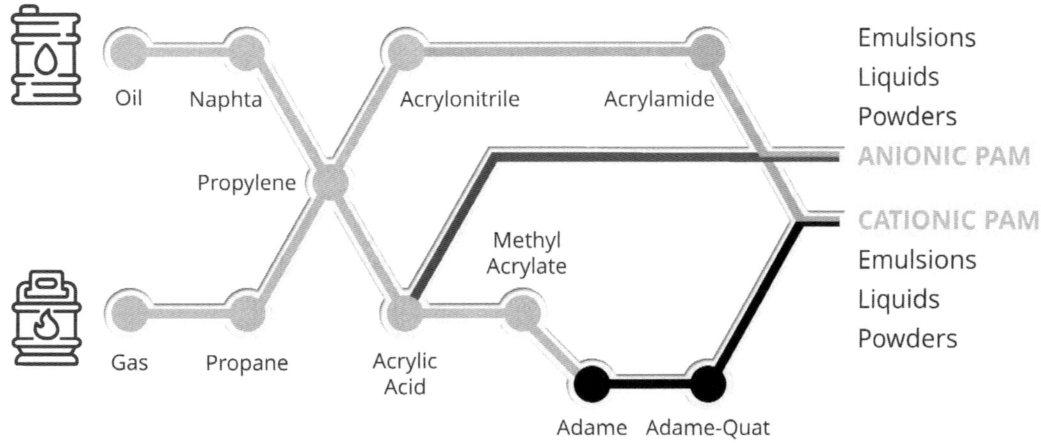

The definition of SNF Polyacrylamides

- Polyelectrolytes are water-soluble chemicals available:
  - As anionic (negatively charged) or cationic (positively charged)
  - In a very wide range of molecular weight (the polymer length)
  - In different structures (linear, branched)
  - In solid or liquid grades

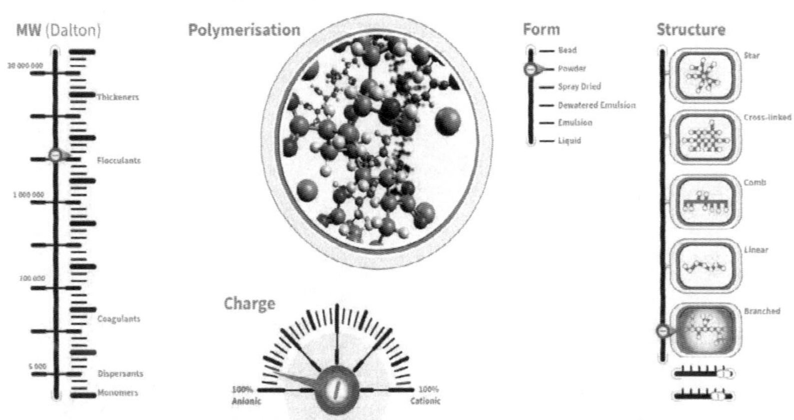

- Our Polymers have several key characteristics that we control during manufacturing:
  - The ionicity (anionic, nonionic and cationic)
  - The molecular weight that can vary from a few thousand to a few million Daltons
  - The structure of the polymer itself and
  - The physical state of the commercial product.

Powder Polymerization Process

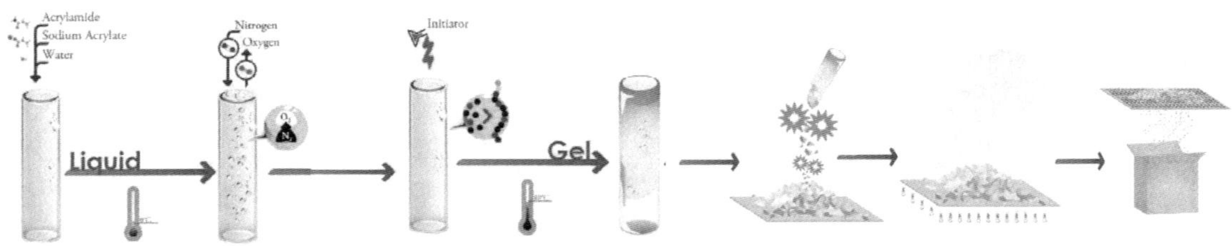

- Dry product to mix with brine to prepare a polymer solution

SNF
WATER SCIENCE

What do polyacrylamides do ?

- Polyelectrolytes are designed to adsorb to dissolved organic carbon and/or suspended solids in the aqueous phase.
  - Adsorption is instantaneous and irreversible.
  - Once the polymer has adsorbed, it forms an insoluble compound and exits the water phase.

SNF
WATER SCIENCE

Viscosity Modification

- Without Polyacrylamide, linear flowing

- With Polyacrylamide, the physical state of water changes

- **This is what happens to the moisture during the agglomeration steps.**
  The water become stickier, more viscous so become more efficient to cover and bind the particles.

SNF
WATER SCIENCE

3 IRON ORE PELLETIZATION

SNF
WATER SCIENCE

STEELMAKING ROUTE

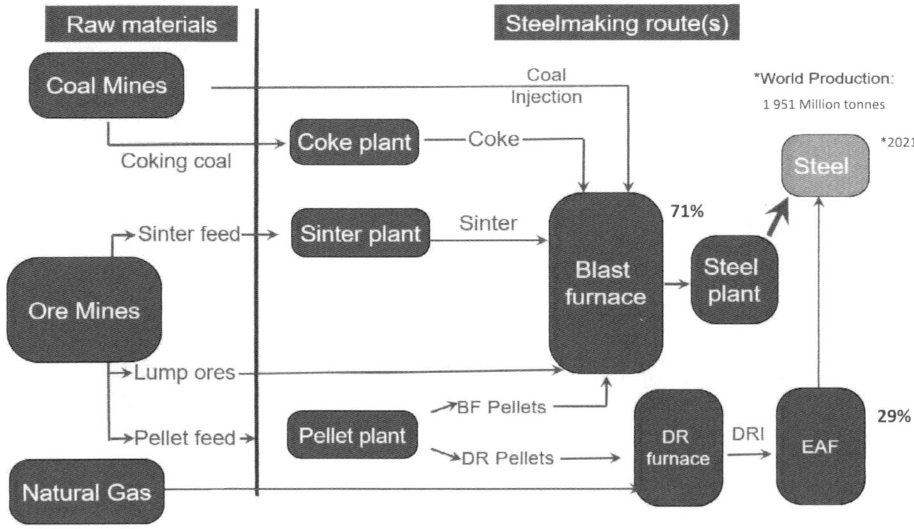

SNF WATER SCIENCE

BALLING PROCESS – General Diagram

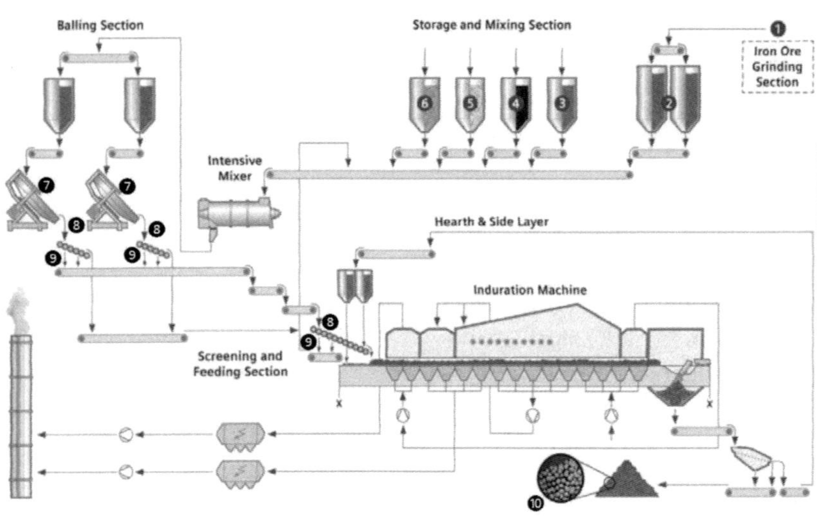

①&② : Iron Ore Concentrates
③: Recycled Dust / fines
④: Coke fines
⑤: Binders
⑥: Fluxes
⑦: Balling pans
⑧: Green pellets
⑨: Rotary sieves
⑩: Final Pellets

SNF WATER SCIENCE

FLOFORM range

Pelletization – Wet Granulation / Balling

- Copolymers & Terpolymers (2 to 3 monomers used to form the binder)
- Mainly powders
- Mixed in production with inorganic compounds (Soda Ash, Lime, Boron ..)
- Can be used in combination with inorganic material: mainly Bentonite
- Dosage : 0,03 to 0,06%

SNF
WATER SCIENCE

Pelletization (balling) process
Key point 1: Controlled migration speed of water

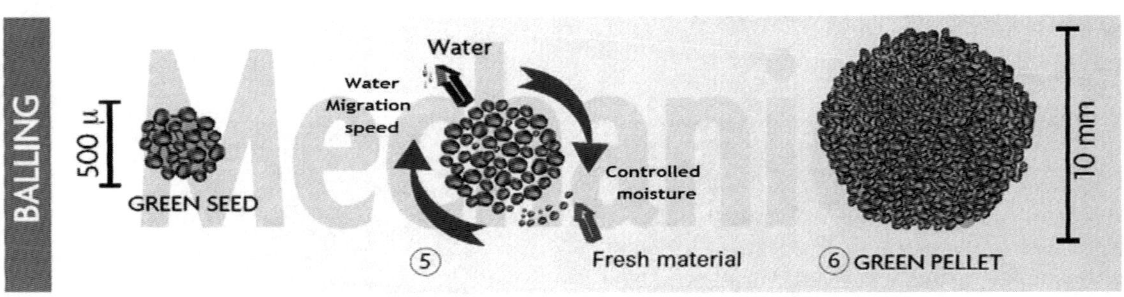

Changing the type of our Polymer (Anionicity, Molecular Weight) allows our binder to be efficient even if the iron ore is reluctant to ball.

No need to raise the dosage (contrary to Bentonite with some Magnetite ores).

SNF
WATER SCIENCE

Pelletization (balling) process
Key point 2: Viscous and sticky pellets surface

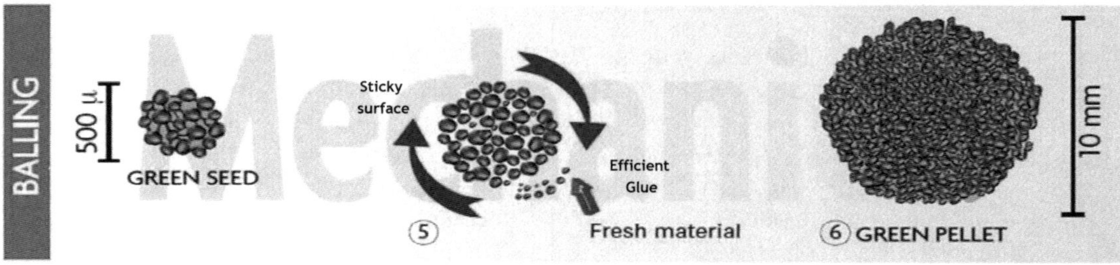

- Our wide portfolio of polymer allows the fine tuning of the final binder formula.
- We can set, at the chosen level, the efficiency of the fresh material's adhesion.

SNF
WATER SCIENCE

LAB DEVELOPMENT

- HEMATITE – AIM: SMOOTH SURFACE
  Higher TI Index

WITH THE CURRENT BINDER: HOLES AND "ORANGE PEEL"

WITH THE NEW DP PRODUCT : SMOOTH

SNF
WATER SCIENCE

LAB DEVELOPMENT

◆ HEMATITE – DRY PELLETS

WITH THE CURRENT BINDER: HOLES AND "ORANGE PEEL"

WITH THE NEW DP PRODUCT : SMOOTH

SNF WATER SCIENCE

LAB DEVELOPMENT – HEMATITE CONCENTRATE

◆ Tests in pellet plant - Comparison with Bentonite

Parameters	Bentonite	FLOFORM
Dosage (kg/T of Concentrate)	5,0	0,5
Green Pellets Moisture (%)	8,84	8,74
Drop Number	2,9	3,2
Green Compression Strength (kg)	1,4	1,33
Dry Compression Strength (kg)	6,21	6,29
Tumble (% +6,3 mm)	95,3	95,3
Cold Compression Strength (kg)	328,5	337
Fe total (%)	67,6	67,9
SiO2 (%)	1,6	1,3
AL2O3 (%)	0,52	0,44
Size (10 mm – 16 mm) (%)	92,4	94,8

Fired Pellet with Bentonite

Fired Pellet with FLOFORM

SNF WATER SCIENCE

LAB DEVELOPMENT – HEMATITE CONCENTRATE

HEMATITE – Comparison with Bentonite – Results from production reports

	Start: Normal Production	Phase 1 with Organic Binder	Phase 2 with Organic Binder	Back to Normal Production
Pellets Properties	Std (Bentonite)	50% Organic Binder	100% Organic Binder	Std (Bentonite)
Duration (Days)	2	2	3	2
Production rate (MT/h)	122	121	124	123
Metallization (%)	95,5	95,2	95,6	95,3
Carbon (%)	2,29	2,36	2,41	2,49
Gas Consumption (Gcal/MT)	2,73	2,73	2,73	2,72

Second phase with 100% OB pellets: very good reducibility, and carbon pickup slightly higher than regular feed mix

SNF WATER SCIENCE

4 SINTERING FLODRI SI PRODUCTS

Property of SNF – Duplication prohibited

SNF WATER SCIENCE

SNF POLYMER EFFECT

The presence of Anionic Polymer raises the micro particle dispersion in water and gives more strength to the binding system at the contact points.

When the change of state arrives, from the liquid phase to the solid phase (drying), micro-particle concentrate at the water bridges and form a solid bridge between the micro-particle (ultra-fines)and the nuclear particles.

At the end of the drying, the fines stick the particle, and the granules are strong enough to resist to the static forces of the sinter furnace.

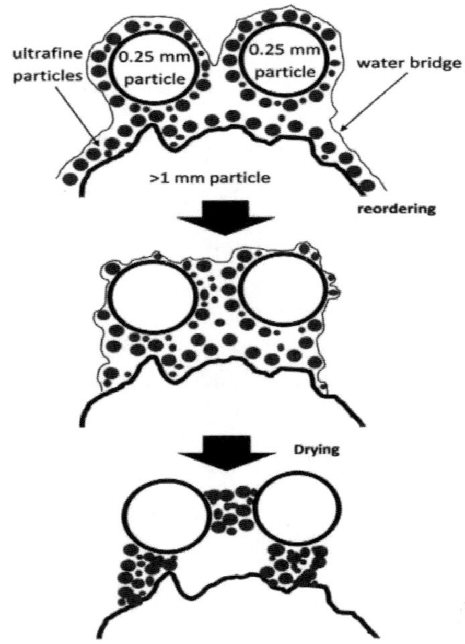

Figure 4. Behavior of micro-particle on granulation.

CASE STUDY

SNF WATER SCIENCE

LAB TRAILS – ARCELOR MITTAL FRANCE

General Flow sheet:

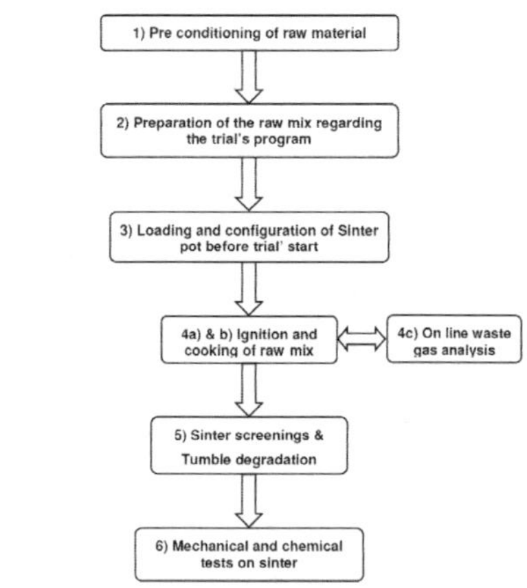

Presentation of Lab devices for Sintering

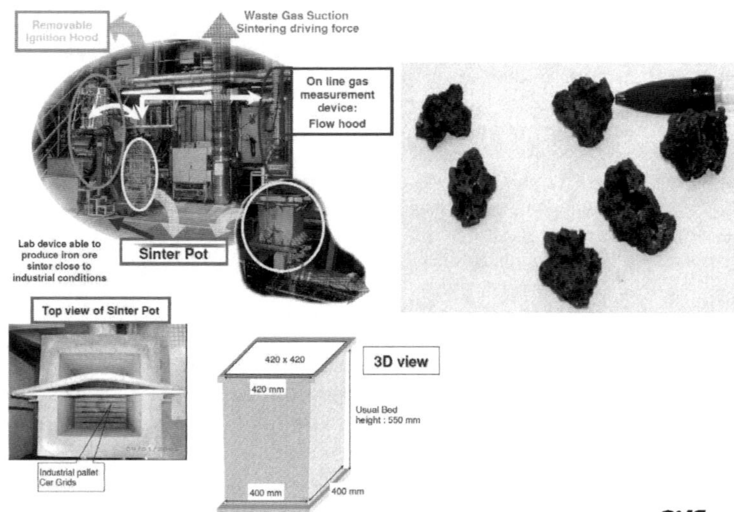

FLODRI SI BINDERS : LABORATORY RESULTS

RESULTS OF THE PILOT TRAIL

WITH FLODRI SI 1150

- Improvement of productivity: + 7.5 to + 10 %

NON – LINEAR ENHANCEMENT OF PRODUCTIVITY

- Sinter quality in agreement with expectations
- No increase on solid fuel consumption
- Slight increase of VOC emissions (especially on CH_4 legislation only on non-CH_4 VOC emissions)
- Improvement of finer fractions resistance (granulation index <250µm): with FLODRI SI 1150, the dry granules are more resistant.

COMPARISON BETWEEN THE BINDERS (CaO & FLODRI SI 1150)

- 0,05% of FLODRI SI 1150 equals the use of 0,1% of CaO, in terms of granulation, productivity and sinter quality.
- Cumulative effect with burnt lime possible, to lower the consumption of CaO.

5 BRIQUETTING : FLOFORM & FLODRI BQ PRODUCTS

SNF WATER SCIENCE

FLOFORM RANGE

Briquetting – Extrusion

- Copolymers & Terpolymers (2 to 3 monomers used to from the binders)
- Powders and liquids
- Usually used pure (no mixing at the production plant)
- Can be used in combination with inorganic materials: Cement, silicates
- Dosage : 1% max for the powders – 2 to 4 % for the liquids

SNF WATER SCIENCE

AREAS FOR BRIQUETTING and EXTRUSION

SNF WATER SCIENCE

NICKEL & COBALT

COAL

CO-PRODUCTS RECYCLING (STEEL & METALS)

SNF WATER SCIENCE

Briquetting process
Plasticity properties given to the agglomerates (briquettes)

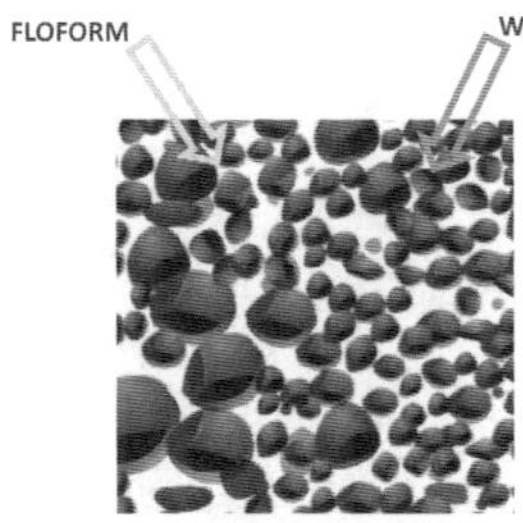

1- Materials – heterogenous sizes

MIXING

2- Polymers hydrates and encapsulates all the particles. "Worm" state

PRESS

3- Agglomerates are well formed and plastics

- **Polymers gives plasticity and strength to the green briquettes.**
  - Agglomerates can withstand many drop after the exit of the press (6 to 10) without breakage.
  - GCS (Green compression strength) is also enhanced
- Our wide portfolio of polymer allows the fine tuning of the final binder formula.

COLD PELLETIZATION PROJECTS

Skipping induration process for Sintering & Pelletization

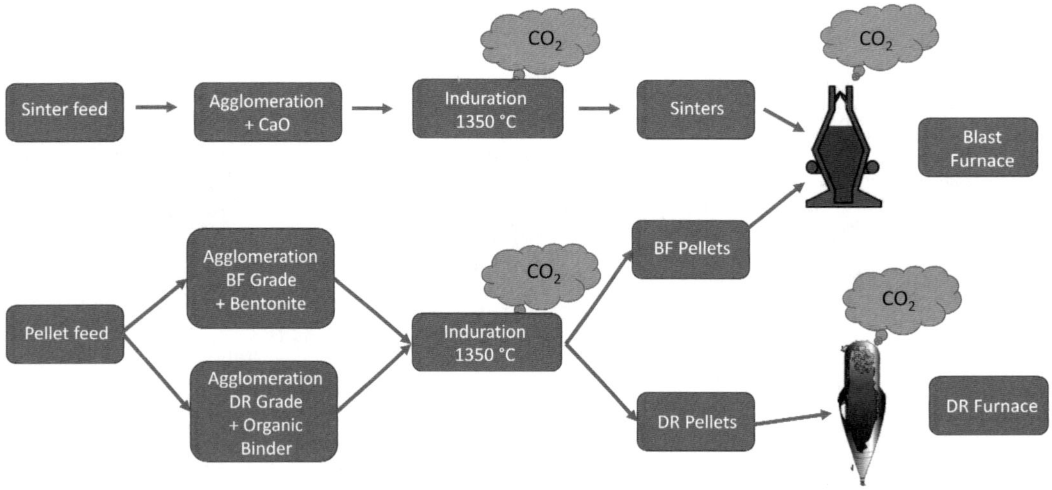

Property of SNF – Duplication prohibited

SNF WATER SCIENCE

First Way: Skipping induration process for Sintering & Pelletization

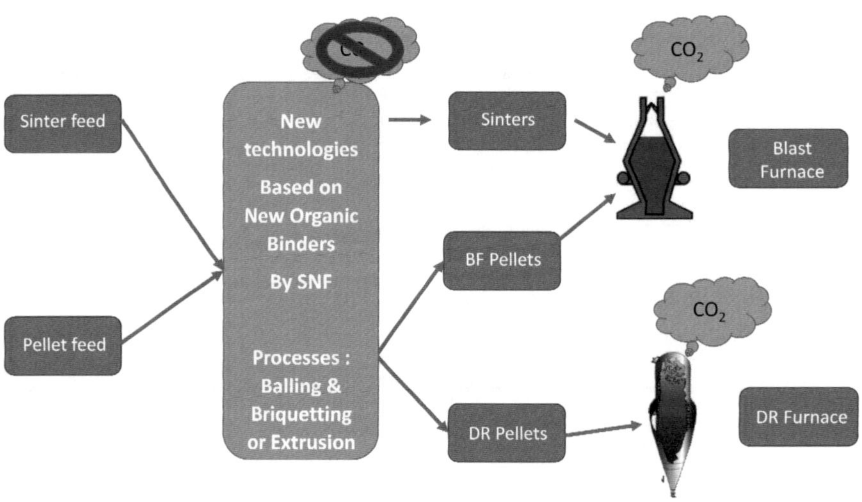

Property of SNF – Duplication prohibited

SNF WATER SCIENCE

FIRST RESULTS WITH FLOFORM

- **FLOFORM New formulas have been tested with first good results in terms of green and dry agglomerates.**
  - Trials made on compaction, using compaction wheels.

Volume of the agglomerates: 6 to 9 cm3

Physical properties on green briquettes

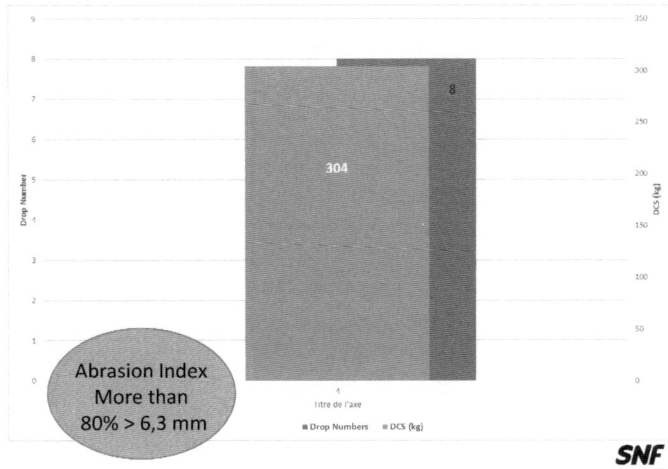

- Trials are still on-going

SNF WATER SCIENCE

CAN INDUSTRY DECARBONIZE STEELMAKING – The EUROPEAN Example

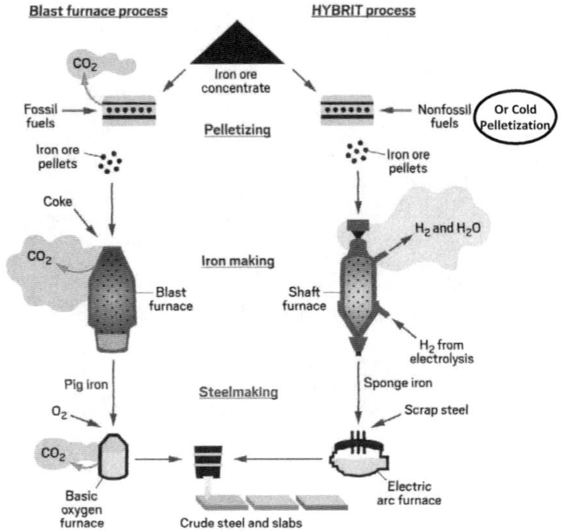

SNF WATER SCIENCE

CAN INDUSTRY DECARBONIZE STEELMAKING – The EUROPEAN Example

BY THE NUMBERS

24%

The percentage of all industrial CO_2 emissions attributed to steelmaking.

7–9%

The percentage of total human CO_2 emissions contributed by the steel industry.

1.86 billion metric tons

The amount of steel produced in 2020.

1.85 metric tons

The average amount of CO_2 emitted by producing 1 metric ton of steel

50,000 wind turbines

The amount of renewable electricity capacity needed to convert Europe's steel industry to hydrogen-based production of direct reduced iron

In 2019: 13 179 Wind turbine offshore were installed

Gilles ZAKOSEK – Project Manager, Mining

gzakosek@snf.com *Mobile : +336 082 568 42*

AUTHOR INDEX